James E. Brook

Elements of Geology

Sir Charles Lyell (1797–1875), founder of modern geology. (By Thomas Coates, Ann Arbor, Michigan, from a photograph of a portrait by T. H. Maguire.)

Throughout a long and laborious life he sought the means of deciphering the fragmentary records of the earth's history in the patient investigation of the present order of nature, enlarging the boundaries of knowledge and leaving on scientific thought an enduring influence.
O Lord how great are thy works and thy thoughts are very deep.   Psalms XCII.5
(Inscription on the tomb of Lyell in Westminster Abbey.)

SECOND EDITION

Elements of Geology

JAMES H. ZUMBERGE

Grand Valley College, Allendale, Michigan

John Wiley and Sons, Inc.

NEW YORK · LONDON

To my Wife, Marilyn

Preface

This edition, like the first, aims to fill the need of a one-semester combined course in physical and historical geology for the nonmajor. The subject material is divided into the two pedagogically traditional units: Part I, The Dynamic Earth; and Part II, The Geological Story. Each part is roughly equal in length although Part I contains ten chapters and Part II only six chapters.

This edition is somewhat longer than the first because new material has been added, especially in the first eleven chapters. Some basic principles of structural geology have been included in Chapter three at the request of several users of the first edition, and a section on volcanology has been incorporated in Chapter five. Other new topics included in this edition but not in the old are the new soil classification scheme of the United States Soil Survey, a discussion of the concept of dynamic equilibrium of landscape development, new data on glaciology, an introduction to paleomagnetism, and a brief treatment of tsunamis.

Many of the first edition illustrations have been retained but several new ones have been added. Four new color plates in which rock and mineral specimens are displayed are included as an aid to the instructor and student who use this book in a nonlaboratory course. In general, the colors seem to be sufficiently accurate to provide a reasonable basis for identification.

Elements of Geology is now about as large as it should ever be. New material added to future revisions should be done so only at the expense of deleting other parts of the book. Some readers may feel that it is already too lengthy, but I believe that in order to provide enough material for instructors of varying backgrounds, the book should be as complete in its coverage of geological subjects as possible.

Of the many people who helped in this revision, I should like to express special thanks to Thomas Coates and Derwin Bell, both of whom provided additional art work for this edition. Suppliers of new photographs are credited in the text where the photographs appear.

Others who made helpful contributions

to me during the course of this revision, and to whom I express my grateful appreciation are Wayne Ault, W. Charles Bell, B. F. Buie, R. M. Denning, John Dorr, E. William Heinrich, K. K. Landes, R. D. Nininger, and R. W. Simonson.

To Mrs. Clemence Cahill and Mrs. Marlene Brandon who spent long hours typing the manuscript, and Miss Jean Ellis who assisted in preparation of the index, I would like to add a sincere note of thanks.

Finally, to my wife, Marilyn Zumberge, and my four children, John, JoEllen, James, and Mark, I express my thanks for their putting up with me during the difficult days when I was deeply involved in this revision.

JAMES H. ZUMBERGE

Grand Rapids, Michigan
May, 1963

Contents

List of Tables

Introduction

There is nothing constant in the Universe,
All ebb and flow, and every shape that's born
Bears in its womb the seeds of change.

Ovid

During the one hundred years since Charles Darwin published his *Origin of Species* (1861), the world of science has expanded its horizons into every walk of life in the civilized world. Elementary school children are exposed to simple scientific experiments, the housewife uses scientifically developed detergents, and the business man pays attention to scientifically conducted polls. Heads of state have scientific advisers and international awards are given for outstanding scientific achievement.

In a world where science rules our very existence some may find themselves thinking of the word, science, in terms of contemporary events such as sending a man to the moon, making a better toothpaste, or building 100 megaton bombs. For others, the world of science is a mere collection of facts which are discovered by a few for the benefit of many.

In the midst of the rush for nations to outdo each other in the many fields of science, it may be of some value to stand back and take a good hard look at this thing which dominates our modern world. What is science?

In a few words, science is the discovery of general natural laws through observation and experimentation. Science is not an organized collection of facts or a catalogue of information about the physical universe, but a dynamic development of concepts based on the logic of deduction and reasoning. The search for scientific truth is never ended nor satisfied. Accepted scientific facts of one generation may be altered or entirely discarded by the next. True science builds on what has gone before to discover the unknown that lies ahead.

Viewed in this perspective, science becomes more than the road to better living and an easier life. It takes on a fuller meaning in that it involves the pursuit of knowledge for the sake of establishing the truth about the world in which we live and the universe to which we belong. Whether these truths established by scientific endeavors are beneficial or detrimental to mankind is incidental.

1

THE SCIENTIFIC METHOD

The acquisition of new knowledge in the world of science is a tedious process. Accidental discoveries are often spectacular because they are unexpected. But in the ordinary pursuit of scientific investigations, the scientist employs the *scientific method.*

The scientific method involves the framing of a new concept or idea to account for certain observed phenomena. The newly formed concept is termed an *hypothesis.* The next step is to predict the consequences of the hypothesis and to devise ways and means of testing these predictions.

When the initial data used for framing a hypothesis are scanty, several *working hypotheses* may be framed, each of which must stand the test of more observation as more pertinent facts are assembled. Only one hypothesis can eventually satisfy all conditions consequent to it. The surviving hypothesis, which eventually is elevated to the rank of a *theory,* may have been one of the original working hypotheses or, what is more likely, may have evolved during the course of testing the others.

In the early days of the Greeks, science as we know it today did not exist. Instead, it was intertwined with philosophy and even mythology. Man had not yet learned to use the scientific method so he was unable to apply rigorous tests and experiments to prove or disprove various hypotheses. Gradually, however, observation, and later, experimentation, cleared the way for real advances in various branches of science.

As the horizons of scientific endeavor expanded, certain broad fields such as physical science, biological science, and medical science developed. Today these broad fields are not as well defined as they were fifty years ago. New hybridized sciences such as *biophysics* indicate the overlapping of what formerly were distinct fields. The space age, too, has ushered in the *planetary sciences,* and we may expect others to appear before the twentieth century has ended.

All scientists, however, regardless of what branch of science they belong to have one common denominator—they all employ the scientific method. That is to say, they carry out experiments and make observations to test some working hypothesis in hopes of establishing a general law as to how natural forces react under certain conditions. In such fields as chemistry, physics, and biology, experiments can be devised whereby the results can be duplicated time and time again, as long as the ingredients and the conditions of their association can be controlled according to the wishes of the scientist.

In other scientific fields, especially those classed as the natural sciences, direct laboratory experimentation is not always feasible, and the scientist must rely more on his ability to observe phenomena as they occur in nature. This process is called field work.

THE SCIENCE OF GEOLOGY

Geology is an earth science, and although there are many facets of it that are conducive to controlled laboratory experiments, a geologist is first and foremost a field observer.

Geology deals with the forces of nature and how they combine to produce the features found on the surface of the continents and the floor of the oceans, as well as deep beneath the ground. Geology is dynamic because it involves physical changes of the earth through enormous spans of time.

HISTORY OF GEOLOGY AS A SCIENCE

The concepts and principles embodied in modern geology evolved over a long period of history. The Greeks indulged in speculative philosophy about the earth and used mythological explanations to account for many phenomena such as earthquakes, volcanoes, and entombed organic remains (fossils). Aristotle (384–322 B.C.) held that all matter could be broken down into four basic elements, air, fire, soil, and water.

The 600 years of the Roman Empire saw some advances in geological thought. During the reign of Tiberius a widely traveled Greek geographer, Strabo, (born 63 B.C.) recognized that the sea had once covered parts of the land. Pliny the Elder (A.D. 23–79), a learned historian and naturalist under the emperor, Vespasian, wrote voluminously on all aspects of natural science. Ironically, he died prematurely in the eruption of Vesuvius which destroyed Pompeii and Herculaneum on the Bay of Naples in A.D. 79. The thirty-seven volumes of Pliny's *Natural History* covered a wide range of subjects, not all of which were scientific in scope, and had a great influence on those who followed him. Of greater value to the domain of geology is the vivid description of the eruption of Vesuvius and accompanying earthquakes by Pliny's nephew and adopted son, Pliny the Younger, (A.D. 61–113) in two letters to the Roman emperor Tacitus.

The Dark Ages retarded the acquisition of scientific knowledge until the end of the Middle Ages, when, in the fifteenth century, the spark of knowledge was rekindled throughout all Europe. In Italy, Leonardo da Vinci (1452–1519) recognized the true origin of fossils as remains of marine organisms which had accumulated on the floors of ancient seas in northern Italy. Somewhat later, George Bauer (1494–1555), a German who wrote in Latin under the name, Georgius Agricola, by which he is better known, published six books on geological subjects. The two best known, *De natura fossilium* (1546) and *De re metallica* (posthumously, 1556), provided the foundations for the fields of mineralogy and mining geology.

During the seventeenth century Nicolaus Steno (1638–1687), a Dane who studied medicine in Copenhagen and spent ten years of his life from 1665 to 1675 in Florence as house physician to the Grand Duke Ferdinand II, was one of the most enlightened geologists of his time. He was the first to realize that the lower layers in a series of strata must be older than the upper. Moreover, Steno recognized that strata were originally deposited in a more or less horizontal position, but that they might become tilted or otherwise distorted through subsequent earth movements.

Although the basic principles of geology were slowly emerging, they still lacked a unifying concept. Geology still could hardly be given the status of a science up until the middle of the eighteenth century. Many of the learned men who took up the study of earth history in the seventeenth and eighteenth centuries were theologians who hoped to find proof of the Noachian deluge in strata of the earth's crust. They were committed to a literal interpretation of Holy Writ which included the Mosaic account of creation and the Flood. Whether from real personal convictions of the scientific authority of Scripture or because of the fear of church censure, most of the natural historians of that time tried to mix geology with theology, an unfortunate circumstance which greatly retarded the development of geology as a science. For the few who dared to take a more liberal view of Genesis the church pronounced judgment. In England the Rev. Thomas

Burnet (1635–1715), who wrote the *Sacred Theory of the Earth* (1681), was dismissed from a court appointment in 1892 because he treated the Mosaic account of the fall of man as an allegory. Another Englishman, William Whitson (1666–1753), was deprived of a professorship in 1701 because of his heterodox views of scripture expressed in *The New Theory of the Earth* (1696). And in Paris, the first great naturalist to present a comprehensive work on the theory of the earth, George Buffon (1707–1788), was forced to recant his views before the Faculty of Theology at the Sorbonne.

It remained for James Hutton (1726–1797), educated in medicine at Edinburgh, Paris, and Leyden, to put into one volume, *Theory of the Earth* (1795), the first modern approach to geology. In the British Isles Hutton founded the so-called *Vulcanist* (or *Plutonist*) group who were opposed to the *Neptunists* led by Abraham Gottlob Werner (1749–1817) in Freiberg, Germany. Werner, an eloquent speaker and inspired teacher, held that all rocks were formed in water, even granite and basalt which are now known to have originated from a molten state. Hutton, as leader of the opposing Plutonist group, proved the true origin of granite and basalt. But more than that, Hutton established for the first time a unifying principle which geology so badly needed. He authored the famous *doctrine of uniformitarianism*. This concept teaches that all geological phenomena of past geological time can be explained through the understanding of modern geological principles and processes. In essence, this doctrine states that the *present is the key to the past*.

The logic of Hutton's geology was so lucid that he gained many followers and collaborators, among which were several who previously supported the Wernerian School of Neptunism. One of Hutton's most ardent supporters and enthusiastic followers was James Playfair (1748–1819) who further elaborated on Hutton's original work and added to it.

The basic thought expressed in the uniformitarian concept was that worldwide catastrophes were not needed to explain past earth history. But catastrophism did not perish immediately. In France, Baron Georges Cuvier (1769–1832) made great strides in studies of fossil animals and was widely renowned throughout Europe for his work. But he taught that practically all the animals which populated the earth in past geological periods were wiped out catastrophically from time to time, and only a few survivors remained from which the next population was developed.

Strong opposition to this theory existed in Germany, France, and England in the early nineteenth century. Sir Charles Lyell (1797–1875) (see frontispiece) did more toward dispelling the catastrophists than any other man. He traveled widely in Europe and North America and wrote voluminously of his travels. He wrote two widely read books, *Principles of Geology* and *Elements of Geology*, both of which are today considered classics in earth science. Lyell supported Darwin's newly founded doctrine of evolution and exerted a profound influence on all geological thought of the late nineteenth and early twentieth century. Lest the reader should get the idea that Lyell was "antichurch," it should be noted that he is one of three geologists buried in Westminster Abbey (see inscription beneath Lyell's picture on frontispiece).

The history of geological thought does not stop with Lyell, of course, but to continue the thread further would be anticlimatic. Lyell's influence gradually displaced the catastrophic school, and there has never arisen a controversy of similar magnitude among geologists since.

What Hutton started, Playfair promoted, and Lyell finished. Modern geological thought and practice all start with the foundations layed by these men.

Although catastrophism in the nineteenth century sense was laid to rest by Hutton, Playfair, and Lyell, we must not close our minds completely in this regard. The extremely short period of time during which man has observed geologic processes in action is less than a mere flick of an eyelash compared to the total length of geologic time. The possibility of catastrophic events of large magnitude in past earth history, especially in the very early stages, cannot be ruled out on statistical grounds alone. We refer here not to volcanic eruptions, violent "tidal waves," or destructive earthquakes, but rather to exceptional activity in the earth's crust of a kind not observed or known to exist. Many geologic features cannot be adequately explained by any known physical process. Although the first attempts at understanding them are, of necessity, based on the extrapolation of natural laws involving the interaction between matter and energy, it is possible and quite probable that past geologic events may have been related to forces and processes that are either no longer operative, or that man's period of observation has been too short to encounter them.

AIMS OF GEOLOGY

Geology involves the knowledge of what is happening on and within the earth today. This requires not only an understanding of the materials involved, such as the rocks and minerals, but also a thorough understanding of the various geologic processes, for example, the way a river moves its load of sediment, or how petroleum moves beneath the ground, or

the mechanisms involved in earthquakes. The first aim in geology is to develop an understanding of earth materials and how these materials are changed and modified through the action of natural forces over a period of time. Part I of this book deals with earth materials and processes.

When this has been accomplished, the student is ready for a second major aim, namely, the reconstruction of the geologic history of the earth. Even the elementary student will soon discover that the various features of the earth were not formed at the same time. Studying the forces that acted at different places on the earth at different times and deciphering the geologic record according to a time reference is an exciting experience.

Essentially, the geologist must answer three basic questions in his study of any geologic feature. First he wants to know, *what happened?* To find out he draws from the reservoir of knowledge that deals with the work of natural forces and agents. Many geologic processes are contemporary and can be viewed in action today. Such things as the growth of a volcano, the movement of a glacier, the development of sinuous river channels, or the way in which rocks are distorted by the application of external forces, are just a few of the many geologic processes that man has studied in minute detail to learn how natural forces modify the earth.

The experimental phase of geology is a rather recent development that has placed the science on a firmer factual basis. There is no question that it will progress in future years through greater emphasis on experimental schemes whereby the forces of nature can be studied under controlled laboratory conditions, thereby placing geology on a quantitative rather than a purely qualitative basis.

The second major question that needs answering by the geologist when he studies some geologic feature, be it a mountain range or a coal bed is, *why did it happen?* In other words, having discovered the *effect,* the geologist then turns to the *cause.* Cause and effect relationships are fundamental in the study of geology, and it must be quite clear even to the casual observer that when the cause of a geologic phenomenon is clearly understood, it is possible to predict future geologic events. Geologists are now on the threshold of predicting the time of future earthquakes, and eruptions of Mauna Loa on Hawaii have been predicted within a few months time of the actual event.

The inability to recognize the difference between cause and effect led early geologists astray. For instance, it was generally assumed by many of the early philosophers that rivers flowed in valleys because the valleys represented a rift or crack in the earth's surface, thereby allowing water to flow in a ready-made channel. Modern geology, on the other hand, has shown that valleys are cut by the erosive power of running water, and from the standpoint of cause and effect relationship, the rivers caused the valleys.

Throughout Part I of this book, cause and effect relationships will be stressed repeatedly. The reader must bear in mind, however, that we can observe the *effects* of past geologic processes today, whereas the *causes* are quite often based on assumptions rather than on known facts. The science will progress as we reduce the number of assumptions and increase our factual knowledge about the cause of geologic processes.

Take the origin of a common rock known as granite as an example. Granite consists of interlocking particles called minerals which are natural chemical compounds. The individual mineral grains are clearly visible to the naked eye. Two hundred years ago, the Neptunists led by Abraham Gottlob Werner argued that all rocks, including granite, were precipitated from sea water. It is true that certain rock types are precipitated in the seas but this is not true of granite. The assumption that granite was a product of sea water precipitation was nullified when the discovery was made that granite is more closely related to the cooling of a molten material such as lava. This deduction was based largely on the manner of occurrence of granite masses in the earth's crust, for it was observed that granite rocks do not generally occur in layers as would be expected if they had formed at the bottom of a widespread sea. Rather, granitic bodies are irregular in shape and actually engulf other rock masses. Such discoveries eventually led to the formulation of the concept that granite was originally a molten mass of material called *magma* which formed beneath the surface of the ground and was later squeezed forcefully into the outer parts of the crust where it changed from a liquid to a solid by cooling. Sometimes the magma reached the earth's surface and poured out as lava.

Today even the magmatic origin of granite is challenged. A large number of geologists believe that although some granites are truly of magmatic origin, most of them form through the alteration of other rock types by the addition of heat and chemical constituents not present in the original rock.

Cause and effect relationships thus are not always obvious. As more and more observational facts are collected about a certain geologic feature, the ideas concerning its origin may have to be altered. And now that model studies are in widespread use in the geologic fields, the possibility of increasing our understanding of the geologic processes and the geologic features they produce is extremely good. Like all sciences, geology is dynamic; it succumbs to new discoveries. Old ideas give way to new concepts as fact gradually replaces guesswork.

CAUSE AND EFFECT IN TIME

The geologist first asks *what* (effect), then *why* (cause), and finally *when?* Thus the third element in basic geologic reasoning involves the placing of the cause and effect into a time continuum, thereby building a geologic time scale—a sequence of geologic events worked out by field observation. Geologic time starts with the origin of the earth and extends to the present. It covers 4 or 5 billion years according to the most recent methods of calculation discussed in Chapter twelve. Naturally, the most recent geologic periods are better understood simply because the geologic features which were formed then have not been erased by subsequent geologic forces. Part II of this book is a brief history of the earth as inferred from the rocks of the earth's crust.

SUMMARY

Geology is an observational science that deals with the natural forces which are acting today and have acted in the past on and within the earth. The geologist employs the scientific method and is guided by the doctrine of uniformitarian- ism to relate cause and effect relationships with reference to earth history. Given the effect, which he can observe directly, the geologists strives to determine the cause and place it in a time continuum.

Laboratory models and controlled experiments have added to the geologist's storehouse of knowledge about the way in which geologic forces modify and alter the earth. The laboratory phase of geology can clarify the forces at work and provide a more quantitive basis for the interpretation of geologic phenomena, but it does not replace the observational work of the field geologist.

REFERENCES

Adams, Frank D., 1938, *The birth and development of the geological sciences,* Dover, Baltimore.

Collier, Katherine B., 1934, *Cosmogonies of our fathers, some theories of the seventeenth and eighteenth centuries* (Columbia University studies in history, economics, and public law, No. 402), New York.

Eiseley, Loren C., 1959, Charles Lyell, *Scientific American,* August, 98–106.

Greene, John C., 1959, *The death of Adam,* Iowa State University Press, Ames, Iowa.

von Zittel, Karl A., 1901, *History of geology and paleontology* (translated from the German by M. M. Ogilvie-Gordon), Walter Scott, London.

Woodward, Horace B., 1911, *History of geology,* Putnam and Sons, New York.

PART 1

The Dynamic Earth

The Earth's Setting

*Astronomy compels the soul to look upwards
and leads us from this world to another.*

Plato

Astronomy is the oldest science known to
man. It deals with the realm of space.
Although one can study geology without
knowing anything about the universe or
solar system, a better perspective of the
earth in time and space is gained if a few
basic facts about the universe are digested
at the very beginning. Furthermore,
even a casual acquaintance with astronomy gives the mind good exercise and
prepares it for what follows later in this
book. The problems of the geologist don't
appear so insoluble when compared to the
problems of the astronomer.

Geology and astronomy overlap; somewhere in the dim past when the solar
system took its present place in the universe and the geologic processes began to
function, the geologist and astronomer
find a common ground. Incidentally,
astronomy is not to be confused with
astrology, the *pseudo* science which deals
with alleged relationships between stars
and their effects on the course of human
events.

In this chapter we consider the universe
and the solar system, and consider some
theories of their origin. The second part
of this chapter deals with the earth as a
planet with special emphasis on the two
main features of its crust, the continents
and ocean basins.

THE UNIVERSE

When you look up at a star on a cloudless night you are really looking back in
time. The earth's nearest star other than
the sun is Alpha Centauri, 4.4 light years
away. The ordinary unit for measuring
distances on earth is the mile or kilometer,
but either of these is much too small for
measuring the distances encountered in
the universe. To state the distance between the stars in miles would be analogous to giving the distance from New
York to London in tenths of an inch.
Instead, the astronomer employs two
units of measurement that are more suitable for interstellar distances. One is the
astronomical unit, the mean distance from

the earth to the sun or 92.9 million miles. The other is the *light year* which is simply the distance traveled by light in one year at a velocity of 186,290 miles per second. It is equal to the number of seconds in one year ($60 \times 60 \times 24 \times 365$) multiplied by 186,290. The product is nearly 6 million million miles! A pair of sharp eyes can see stars almost 2 million light years away. With the 200-inch Hale telescope on Mt. Palomar man can peer nearly 2 billion light years into space.

■ GALAXIES. The early Greeks regarded the universe as a hollow sphere, the inside of which was studded with stars. The earth was the stationary center of this heavenly sphere which rotated on an inclined axis. This picture was not appreciably changed until the sixteenth century when Copernicus (1473–1543) propounded the revolutionary idea that the earth revolved around the sun, thereby making the sun the center of the universe. This theory prevailed until the middle of the nineteenth century when

the discovery was made that the sun was only one of millions of stars in the disc-shaped galaxy of stars now called the Milky Way or The Galaxy. Later work showed the diameter of the galaxy to be about 80,000 light years, and the sun to be situated in an insignificant position some 26,000 light years from the center. The Milky Way appears as a broad bright band stretching across the sky and radiates the combined light of millions of stars in our own galaxy.

The Milky Way was the known universe until 1923 when the American astronomer, E. P. Hubble (1889–1953), discovered indisputable evidence that other galactic systems existed outside of our own galaxy. These were given the name "island universes" in recognition of the fact that they represented separate assemblages of stars beyond what was then the known universe. An estimated 1 billion of these island universes or exterior galaxies as they are now called, exist within range of the 200-inch Hale tele-

Figure 2-1. A spiral nebula 6 million light years away. This galaxy, like the Milky Way, is composed of billions of stars. The white specks in the picture are stars of our own galaxy. (Photograph of E. W. Dennison, University of Michigan Observatory.)

Figure 2-2. Diffuse gases, mostly hydrogen, in our own galaxy, about 7500 light years away. (Photograph of Albert Boggess III, University of Michigan Observatory.)

scope. They appear to be distributed more or less uniformly in space. Local galaxies, those lying between 150,000 and 1,500,000 light years from the earth, range in size from 2000 to 120,000 light years in their longest dimension. All galaxies are either elliptical, irregular, or flat discoidal in shape. The latter are especially intriguing because they appear to be rotating or spiraling like a giant pin wheel (Fig. 2-1).

The nearest galaxies to the Milky Way are two irregular shaped assemblages of stars known as the Magellanic Clouds which are actually visible to the naked eye in the southern hemisphere. They are 150,000 light years distant and have diameters of 20,000 and 30,000 light years. A single galaxy may contain tens of billions of stars, some of which are distinctly visible by special photography through large telescopes. Other galaxies are so densely populated with stars and gases (Fig. 2-2) that their light combines to produce a diffused zone of brightness. The bright band of the Milky Way is an example of this condition in our own galaxy.

■ THE EXPANDING UNIVERSE. Probably the most intriguing thing about the universe in addition to its incomprehensible size is the apparent fact that it is expanding at a tremendous rate. The evidence for this assertion lies in the manner in which the light coming from the exterior galaxies shifts toward the red (long wave) end of the light spectrum; This is known as the Doppler effect. The "red shift" is caused by the stretching of the light waves as they leave the receding galactic source just as the pitch of the horn of a fast moving automobile is lowered as the car speeds away from the listener. The rate of expansion of the universe increases in all directions away from us in almost direct proportion to the distance of each galaxy from the earth. The expansion, however, does not take place within the galaxies themselves.

The theory of an expanding universe poses some interesting questions and suggests some obvious corollaries. When did the expansion begin and how long will it continue? In answer to the first question, it can be shown that, at the present rate of expansion, the universe would have had a "beginning" about 5 billion years ago. This age agrees with the presently accepted age of the earth of 4.5 to 5 billion years, and implies that the solar system and the whole universe came into existence at nearly the same time. As to how long the expansion will continue, only educated guesses have been proposed. Some astronomers believe that rate of expansion is diminishing and will continue to decrease until contraction sets in. Contraction will continue until the galaxies get so close together that expansion will begin again. Another suggestion is that the universe is in a steady-state condition. Expansion is caused by the continuous emergence of new matter so that the density of galaxies is kept constant in the universe.

Astronomy demonstrates in a dramatic way the fact that science never becomes a closed book. New discoveries always bring new problems and pose new questions. The search for the answers stimulates further research and further discovery. Astronomy is old yet excitingly new; is there any other field of knowledge that can better equip us for entrance into the space age?

THE SOLAR SYSTEM

The sun is the center of the solar system. Bound to the sun by gravitational forces are the other elements of the system which include nine planets and their thirty-one moons or satellites, myriads of asteroids, thousands of comets, and innumerable meteors (Fig. 2-3). The farthest planet, Pluto, is about forty times more distant from the sun than the earth is, but compared to distances in our own galaxy, to say nothing of the universe, the solar system is very small. Indeed, an observer on the nearest star Alpha Centauri, using the largest known telescope, could not discern the planets of the solar system because of their small size. Hence, many other similar systems could exist in the universe, but would be undetected by astronomers because of inadequate instruments. Up to now only one solar system is known to exist. Table 2-a summarizes the known facts about the major elements of the solar system.

■ THE SUN. The sun is a star in the Milky Way. Its diameter is 860,000 miles and it rotates on its axis once every 25 days. Chemically, the sun is a gaseous mass of hydrogen that is constantly being changed into helium at extremely high temperatures. Part of this heat reaches the earth, and were it not for the sun the earth would be a lifeless planet. Even though the sun is entirely gaseous in composition, it contains 99 per cent of the mass of the solar system.

■ THE PLANETS. Moving in nearly the same plane around the sun are nine planets and their satellites. The smaller inner four planets in order of increasing distance from the sun are Mercury, Venus, Earth, and Mars. The outer group consists of Jupiter, Saturn, Uranus, Neptune, and Pluto. Astronomers are agreed that all the larger planets have been discovered. The most recent discovery was Pluto, the farthest planet from the sun, whose position in space was predicted by astronomers more than a decade before the actual discovery in 1930.

The only planets for which no moons are known are Mercury, Venus, and

Table 2-a. Facts About the Solar System

	AVERAGE DISTANCE FROM SUN (MILLIONS OF MILES)	MEAN DIAMETER (MILES)	DENSITY (WATER 1)	LENGTH OF TIME FOR ONE TRIP AROUND THE SUN (EARTH UNITS)
Mercury	36	2,900	6.1	88 days
Venus	67	7,600	5.06	226 days
Earth	93†	7,913	5.52	365 days
Mars	142	4,200	4.12	1.9 years
Jupiter	483	86,800	1.35	12 years
Saturn	886	71,500	0.71	29 years
Uranus	1,782	29,400	1.56	84 years
Neptune	2,793	28,000	2.29	165 years
Pluto	3,670	3,600	(?)	248 years
Sun	—	864,000	1.41	—
Moon	93	2,163	3.33	—

* Data from Robert H. Baker, 1959, *Astronomy,* 7th ed., D. Van Nostrand Co., Princeton, N.J.
† The average distance from earth to sun, 92.9 million miles, is one *astronomical unit.*

Pluto.   The earth has only one, whereas Saturn has nine and Jupiter twelve. Mars and Neptune have two each, and Uranus has five.

Planets do not radiate any light of their own but merely reflect sunlight.   Although man has speculated about the possibility of life on other planets, the only possibility lies on Mars.   The other planets are either too hot or too cold and contain no atmosphere at all or have atmosphere consisting of gases lethal to life as we know it on earth.

As for Mars, a remote possibility exists that its surface may be inhabited by extremely simple vegetational forms.   This inference is based on the color changes seen on the planet at different seasons of the year.   Mars' atmosphere is void of oxygen and contains less than 1 per cent of carbon dioxide and traces of water. Nitrogen is probably the main constituent of the Martian atmosphere.   Polar ice caps expand and contract with the seasons on Mars, and in its equatorial regions, temperatures reach 50°F.

The alleged "canals" of Mars are probably an illusion caused by the merging of complicated detail when viewed with in-adequate magnification.   Modern astronomers using photographic techniques have not been able to photograph a "canal system" that coincides with drawings of the earlier investigators.   Recently, the darker areas of Mars' surface have been related to emanations of volcanic dust clouds from Martian volcanoes, but this idea is not widely supported.

THE ORIGIN OF THE SOLAR SYSTEM

The human mind has a great relish for origins, and the speculations concerning the origin of the solar system have been no less intense than the efforts of man to determine the origin of life itself.   In the past 200 years three major theories evolved, each of which has serious defects in the light of modern astronomy.   Today, a new concept is rapidly gaining prominence in the minds of astronomers.   A brief summary of the older hypotheses will be given first, followed by a general statement of the more recent concept of the origin of the solar system.

■ CONDITIONS THAT ANY HYPOTHESIS MUST SATISFY.   Before any intelligent idea can be expressed concerning the origin of the solar system, it is mandatory that this hypothesis be compatible with all known facts about the system, and it must agree quantitatively with known physical and chemical laws.

Generally speaking, the solar system has all the earmarks of an orderly system rather than a haphazard arrangement of bodies. This condition requires a common origin for all units in the system, and because of this, it is proper to view the elements of the solar system as an organized whole rather than as individual components.

■ KNOWN CHARACTERISTICS OF THE SOLAR SYSTEM. The following statements summarize the factual data about the rela-

tionships of the planets to the sun, and can be regarded as the basic elements that need explaining in any theory of origin.

1. All planets revolve around the sun in the same direction in nearly circular orbits, most of which lie almost in the same plane (Fig. 2-3).

2. The satellite systems of the planets exhibit the same regularities except for a few outer satellites that move in the opposite direction.

3. The sun's rotation is in the same direction as the planetary orbits (Fig. 2-4).

4. The sun has 2 per cent of the total angular momentum of the solar system.

The uniform relationship of the planets

Figure 2-3.   Sketch of part of the Solar System in which the observer is located beyond Jupiter. (After Herbert S. Zim and R. H. Baker, 1956, *Stars,* Simon and Schuster, New York, p. 123.)

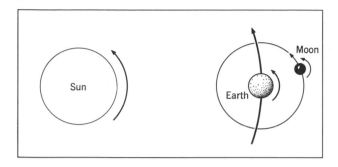

Figure 2-4. Sketch showing the rotation of the earth, sun, and moon. Not to scale.

to the sun is contrasted with the apparent eccentricity of comets. Comets move in highly elliptical orbits that are strongly inclined to the orbital plane of the planets (Fig. 2-5). It is quite logical to assume that because comets do not bear the same orderly relationship to the sun that the planets do, they must have a different although not unrelated origin.

■ KANT-LAPLACE NEBULAR HYPOTHESIS. This idea was developed by the independent efforts of a German philosopher, Immanuel Kant (1724–1804) and a French mathematician, Pierre Simon Laplace (1749–1827) in the late eighteenth century. The hypothesis assumed the existence of a large globular mass of gas, slowly rotating. The gravitational pull inherent in the initial mass caused contraction, which in turn caused an increase in rotational velocity according to the law of conservation of angular momentum. Eventually the gaseous mass became flattened into a discoidal shape. Gaseous rings near the outer rim of this system became detached or separated from the shrinking mass from time to time, each ring eventually condensing to form a planet (Fig. 2-6). The central mass contracted and became the sun, whereas the rings shed during contraction went through the same process of contracting and shedding of rings to form the satellites of the planets.

The fatal objection to this hypothesis is that the sun is rotating too slowly in comparison to the planets for this mechanism to have worked. If the Kant-Laplace system of origin actually did take place, the sun should have the greatest angular momentum because it is the most massive element of the solar system and lies at the center of the system. Actually, the sun has only 2 per cent of the total angular momentum.

■ THE CHAMBERLIN-MOULTON HYPOTHESIS. In this theory, proposed by an American geologist, T. C. Chamberlin, and an astronomer, F. R. Moulton, the sun was regarded as a star which existed before

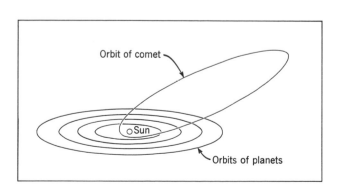

Figure 2-5. Sketch showing the relationship of the orbits of planets and comets.

Figure 2-6.   Sketch illustrating a stage in the development of the Solar System according to the Kant-Laplace hypothesis.

the planets were formed.   Another star passed close to the sun thereby exerting a strong gravitational pull.   The material torn from the sun was dragged along in the direction of movement of the passing star.   The disrupted material pulled from the sun condensed into solid particles or "planetesimals," each pursuing its own orbit around the sun.   Larger clusters of planetesimals were nuclei to which other planetesimals were welded by collision, eventually forming the planets.   Still other knots or clusters of planetesimals, fortuitously located near the clusters from which the planets formed, formed the satellites.

According to this hypothesis, the angular momentum of the planets was derived from the pull of the passing star.   But the major difficulty with that idea is that such a sideways motion of planetesimals could not be produced by the passing star, because, when it was about 100 million miles away from the sun it would be moving almost directly away from it.

■ THE JEANS-JEFFREYS TIDAL FILAMENT HYPOTHESIS.   This hypothesis also involves an original sun that had a close encounter with a passing star. The idea was conceived by Sir James Jeans (1877–1946), a physicist, and Sir Harold Jeffreys (1891–   ), a British astronomer. Tidal action of the passing star pulled from the sun a gaseous filament which later broke into individual gaseous globules, each of which eventually condensed into a planet. Some of these newly formed planets were further disrupted during their first trip around the sun in an eccentric orbit, thus providing material for the eventual development of the satellites.

Like the planetesimal hypothesis, the tidal filament concept suffers from the inability of the passing star to impart the proper angular momentum to the gaseous filament. Furthermore, astronomers eventually showed that a hot filament pulled from the sun would not form solid planets but would simply diffuse into space.

■ THE TURBULENT HYPOTHESIS. The most recent idea of the origin of the solar system links its beginning to the turbulence of a gaseous dust cloud or nebula, roughly in the shape of a disc with a diameter of the same order of magnitude as the solar system. This solar system nebula was only one of many "swirls" of primordial dust and gas, some of which formed galaxies. Each of the separate gaseous discs was a giant eddy in a huge hierarchy of eddies resulting from turbulence in the initial mass of gas and dust which formed the incipient universe.

The dust-gas cloud shrank under its own gravitational attraction, with a resulting increase in rotational speed in accordance with the law of conservation of angular momentum. Continued shrinking resulted in a nucleus which eventually became the sun, and the remainder of the gaseous dust cloud collapsed into a disc rotating around the nucleus. Turbulence in the disc resulted in the planets and their satellites.

This hypothesis is a bit too complex to treat in detail here. It does account for the regularities as well as some of the irregularities in the solar system. All the planets and satellites of the inner planets were part of the original planetary system of eddies. They all revolve in the same direction as the Earth-Moon-Sun system. The satellites of Neptune and Saturn as well as the three outer satellites of Jupiter have retrograde orbits. According to the turbulent hypothesis, these satellites were captured at a later date, after the planets had condensed to about their present size. The idea that the Moon is an offspring of the earth, having developed by a great rupture induced by solar tides, is not seriously entertained by astronomers.

Comets, according to the turbulence idea, are "leftovers" formed from the scattered innermost parts of the original cloud. Their extremely eccentric orbits (Fig. 2-5) are due to attraction by passing stars.

The turbulent or dust cloud hypothesis explains many known facts about the solar system, but it still does not explain away the small amount of angular momentum of the sun. That is, it cannot explain the sun's rotation if that rotation originated from the same motion of the original dust cloud which produced the present orbital movement of the planets. Perhaps there exists an unknown mechanism by which angular momentum was transferred from the inner part of the system to the outer part. As yet, we don't know and must conclude, therefore, that even though the concept of turbulence has many attractive features, it does not necessarily represent the final answer to the question of the origin of the solar system.

■ ORIGIN OF THE EARTH'S ATMOSPHERE. Possibly the earth's original atmosphere contained water vapor, hydrogen, ammonia, methane, and some hydrogen sulfide. Various chemical changes induced by solar radiation would dissociate hydrogen from water vapor, thereby leaving the freed oxygen to combine with ammonia, forming water and free nitrogen. The combination of oxygen and methane would yield carbon dioxide and more free water.

One prominent geologist holds the view that the earth's atmosphere is not residual from a primordial gaseous envelope surrounding the earth, but that the original atmosphere contained only carbon dioxide and nitrogen. To this simple protoatmosphere, various other gaseous constituents have been added during the course of geologic time by the emanations from volcanoes. Such volatiles as water vapor, carbon dioxide, carbon monoxide, and nitrogen accumulated gradually. In either theory the time at which free oxygen started to accumulate is still a problem.

THE EARTH'S MAJOR FEATURES

It is proper at this point to leave the realm of space and take a closer look at the main point of interest insofar as this book is concerned, the earth. To begin with, let us consider the two major features of the earth, the continents and ocean basins, and pay particular attention to the distinguishing characteristics of each. This is a necessary step before we can proceed further in the study of geology.

The total area of the earth is 196.5 million square miles of which 57.5 million square miles or 29 per cent is land, and 139.0 million square miles or 71 per cent is ocean. The continents vary greatly in size from Eurasia (20.9 million square miles) to Australia (2.9 million

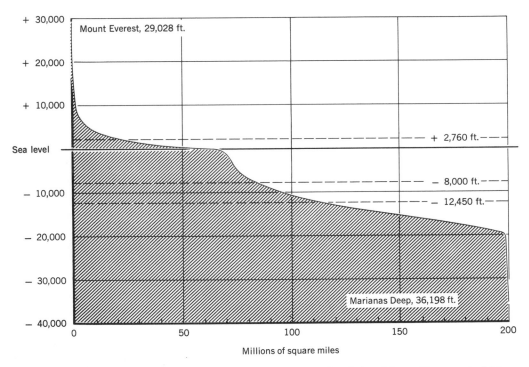

Figure 2-7. Graph showing cumulative area of the earth's surface below Mount Everest, the highest known peak. Average land elevation: 2760 feet above sea level. Average ocean depth 12,450 feet below sea level. Average elevation of the crust of the solid earth: 8000 feet below sea level. (Data in part from Encyclopedia Britannica).

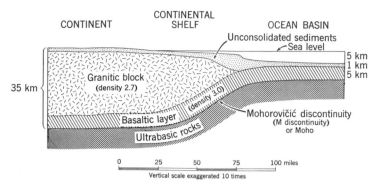

Figure 2-8.   Diagrammatic cross-section of a segment of the earth's crust showing the difference in thickness of the crust beneath the continents compared to the ocean basins.   The base of the crust is defined by the Moho.   (Based on a diagram by J. Tuzo Wilson in G. P. Kuiper (ed.), 1954, *The solar system,* vol. II, *The earth as a planet,* University of Chicago Press, Chicago.)

square miles).   The continental masses are unevenly distributed over the surface of the globe, with more than two-thirds north of the equator.

In the writings of many authors reference is commonly made to the "seven seas," but in detail it is difficult to draw completely natural boundaries to the oceans since they are all inter-connected. The three largest, Pacific, Atlantic, and Indian converge around the Antarctic continent, and the ice-covered Arctic Ocean is connected to the Atlantic and Pacific by relatively narrow straights.

Besides the variation of distribution of land and sea there exists also considerable difference in elevation of the earth's solid surface.   The highest point, Mt. Everest in the Himalayas of Nepal is 29,028 feet above sea level, and the deepest ocean sounding of 36,198 feet below sea level occurs in the Mariana Trench south of the island of Guam in the western Pacific.

The average elevation of the continents is 2760 feet above sea level, a little over $\frac{1}{2}$ mile, and the average ocean depth is 12,450 feet or roughly $2\frac{1}{3}$ miles.   Figure 2-7 portrays graphically the cumulative areas of the continents and ocean bottoms above and below sea level, the standard reference plane of all vertical measurements on the earth.

The more or less rigid shell covering the earth constitutes the earth's crust. The crust includes the rocks of the continents as well as the rocks beneath the ocean floor.   The lower boundary of the crust is 20–25 miles (30–40 kilometers) beneath the surface of the continents and only about 3 miles beneath the ocean floor (Fig. 2-8).   This boundary is known as the Moho or M *discontinuity;* both terms stand for Mohorovičić, a Yugoslavian geophysicist who first demonstrated the existence of the boundary in 1909.   The Moho separates the earth's crust from the *mantle,* which is composed of denser ultrabasic material—the details of which are discussed in a later chapter.

The fundamental difference between the continental blocks and ocean basins is *not* to be found in the fact that the former generally lie above sea level and the latter are submerged, but rather in the fact that the two are composed of different crustal materials.   The continents are underlain by a rock type known as *granite* (density 2.7), which is not found in the oceans.   Instead a heavier rock type, *basalt* (density 3.0) underlies the floor of all ocean basins.   Inspection of

Figure 2-8 shows that the lighter granitic continental block is "floating" on the heavier basaltic "sea."

The light granitic crustal materials are commonly referred to as the *sial*, a coined word taken from the first two letters of the words *si*licon and *al*uminum. These two elements occur in great abundance in granitic rocks. The basaltic crustal material beneath the ocean basins is identified by the word *sima*, a word derived from *si*licon and *ma*gnesium, the chief constituents of basaltic rocks. The terms sialic crust and simatic crust refer to the continents and ocean floors respectively.

The granitic rock is not exposed everywhere on the earth's surface because it is covered by other rock types and soil which came into being after the continental masses were formed. The basaltic material beneath the oceans is covered with about a half mile (1 kilometer) thick layer of oceanic muds, silts and oozes, but in some places in the ocean basins, notably in the Pacific and Atlantic, volcanic peaks composed of lava rise above the ocean floor. The Hawaiian Islands are outstanding examples of volcanic islands which rise 35,000 feet above the surrounding ocean floor. The absence of any granitic rock types on the floors of the ocean basins is of singular importance in deciphering the origin of each.

THE OCEAN BASINS

No phase of earth science has made greater studies since the end of World War II than oceanography. Geologists are interested in the ocean floors because of the hidden clues there that may hold the answers to many of the questions about earth history.

But in a much broader sense, all mankind has a stake in the oceans. Certainly in this last half of the twentieth century the oceans may well have to supply a multiplying population with food and water, to say nothing of the vast mineral resources that now lie untouched on their unexplored floors. Special vessels are needed to carry the scientist to the sea and expensive instruments are required to permit him to look into its depths.

The more powerful nations of the world have recognized the need for stepping up oceanographic research and are supporting expensive scientific voyages. The United States government will build several new oceanographic ships during the 1960's, and the USSR already has several in operation. Both countries along with many others will participate in the Indian Ocean Expedition of the 1960's in a joint effort to acquire new knowledge about a vast unexplored segment of our planet which someday may be of vast importance to the survival of mankind.

It is tempting to devote a larger segment of this book to this recently revitalized phase of earth science, but the reader will have to be satisfied with only a brief look at the ocean basins, and he must search through the references at the chapter's end to further satiate his appetite for more information.

■ PHYSICAL FORM OF THE OCEAN BASINS. The millions of cubic miles of sea water hide the ocean bottoms from man's view. Before the 1920's, he depended on mechanical depth measuring techniques which basically amounted to lowering a weighted wire over the ship's side until it reached bottom. Such depth measurements were not only inaccurate but also laborious and time consuming. Not until the development of the modern echo sounding devices, based on the principal of the velocity of sound waves in water, did a more accurate picture of the configuration of the ocean floor emerge. The old sounding techniques were so widely scattered that all the details of sea bottom topography went unrecognized. Not too long ago the sea floor was visualized as a rather flat featureless plain with a few broad plateaus and isolated volcanic peaks rising from its depths.

This concept has radically changed. Today, new continuously recording sounding equipment draws an accurate bottom profile beneath the track of every modern ship on the high seas. Precision navigation permits pin-point plotting of even minor details of the sea floor and provides the basis for constructing oceanic charts, the likes of which were not dreamed of earlier in this century. These charts reveal the startling fact that the topography of a large part of the sea floor is more rugged than the dry land.

The main features of the ocean basins are (1) the continental margins which contain the continental shelves and the continental slopes with their incised submarine canyons; (2) deep arcuate trenches and associated island arc systems; (3) the Mid-Ocean Ridge system; and (4) sea mounts or guyots on the ocean floor.

The continental shelves are really submerged margins of continents owing to the fact that the present volume of water in the oceans is larger than the capacity of the ocean basins. Continental shelves characteristically have a seaward slope of about 10 feet per mile and range in width from less than one mile to several hundred miles. The seaward margins of the shelves are usually somewhat less than 600 feet deep but may vary from less than 200 feet to 3000 feet. Recent studies of the continental shelves reveal that they are underlaid by a thick layer of sediments (Fig. 2-8) the base of which lies lower than the deep floor of the open ocean.

The continental slopes fringe the outer margins of the continental shelves (Fig. 2-9) and are cut by deeply incised channels called *submarine canyons.* Many of the more prominent canyons such as the Hudson Canyon off the Atlantic coast are comparable in scale to the Grand Canyon of the Colorado River. Some of the submarine canyons are associated with mouths of rivers and are considered to be seaward extensions of these rivers when sea level was lower. But the fact that many of the lower reaches of the canyons descend to great oceanic depths makes this theory of origin untenable. These depths are too great to be accounted for by lowering of sea level. It is possible that the lower segment of such canyons were cut by muddy and silty currents flowing down the continental slopes. This is known as the *turbidity current hypothesis,* a view that has widespread acceptance by many prominent geologists the world over.

The deepest soundings of the oceans are of the order of 6 to 7 miles and consistently occur in deep curved troughs or *arcuate trenches,* which are normally associated with chains of volcanic islands called *island arcs.* The latter are chains of submarine mountains with only the highest peaks protruding above sea level, as for example, the Mariana Islands which parallel the deep arcuate Mariana Trench. Other examples of the island arc and associated trenches systems are the Aleutian chain (Figs. 2-10 and 2-11); the Philippine, Japanese, and Kurile Islands; and the Puerto Rico trench curving southward around the Lesser Antilles to the island of Barbados. South of Barbados the trench is believed to be filled by sediments rapidly carried by turbidity currents from the mouth of the Orinoco River in Venezuela. Other sediment-filled trenches are also known, and it is argued by some that the deep nonfilled trenches retain their present configuration because no large river systems are near enough to supply silt and mud from which turbidity currents can form.

The Mid-Ocean Ridge system is a

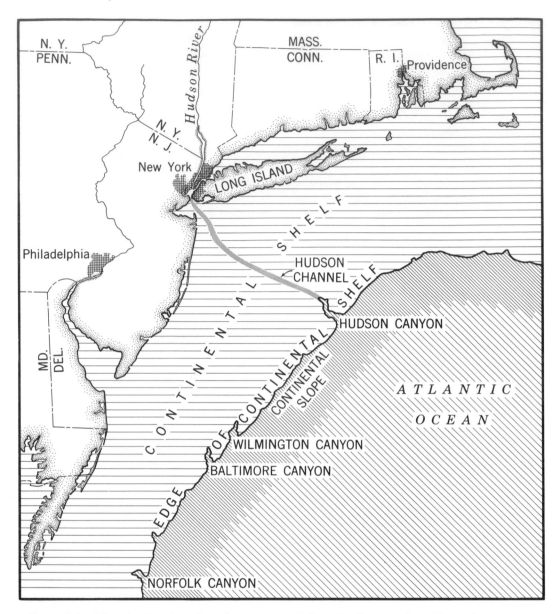

Figure 2-9. Map showing the submarine canyons off the Atlantic coast of the United States. The canyons are restricted to the edge of the continental shelf. Some, like the Hudson Canyon, are connected to the mouths of submerged channels across the continental shelf. (Based on A. C. Veatch and P. A. Smith, 1939, *Atlantic Submarine Valleys of the United States and the Congo Submarine Valley,* Geological Society of America, Special Paper 7, Plate I.)

world-encircling submarine mountain range some 40,000 miles in length that can be traced through the Atlantic, Indian, and Pacific oceans (Fig. 2-12). The best-known segment of this undersea mountain system is the Mid-Atlantic Ridge, a 1000-mile wide belt of peaks and ridges rising some 2 miles above the surrounding ocean floor. Only a few of its highest peaks emerge to form islands

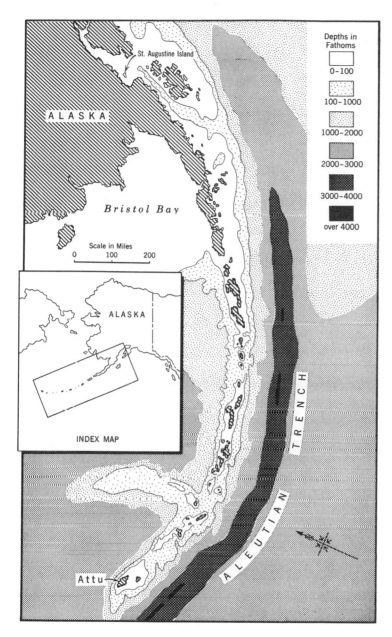

Figure 2-10. Map of the Aleutian Islands, an island arc with an adjacent arcuate trench on its convex side. (Submarine topography based on a map of Alaska by the National Geographic Society, 1956.)

such as the Azores and Ascension Island. The curious thing about the Mid-Atlantic Ridge and other parts of the entire Mid-Ocean Ridge system is that a rift or valley occupies the central portion of the range and more or less defines the axis or backbone of the whole system. This median rift is narrow—only 20 to 80 miles wide—compared with the width of the Mid-Ocean Ridge, and ranges in depth from $\frac{1}{2}$ to $1\frac{1}{2}$ miles. In some places the rift extends into the continents, as for example, the Gulf of California, the Red Sea, and the East African rift valleys.

Another quite recent discovery is the fact that this extensive subocean rift marks the position of many earthquake centers. In fact, when it became known

Figure 2-11. St. Augustine Island, Alaska, a volcanic island in the Aleutian island arc system. See Figure 2-10 for location. (Photograph by the U.S. Air Force.)

that the oceanic rift followed the Mid-Ocean Ridge, and that the rift was coincident with an active earthquake belt, research vessels such as Columbia University's *Vema* crossed the earthquake belt in many unsounded parts of the ocean where no submarine ridges were previously anticipated and found the ridge and associated rift where they were predicted. It now appears that the Mid-Ocean Ridge is a major morphologic feature of the earth that has an important bearing on the nature and history of the earth's crust.

The deep ocean basin, 12,000 to 15,000 feet deep, contains vast reaches of more or less featureless topography interrupted only by *sea mounts* and *guyots*. The former are submarine volcanic peaks that do not reach the surface and the latter are flat-topped sea mounts that occur by the hundreds in the Pacific. They apparently represent truncated volcanic cones whose peaks were planed off by wave action in the distant geologic past after which time they subsided to depths 3000 to 6000 feet below sea level. Many of the submerged volcanic peaks of the Pacific are capped with coral reefs that continued to grow upward as the islands sank, thereby maintaining an islandic surface a few feet above

sea level even though the base of the island was sinking. Such *coral atolls* abound in great numbers in the island arc systems of the Pacific ocean.

■ ORIGIN OF THE CONTINENTS AND OCEAN BASINS. It is highly improbable that we will ever know what the newborn earth looked liked. The best we can do is to assemble the known facts and speculate on what process or processes could explain them. Such speculation has given rise to several hypotheses, each of which has some merit.

The facts are rather meager. All continents are granitic and at least a part of every continent contains rocks that are 2 to 3 billion years old. The crustal material of the ocean basins is basaltic in composition; no granitic material has ever been found in the oceanic segments of the earth's crust.

One of the older ideas of continental origin involves the concept that the original earth was molten throughout with a crustal composition equal to a mixture of granitic and basaltic constituents. As the crust solidified through cooling, it separated into two major rock types, granite and basalt. The mechanism of separation is called *differentiation,* a process whereby the heavier or basaltic rock

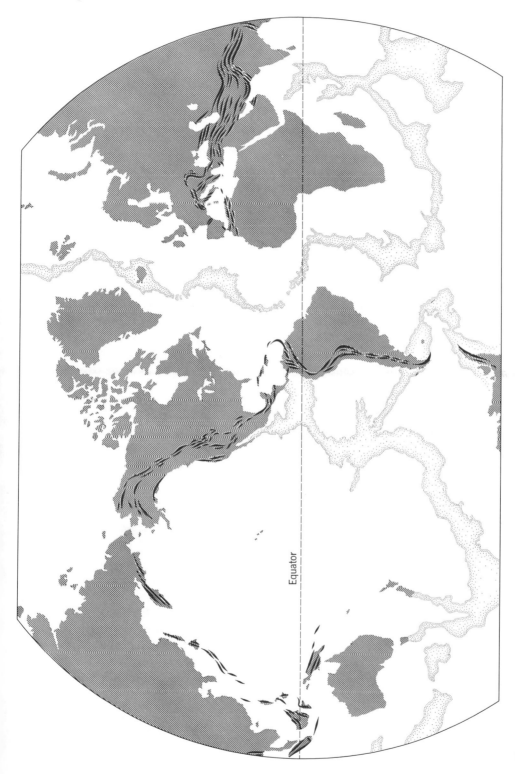

Figure 2-12. Map of the world showing the Mid-Ocean Ridge system in stippled pattern. Black bands show trends of the major mountain ranges of the continents. (Based on Plate 2 of the American Geographic Society Atlas, 1960).

Equator

material solidified first and settled to the base of the remaining molten material. The remaining light granitic material eventually cooled to form the continental part of the crust. This explanation accounts for the *difference* in composition of oceanic and continental crustal segments but does not account for the *distribution* of continents and ocean basins.

Perhaps the initial crust was not homogeneous in composition but rather more granitic in some places than in others. According to this hypothesis in its original form, the cooling of the crust and concurrent development of granitic continental blocks left the newly formed continents in approximately their present relative positions on the earth's surface.

A modification of this point of view argues that only one such "protocontinent" was formed and that it subsequently broke into smaller parts later in earth history, each part "drifting" to some position on the earth's surface (Fig. 4-2). This hypothesis of *continental drift,* proposed independently by F. B. Taylor, an American, and A. Wegener, a German, early in this century, has more widespread acceptance in Europe, Africa, and South America than it has in Canada or the United States.

A more recent hypothesis, propounded by J. Tuzo Wilson, a Canadian geophysicist, suggests that in the early phases of earth history no continents existed. Instead the earth's newly solidified crust was essentially basaltic in composition. The temperature immediately below the solid crust was higher than it is today. As further cooling progressed, gases and lava escaped through cracks in the crust. Water vapor in the gas condensed to form water and the other gases formed the atmosphere. The lava built volcanic mountains of the type found in present day island arc systems. Later the volcanic chains were altered to granitic material, thereby forming the nuclei of future continents. The sediments, eroded from these continental nuclei and deposited on fringing continental shelves, were later altered to granitic material and became part of the original nuclei. Arcuate island arc and trench systems continued to form around the fringes of the young continents, and the process repeated time after time, each cycle adding a new mass of granitic material to the continents. The continents are thus conceived as the result of an accretionary process of growth which is still in progress.

Perhaps the most recent hypothesis on the origin of the oceans and continents is that of Heezen, an American geologist. He proposed that the earth is expanding and has been ever since the crust cooled and left a granitic layer over the entire surface. Expansion of the planet caused the granitic crust to crack and break up into segments separated by basaltic material that originally lay beneath the granitic crust. According to this hypothesis the continents have retained their original size but the oceans have enlarged from cracks in the primeval crust of the earth to their present size. The rift along the axis of the Mid-Atlantic Ridge is the most recent "crack" in the crust owing to continued expansion of the earth.

SUMMARY

The earth is one of nine planets in the solar system of which the sun is the center. The solar system appears to be about the same age as the universe, 4.5 to 5 billion years. Older ideas of the origin of the solar system envisioned the planets as remains of material torn from the sun by a passing star (Chamberlin-Moulton and Jeans-Jeffreys Hypotheses), or condensation of a globular mass of gas (Kant-Laplace Hypothesis). The present thinking of many astronomers is embodied in the dust cloud hypothesis in which turbulence produced a system of eddies, each of which contracted and condensed to form a planet in the solar system. All theories have difficulty in accounting for the low angular momentum of the sun.

The earth's crust consists of two main parts; the light granitic continents (density 2.7) which occupy only 29 per cent of the earth's surface and the ocean basins underlain by basalt (density 3.0) which comprise 71 per cent of the Earth's surface. The ocean basins are filled with sea water to an average depth of $2\frac{1}{3}$ miles and the continents have an average elevation above sea level of a little more than $\frac{1}{2}$ mile. The base of the crust is the M discontinuity or Moho which lies 20 to 25 miles beneath the continents but only about 3 miles beneath the ocean bottom.

One of the major features of the ocean basins is the Mid-Ocean Ridge of which the Mid-Atlantic Ridge is the best known segment. This ridge coincides with a belt of earthquakes. Other oceanic features are the island arc systems and their associated deep trenches, the submarine canyons along the continental slopes, and guyots and sea mounts rising from the deep ocean floor.

The origin of continents and ocean basins is related to the initial crust of the earth which probably cooled from a molten state. Whether the original continents were in their present relative position, shifted about through geologic time, or grew from nuclei is still debated.

REFERENCES

Ewing, Maurice, 1961, Shape and structure of ocean basins, in *Oceanography,* edited by Mary Sears, Pub. 67, American Association for the Advancement of Science, Washington, D.C.

Heezen, Bruce, 1960, The rift in the ocean floor, Sci. American, October.

Kuiper, G. P. (ed.), 1954, *The solar system,* vol. II, *The earth as a planet,* University of Chicago Press, Chicago, Chapter 4, The development and structure of the crust, by J. Tuzo Wilson, and Chapter 6, The geochemistry of the crust, by Brian Mason.

McLaughlin, D. B., 1956, *The origin of the solar system* (unpublished mimeographed synopsis).

Poldevaart, A., 1955, *The crust of the earth,* Geological Society of America, Special Paper 62.

Reynolds, J. H., 1960, The age of the elements in the solar system, *Scientific American,* **203,** No. 5, p. 171–182.

Scientific American, 1955, *The new astronomy,* New York, Simon and Schuster.

Spilhaus, Athelstan, 1959, Turn to the sea, National Acad. Sci., National Research Council, Washington, D.C.

Urey, H. C., 1952, *The planets, their origin and development,* Yale University Press, New Haven.

Von Arx, W. S., 1962, *An introduction to physical oceanography,* Addison-Wesley Publishing Co., Reading, Mass.

The Earth's Crust

To a person uninstructed in natural history,
his country or seaside stroll is a walk through a gallery
filled with wonderful works of art,
nine-tenths of which have their faces turned to the wall.

Thomas Henry Huxley

The gross features of the earth's crust are the continents and ocean basins. The continents, at least, would be visible from an observer on the moon, and would be distinguishable from the vast expanse of ocean that separated them. The geologist does not take the space approach to the study of the planet on which he lives because he is able to study at least parts of it in considerable detail. Although the major effort during the first half of the twentieth century has been directed toward those parts of the crust above sea level, the last half of this century will see a greater trend toward extracting samples of rock and sediment from the ocean floors and continental shelves.

Having surveyed, briefly, the gross crustal features of the earth, we are now ready to examine the finer details of crustal materials, especially the rocks and minerals exposed on the land surface. This chapter deals with the way in which the most common elements of the earth's crust are found in minerals and rocks, the basic units of the inorganic world.

ELEMENTS AND COMPOUNDS

The ancient philosophers believed that only four elements existed in nature. These were fire, air, water, and earth. Gradually, this concept was dispelled as the science of chemistry evolved through the efforts of many workers. By 1960, some 102 elements were known: 10 of these were discovered after 1940. At least 94 are naturally occurring, but only 8 occur in amounts greater than 2 per cent in the earth's crust (Table 3-*a*).

An element is a substance that cannot be separated into simpler forms of matter by ordinary chemical means. The elements of the earth's crust usually occur in chemical union with each other. That is, they rarely occur in their simple form. Elements occurring alone in nature are called *native elements* of which gold, silver, copper, and carbon are examples (Plate I-*A, B, C*).

Two or more elements chemically united form a *compound*. Any specific compound has exactly the same number

Table 3-a.　The Common Elements of the Earth's Crust

ELEMENT	PER CENT BY WEIGHT*
Oxygen (O)	46.60
Silicon (Si)	27.72
Aluminum (Al)	8.13
Iron (Fe)	5.00
Calcium (Ca)	3.63
Sodium (Na)	2.83
Potassium (K)	2.59
Magnesium (Mg)	2.09
All others	1.41

* From Brian Mason, 1952, *Principles of Geochemistry*, New York, John Wiley and Sons, p. 42.

of constituent elements combined in a definite proportion. This means, for example, that pure sodium chloride (NaCl) —ordinary table salt—found anywhere on earth, has exactly the same proportion of sodium to chlorine.

On the other hand, air is not a compound but rather a *mixture* of elements and compounds. Thus a compound can be represented by a chemical formula whereas a mixture cannot. Hence, for pure water, we can write H_2O, but for air we can only note that it consists of oxygen, nitrogen, carbon dioxide, water vapor, and other minor constituents, in varying percentages, depending on local conditions of the atmosphere.

NATURAL ELEMENTS AND COMPOUNDS

An inorganic element or compound in its natural state is a *mineral*. More precisely, a substance must fulfill four conditions before it can be properly called a mineral. These conditions are as follows:

1. It must occur naturally as an inorganic substance.

2. Its composition must be such that it can be represented by a chemical formula.

3. It must have a definite internal structure (i.e., it must be crystalline).

4. Its physical properties must be fixed and controlled by composition and structure.

The *external appearance* of some minerals is evidence that some orderly arrangement of the constituents exists in the mineral. For example, Fig. 3-1 shows several different minerals, each of which occurs naturally in some precise geometric form called a *crystal*. Not only does each of these crystals have a distinct *external* shape and configuration, but the *internal* arrangement of the constituent atoms is different for each. Or, stated differently, every mineral species consists of a distinct geometric arrangement or latticework of its atomic constituents, and this three-dimensional arrangement controls the shape of the crystal. But to say that a mineral is crystalline does not imply that it must necessarily have a perfect external geometric form; it simply means that the internal position or arrangement of the atoms of the mineral is the same for all specimens of that particular mineral species, and depending on the conditions under which it formed, it may exhibit a definite external form.

A logical question is, how can the internal arrangement of atoms be known for a given mineral? The answer lies in two discoveries made more than two hundred years apart. The first involved the measurement of the angle at which certain crystal faces met. It was found that these interfacial angles were constant in specimens of the same mineral species. Using table salt as an example again, we know that the faces (or sides) of the box-like crystals always form an angle of 90°, a right angle. From this law of the *constancy of interfacial angles*, workers of the early eighteenth century deduced that the external shape of a given mineral must be controlled by the internal geometric arrangement of the constituent atoms.

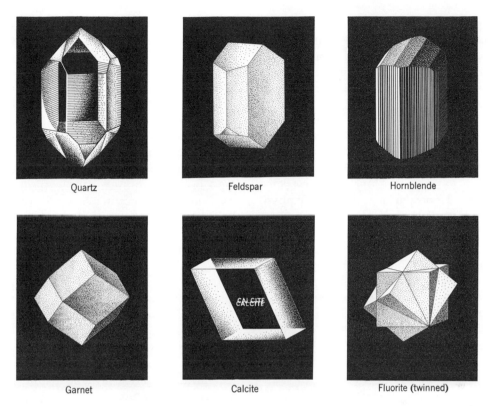

Figure 3-1. Crystals of some common minerals. The natural shape of minerals are determined by the internal arrangement of their constituent elements.

The second discovery and actual verification of this deduction came in the early part of the twentieth century, when the use of X rays was introduced into the field of mineralogy. X rays beamed through a crystalline substance are diffracted by the layered arrangement of the atoms making up the crystal. The amount and direction of diffraction can be measured and are an index of the internal structure of the mineral. Every mineral species has a characteristic X ray diffraction pattern which can be used to calculate the spacing between atoms in that particular mineral.

What is the purpose of discussing the details of crystalline materials and the arrangement of atoms in the mineral substances? Perhaps the main reason is to develop the concept that the elements of the earth's crust occur in combination with each other because of certain affinities which the various elements have for each other, and that the mineral species are fixed in their physical and chemical composition because of the manner in which the constituent atoms are linked or bound together. We could digress further into theoretical considerations of the nature of the bonding agents that hold atoms together or a discussion of the finer points of the ideas concerning the structure of atoms. Suffice to say, however, that an orderly arrangement of the atoms in any mineral is evidence that the forces of nature do not function in a haphazard way, but act according to laws that are irrevocably established.

■ PHYSICAL PROPERTIES OF MINERALS. So far, we have shown that at least one physical property of a mineral, its geometric shape, is controlled by its internal structure. Other physical properties are hardness (resistance to abrasion), optical properties, cleavage, fracture, and specific gravity.

A mineral's physical properties provide a good means of identifying individual mineral species. The physical properties of a single mineral are invariable, or at most, variable within very restricted limits. Hence, to know a few basic physical properties about the common rock-forming minerals is tantamount to knowing the mineral itself. Once a mineral has been identified on the basis of its physical properties, its chemical composition can be stated because all specimens of the same mineral species have identical physical properties and chemical compositions.

■ CLASSIFICATION OF MINERALS. The common minerals are identified on the basis of their physical properties, but the mineralogists have arranged the various minerals into groups or categories based on chemical composition. Since it is already known that about 10 per cent of the 102 known elements constitutes nearly 98 per cent of the earth's crust, it is understandable that only about two dozen important minerals exist in the common rock types.

The following paragraphs provide additional information on the minerals listed in Table 3-*b*. Plate I illustrates some of the more common types. Note that the name of a mineral has no genetic relationship to its chemical formula. Most mineral names are derived from some Greek or Latin root, the meaning of which was supposed to be related to certain properties of the mineral. A more recent practice of mineralogists is to name a newly discovered mineral after the name of a person.

NATIVE ELEMENTS. Among this group are some of the most precious metals such as *gold* (Au), *silver* (Ag), and *platinum* (Pt).

Also included are two minerals that demonstrate the importance of structure over composition. Both *diamond* and *graphite* are composed of pure carbon (C) but they differ widely in their physical properties which is a reflection of the way in which the carbon atoms are arranged in each. In diamond, the carbon atoms are closely packed and strongly bound to each other, an arrangement which explains the hardness of this gemstone. In graphite, the carbon atoms occur in a layered structure which accounts for the flaky and slippery property of that mineral. Diamond, besides being highly valued for its use as a gem, is also widely used in industry as an abrasive agent. By far the largest proportion of diamonds is used for industrial purposes. Diamonds are now made synthetically for industrial use.

OXIDES. An element combined with oxygen is an oxide. Not all elements are chemically or physically able to unite with oxygen. In nature, the most ubiquitous oxides are those containing iron. *Magnetite,* $FeFe_2O_4$ or Fe_3O_4, and *hematite,* Fe_2O_3, are two common iron oxides. *Limonite,* $Fe_2O_3 \cdot nH_2O$, is a name given to a mixture of hydrous iron oxides, and is really not a mineral in the strictest sense. All three are common rock-forming constituents, and both magnetite and hematite are the major sources of iron in iron ore. Quartz, SiO_2, is the most common of all oxides, but because of its structure, it is discussed under the silicate group.

SULFATES. Minerals containing sulfur and oxygen plus another element are known as sulfates. The most common sulfate mineral is gypsum, $CaSO_4 \cdot 2H_2O$, which is widely used for making plasters and plaster board. It is formed by precipitation from sea water.

CARBONATES. These minerals are important rock-forming materials and occur in great quantities in rocks known as limestone. *Calcite,* $CaCO_3$, and dolomite, $CaMg(CO_3)_2$, are the two most common

Table 3-b.   Some Common Rock-Forming Minerals and Their Chemical Composition

CHEMICAL GROUP	MINERAL NAME	CHEMICAL COMPOSITION*
Native Elements	Gold	Au
	Copper	Cu
	Diamond	C
	Graphite	C
Oxides	Hematite	Fe_2O_3
	Magnetite	$FeFe_2O_4$
	Limonite	$Fe_2O_3 \cdot nH_2O$
	Quartz†	SiO_2
Sulfides	Pyrite	FeS_2
	Chalcopyrite	$CuFeS_2$
	Galena	PbS
Sulfates	Gypsum	$Ca(SO_4) \cdot 2H_2O$
	Anhydrite	$Ca(SO_4)$
Carbonates	Calcite	$Ca(CO_3)$
	Dolomite	$CaMg(CO_3)_2$
Haloids	Halite	NaCl
	Fluorite	CaF_2
Silicates	Quartz	SiO_2
	Olivine	$(Mg, Fe)_2SiO_4$
Pyroxenes	Augite	$Ca(MgFeAl)(AlSi)_2O_6$
Amphiboles	Hornblende	$Ca_4Na_2(MgFe)_8(AlFe)_2(Al_4Si_{12}O_{44})(OH,F)_4$
Micas	Muscovite	$KAl_2(AlSi_3O_{10})(OH)_2$
	Biotite	$K(Mg,Fe)_3(AlSi_3O_{10})(OH)_2$
	Chlorite	$(MgFeAl)_6(AlSi_4O_{10})(OH)_8$
	Talc	$Mg_3(Si_4O_{10})(OH)_2$
	Kaolinite	$Al_2(Si_2O_5)(OH)_4$
Feldspars	Orthoclase	$K(AlSi_3O_8)$
	Microcline	$K(AlSi_3O_8)$
	Plagioclase	Isomorphous mixture of Ab and An
	Albite (Ab)	$Na(AlSi_3O_8)$
	Anorthite (An)	$Ca(Al_2Si_2O_8)$

* Chemical formulas based on Wm. H. Dennen, 1960, *Principles of Mineralogy,* revised printing, New York, Ronald Press Co.

† Chemically, an oxide; structurally, a silicate.

carbonates.   Commercially these minerals and the rocks containing them are valuable sources of calcium and magnesium carbonates which are used in the cement industry and also in the iron and steel refining process.   Like the sulfates, they are derived from sea water.

HALOIDS.   The name haloid comes from halogen, meaning "salt producer." The chief minerals of this group are halite, NaCl, and fluorite, CaF_2.   Halite is common table salt and occurs in large quantities as discrete layers of rock.   Its importance to mankind is obvious. Fluorite is not as widespread in occurrence as halite, but it is found in veins and in association with calcite and dolomite deposits.

SILICATES. Members of this group are by far the most important rock-forming minerals and it is necessary to go into a little detail about them to get a better understanding of them. Structurally, they are considerably more complex than halite with its simple arrangement of sodium and chlorine atoms in a boxlike pattern.

The silicate group of minerals is subdivided on the basis of the different internal structures revealed by X ray analysis. The basic "building block" of all silicate minerals is the SiO_4 tetrahedron shown in Fig. 3-2. It consists of one atom of silicon, Si, surrounded by four atoms of oxygen equidistant from the silicon atom. Note that the oxygen atoms are considerably larger than the silicon atom, and in the diagram showing the SiO_4 tetrahedron, the silicon is hidden from view.

Quartz. Although *quartz* is chemically an oxide, it is structurally akin to the silicate group because it contains the silica tetrahedron. In quartz the silica tetra-

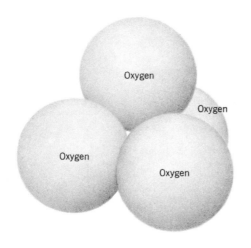

Figure 3-2. Diagram of the SiO_4 tetrahedron. Four oxygen atoms are equally spaced around a silicon atom which is not visible in the diagram. This unit of four oxygen atoms and one silicon atom is the basic building block of all silicate minerals.

hedrons are grouped in a three-dimensional framework in which the ratio of silicon to oxygen is $1:2$. In a single tetrahedron the ratio of silicon to oxygen is $1:4$, but in quartz, all the oxygen atoms are shared by adjacent silica tetrahedrons, hence the formula for quartz is SiO_2.

Pyroxene Group. The silica tetrahedrons are arranged in single chains that are held together by other atoms such as calcium, Ca; magnesium, Mg; and iron, Fe. A very common example of a pyroxene is augite, a black mineral found in many igneous rocks.

Amphibole Group. The silicates of this group have a double-chain arrangement of the silica tetrahedrons. Aluminum substitutes for silicon in the SiO_4 tetrahedrons in some cases, and the double chains are linked together by calcium, magnesium, or iron. An important difference between the amphiboles and pyroxenes is that the amphiboles contain a water molecule, which makes them hydrous. The most common amphibole mineral is *hornblende,* a black mineral which is an important rock former.

Mica Group. Chemically the micas contain a wide range of component elements but structurally they have one thing in common. They consist of sheets or layers of linked tetrahedrons; hence the term *sheet structure* is applied to all micas. This sheet structure explains why the micas have the property of separating into thin flexible layers or plates, a property called *cleavage.* Many minerals have this property, but mica has the most perfect cleavage of any common mineral.

Two important rock-forming minerals of the mica group are *muscovite* and *biotite.* The first is transparent with thin cleavage plates, and the second is brown to black. Muscovite is a hydrated potassium aluminum silicate, and biotite contains all these constituents plus iron and magnesium.

Feldspar Group. No other group of minerals is as abundant in the rocks of the earth's crust as the feldspars. This fact is

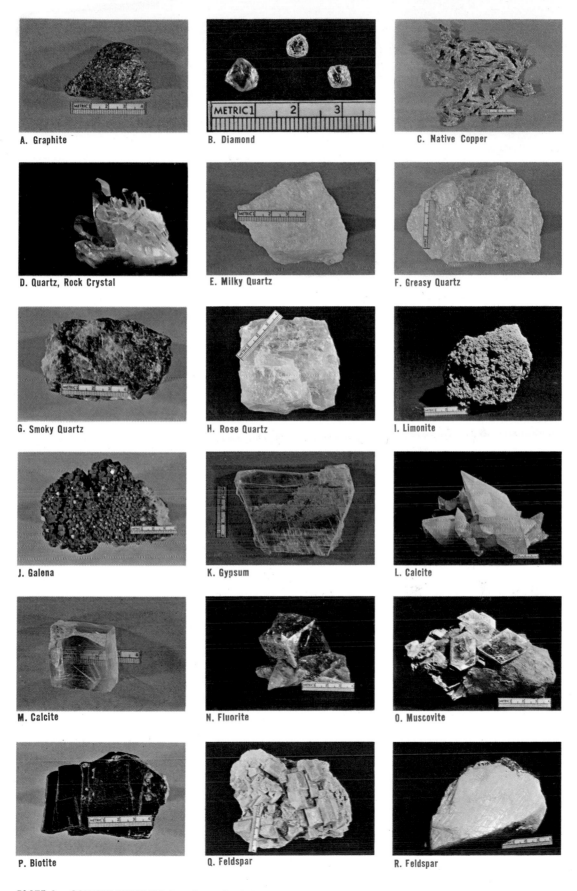

A. Graphite

B. Diamond

C. Native Copper

D. Quartz, Rock Crystal

E. Milky Quartz

F. Greasy Quartz

G. Smoky Quartz

H. Rose Quartz

I. Limonite

J. Galena

K. Gypsum

L. Calcite

M. Calcite

N. Fluorite

O. Muscovite

P. Biotite

Q. Feldspar

R. Feldspar

PLATE I.   COMMON MINERALS (see Appendix A for further details)

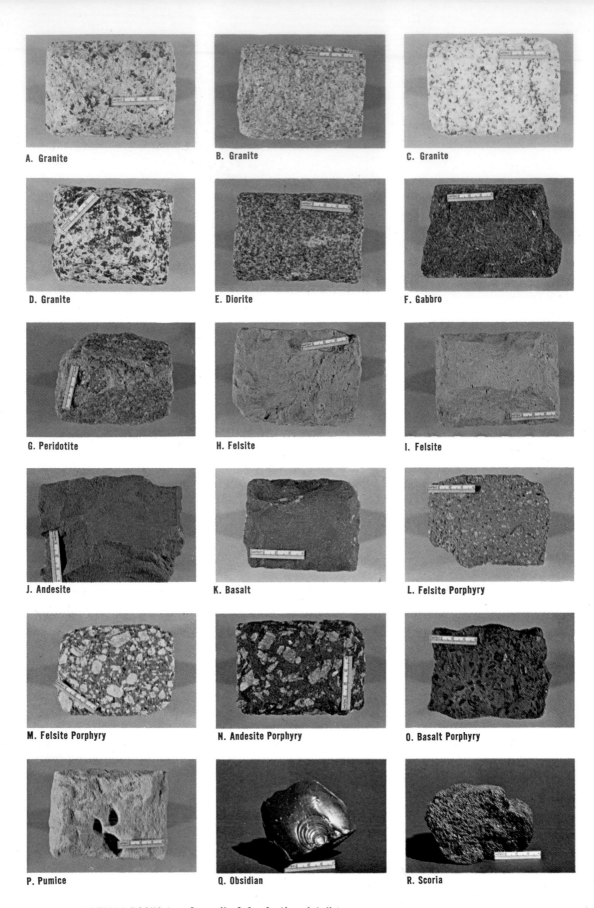

A. Granite

B. Granite

C. Granite

D. Granite

E. Diorite

F. Gabbro

G. Peridotite

H. Felsite

I. Felsite

J. Andesite

K. Basalt

L. Felsite Porphyry

M. Felsite Porphyry

N. Andesite Porphyry

O. Basalt Porphyry

P. Pumice

Q. Obsidian

R. Scoria

PLATE II.   IGNEOUS ROCKS (see Appendix A for further details)

A. Sandstone

B. Sandstone

C. Fossiliferous Sandstone

D. Arkose

E. Conglomerate

F. Breccia

G. Shale

H. Fossiliferous Limestone

I. Chert

J. Chert

K. Rock Gypsum

L. Rock Gypsum

M. Diatomaceous Earth

N. Chalk

O. Rock Salt

P. Coquina

Q. Peat

R. Anthracite

PLATE III. SEDIMENTARY ROCKS (see Appendix A for further details)

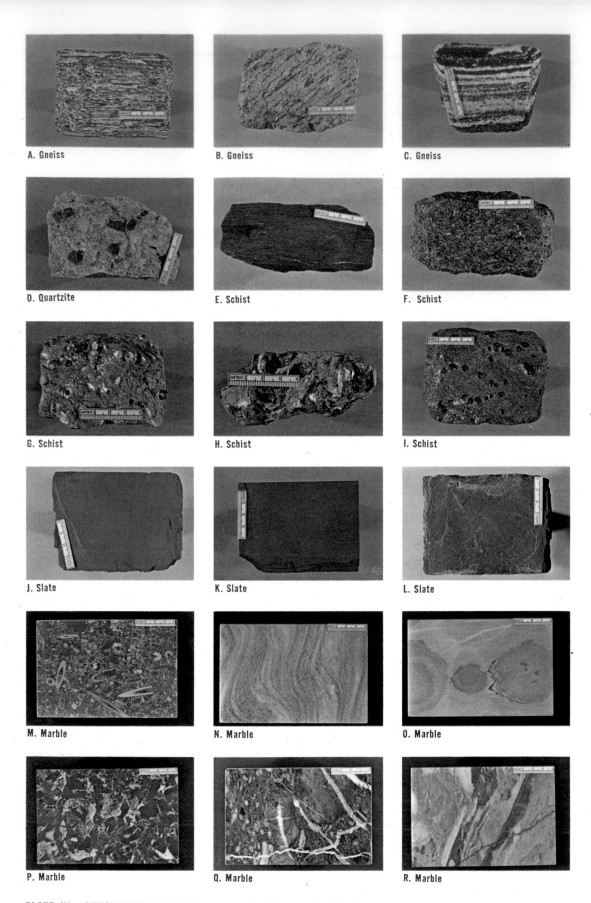

A. Gneiss

B. Gneiss

C. Gneiss

D. Quartzite

E. Schist

F. Schist

G. Schist

H. Schist

I. Schist

J. Slate

K. Slate

L. Slate

M. Marble

N. Marble

O. Marble

P. Marble

Q. Marble

R. Marble

PLATE IV. METAMORPHIC ROCKS (see Appendix A for further details)

brought out when it is noted that these minerals are composed entirely of the eight most abundant elements of the earth's crust (Table 3-*a*). *Orthoclase* feldspar, $KAlSi_3O_8$, is usually pink to flesh colored and is the chief mineral in granites. *Plagioclase* feldspar (varying mixtures of $NaAlSi_3O_8$ and $CaAl_2Si_2O_8$) also occurs in granites and rocks of similar origin. Feldspars are extremely important as rock-forming minerals. In fact, one whole class of rocks (igneous rocks) is classified on the basis of the kind and amount of feldspar present.

The plagioclase feldspars are interesting from another point of view because they form a continuous series of different minerals depending on the amounts of the two end members, *albite,* $NaAlSi_3O_8$, and *anorthite,* $CaAl_2Si_2O_8$, present in the specimens. Such a series is called *isomorphous,* meaning like in form. In other words, a plagioclase mineral may have any proportion of albite to anorthite, ranging from pure albite to pure anorthite. The unlimited variations of amounts of albite and anorthite in a plagioclase mineral are possible because the sodium of the albite and calcium of the anorthite are nearly the same size, thereby allowing one to proxy for the other in the structural framework.

The *isomorphous substitution* explains why the plagioclase feldspars are rarely found in pure form (i.e., albite or anorthite), but more commonly consist of an intermediate mixture of the two end members of the series. Isomorphism is common in other mineral groups, but it is especially important in the plagioclase feldspars from the standpoint of igneous rock classification.

ROCKS

A rock is a compositional unit, usually an aggregate of minerals, forming a significant part of the earth's crust. Rocks are the major units studied by the field geologist. He differentiates one rock type from another and plots the boundaries or contacts between the different kinds of rocks on a map, thereby constructing a geologic map. When the map is complete the geologist can draw general conclusions about the relationship between the rock units so far as their time of origin is concerned and about their potential use to mankind.

Three main categories of rocks exist, and each is further subdivided on the basis of distinguishing characteristics such as mineralological composition and texture. The three major groups are *igneous, sedimentary,* and *metamorphic.*

■ IGNEOUS ROCKS. Igneous rocks are by far the most abundant of the earth's crust. Their chief distinction is that they were formed from a hot molten mass called *magma.* Lava is magma that has reached the earth's surface through cracks and fissures, and has cooled until it has congealed into rock.

Magma might be defined as a complex high-temperature solution of silicates containing water and other gases. Magma originates below the surface of the earth, probably in the upper mantle. Since rocks at these depths are under high pressure, they can exist in the solid state at very high temperatures. If the pressure is lowered by any means, however, the very hot rocks will change to the liquid state and become mobile. The accumulation of heat from a local radioactive source in the crust might also produce magma.

Once in the liquid state, the newly formed magma works its way toward the surface, either by the melting away of the overlying rocks (assimilation) or by forcing them aside. During the process of forcing its way into the surrounding and overlying hard rock, a process called *intrusion,* the magma cools. Initially the magma may have a temperature in the 1000–2000°F range, but eventually it will cool to the temperature of the enclosing medium, either rock or atmosphere.

The cooling rate of the magma is highly important in terms of the physical appearance of the igneous rock. Slow cooling permits the growth of megascopic crystals, that is, crystals large enough to be identified with the naked eye. Such rocks possess a *coarse* or *granitoid texture* (Plate II-*A* through *G*). More rapid cooling, on the other hand results in microscopic crystals, which are clearly discernable only under a microscope or hand lens. These rocks have a *fine-grained* or *felsitic* texture (Plate II-*H* through *K*). Furthermore, if the magma should break through to the surface and cool under atmospheric conditions, it literally freezes so quickly that the various atoms cannot arrange themselves into the different structural arrangements of the silicate minerals; hence, no crystals are formed and the rock is said to have a *glassy* texture (Plate II-*P, Q, R*).

In some igneous rocks the magma underwent two stages of cooling. Evidence for this lies in the fact that certain igneous rocks contain large crystals, indicative of slow cooling, imbedded in a matrix of microscopic crystals, indicating more rapid cooling. The large crystals are called *phenocrysts* and the crystalline aggregate in which they are imbedded is called the *groundmass*. The rock itself is termed a *porphyry*. Such a relationship suggests that the magma was injected into a cooler environment after the first crystals formed (Plate II-*L* through *O*).

The cooling of a magma is a complex chemical process, but generally speaking the various silicate minerals are precipitated in a definite manner. The *ferromagnesian* minerals (iron and magnesium silicates) such as olivine and augite, which reach saturation early (at high temperatures), are among the first to be crystallized. These are followed by hornblende and biotite, then by the feldspars (pla-gioclase before orthoclase), and finally quartz.

The resulting igneous rock is thus a function of both the original composition (mineral constituents) of the parent magma and the rate of cooling (texture). It is on this basis that a general classification of igneous rocks can be made. Table 3-*c* gives a brief classification of the common igneous rocks, and Plate II illustrates some common examples.

A rock with a high proportion of ferromagnesian minerals has two general characteristics. It is usually dark-colored and has a specific gravity of about 3. In contrast, an igneous rock with a high quartz and orthoclase feldspar content is commonly light colored and has a specific gravity of about 2.7. This explains how several different types of igneous rock might be generated from the same parent magma. For example, an original magma could be divested of most of its ferromagnesian silicates because they are the first to form solid crystals as the magma cools, and they are also heavier than the remaining still-molten magma. They would thus tend to sink to the bottom of the magma chamber, leaving a residual magmatic solution of a different composition, which, when completely crystallized, would produce a light-colored igneous rock of high quartz and orthoclase content. The process whereby two distinct rock types are produced from a common magma is called *differentiation*.

■ OCCURRENCE OF IGNEOUS ROCKS. In general, igneous rocks are formed in the earth's crust in two ways. Either they crystallize beneath the crust, in which case they are *intrusive,* or they solidify at the surface and are termed *extrusive*. The intrusive rocks have a coarse texture as opposed to the fine grain or glassy texture generally displayed in the extrusive rocks.

INTRUSIVE MASSES. Although intrusive rocks were formed at a considerable

Table 3-c.   Classification of Igneous Rocks *

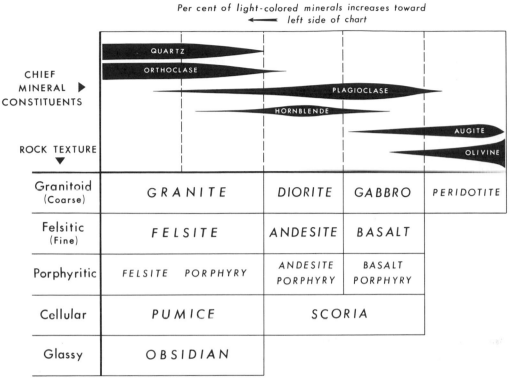

Per cent of light-colored minerals increases toward
← left side of chart

CHIEF MINERAL CONSTITUENTS ▶				
QUARTZ				
ORTHOCLASE				
		PLAGIOCLASE		
	HORNBLENDE			
			AUGITE	
			OLIVINE	

ROCK TEXTURE ▼				
Granitoid (Coarse)	GRANITE	DIORITE	GABBRO	PERIDOTITE
Felsitic (Fine)	FELSITE	ANDESITE	BASALT	
Porphyritic	FELSITE PORPHYRY	ANDESITE PORPHYRY	BASALT PORPHYRY	
Cellular	PUMICE	SCORIA		
Glassy	OBSIDIAN			

* From James H. Zumberge, 1957, *Laboratory manual for physical geology*, Dubuque, William C. Brown.

depth below the surface in past geologic time, they now protrude at the surface, because the rock into which they were intruded has been removed by the slow but persistent forces of erosion. The geologist therefore has the opportunity to study the intrusive rocks now exposed at the surface even though they were formed in the depths. Studies of many different intrusive units have revealed the presence of several different shapes and sizes of intrusive rock masses.

Figure 3-3 shows a diagrammatic cross section of some intrusive rock masses. The *batholith* is the largest of all intrusive bodies. In plan view it may be circular, elliptical, or quite irregular, but its area of surface exposure is always greater than 40 square miles. Most batholiths increase in size with depth and extend to a depth

of many miles. No drill hole or boring has ever penetrated to the base or bottom of a batholith. The three-dimensional picture of some batholiths is well known from their occurrence in mountain ranges. A *stock* is a small batholith and differs only in size of exposed surface area, less than 40 square miles.

Dikes are tabular intrusive masses ranging in thickness from a few inches to over 100 feet (Fig. 3-3). They probably represent a crustal fracture into which magma was injected (Fig. 3-4). Where they are exposed at the surface, dikes commonly form ridges which can be traced for miles across the countryside. Dikes are *discordant* because of the manner in which they cut across trends of rocks they intrude. Dikes are commonly basaltic in composition, but some are

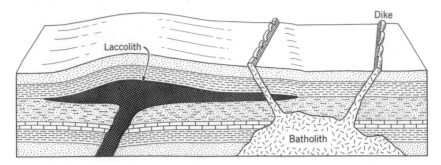

Figure 3-3. Diagrammatic cross section illustrating three kinds of intrusive rock masses. The dikes occur at the surface because the enclosing rock has been eroded away. Both the batholith and laccolith will crop out at the surface when the overlying rock has been removed by erosion.

extremely rich in quartz, orthoclase, and muscovite, and are very coarse grained in texture. These *pegmatite* dikes are important sources of commercial-grade mica, feldspar, and other minerals.

Another tabular intrusive rock mass is the *sill*. It is a layer of cooled magma between two pre-existing rock layers, and hence is *concordant* in contradistinction to a dike. If the magma forces the overlying rock into a dome or arched shape, the resultant intrusive mass is called a *laccolith* (Fig. 3-3).

In recent decades the magmatic theory of the origin of granite has been challenged. Many geologists argue that granites are produced by the change or alteration of other rock. The change is so pronounced that the character of the original rock is completely obscured. This process is called *granitization*. Geologists who favor the granitization theory argue that it is impossible to believe in the intrusion of magmas because no one has successfully explained what happened to the rock displaced by the magma. Some granitic masses have volumes of thousands of cubic miles.

Geologists who believe in the magmatic origin of granite say that some of the original country rock was thrust aside and some of it was dissolved or assimilated by the invading magma. The proponents of the granitization hypothesis claim that this is not a valid explanation and hold that the only plausible

Figure 3-4. Pegmatite dikes cutting granite in the Wet Mountains, Colorado.

means of forming a large granitic body is by an *in situ* process of alteration of the rock that previously occupied the same space. The controversy is not resolved, but most geologists agree that granite is formed by the crystallization of magma as well as by granitization. The main difference of opinion lies in the total amount of granite produced by the two mechanisms. Those who favor the granitization hypothesis claim that at least three-fourths of the known granitic masses of the earth's crust are the result of the granitization process, whereas the supporters of the magmatic theory argue that three-fourths of all granitic bodies are derived from the crystallization of magma.

EXTRUSIVE ROCKS. The most common type of extrusive rock is the lava flow. Thick lava flows, like sills, are tabular in shape and may range in thickness from a few feet to several hundred feet. Although lavas are usually associated with volcanoes, it does not follow that all lavas are ejected from volcanic cones. Some apparently oozed or welled out of crustal fractures without the spectacular fireworks attending volcanic eruptions. Lava flows display a characteristic pattern of cracks or fractures when exposed in cross section. The fractures or joints form a columnar pattern (usually hexagonal) which develops during the cooling process and is very likely the result of shrinkage (Fig. 3-5).

Figure 3-5. The vertical columns in Devil Postpile National Monument, Madera County, California, were formed when an ancient lava flow cooled. The basalt columns are about 2 feet in diameter and most of them are six-sided although some have four, five, or seven sides. (Photograph by Sierra Club, Courtesy of the U.S. Geological Survey.)

Successive lava flows have accumulated in aggregate thicknesses of many thousands of feet, as for example, the mile-thick Columbia Lava Plateau of the northwestern United States and the Deccan Lava Plateau of India.

Yellowstone Park in northwestern Wyoming is underlain by extensive lava flows, some of which are still cooling as indicated by the hot springs and geysers that originate when surface waters seep into the joints of the flows and are heated by the still hot rock.

DIFFERENCES BETWEEN SILLS AND FLOWS. Some sills are intruded so close to the surface that they develop a hexagonal joint pattern and other characteristics of lava flows. Certain conditions, developed at the time of origin of the sill or flow, aid the field geologist in distinguishing between them in the field. The possibility of confusion is readily appreciated when we consider the fact that both flows and sills are tabular, both may have identical textures and composition, and both may exhibit a well-developed hexagonal joint pattern. The possibility of mistaking a flow for a sill is increased if only part of the rock mass is visible to the observer.

The problem is usually resolved by a thorough examination of the *zone of contact* between the igneous mass and the adjoining rock *above and below* the sill or flow. A sill bakes the part of the rock it intrudes and may actually tear off parts of the intruded rocks and incorporate them into the still molten magma as fragments which are called *inclusions* (Fig. 3-6). These baked contacts as well as inclusions from the overlying and underlying rock layers characterize both the top and bottom portions of the sill.

A flow also bakes the surface over which it moved while in the liquid state, and some of the fragments of the underlying rock also occur as inclusions near the base of the flow. The surface of the flow, however, is not in contact with any

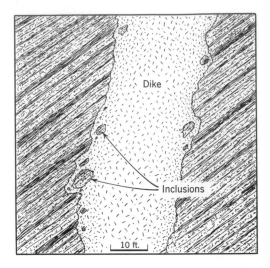

Figure 3-6. Inclusions are rock fragments derived from the intruded rock and incorporated into the intrusive rock. Inclusions may occur in any igneous rock.

other rock when it forms. But some flows are buried at a later date by another deposit. In this case, the younger sedimentary deposit on top of the flow will contain fragments of the flow rock in it, thereby revealing the true sequence of events and relative age relationships of the various rock units. Figure 3-7 shows a series of diagrams illustrating a hypothetical situation in which both a sill and lava flow bear a distinct realtionship to the sedimentary rocks that existed before and after the igneous rocks were formed.

This digression on the field relationships of flows and sills with adjoining rock units is given as an example to show how important field investigations are in the study of geology. A single hand specimen of a fine-grained igneous rock would not always reveal its field relationships. The importance of field studies in working out the relative sequence of geologic events is obvious from this example.

Another group of extrusive rocks consists of the *pyroclastics*. These are all associated with volcanism and represent

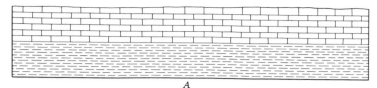

A

Undisturbed rock layers. Limestone above, shale below.

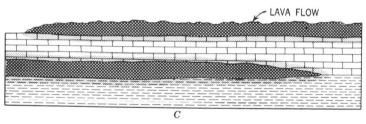

B

Sill intruded between shale and limestone. Note alteration of limestone and shale near top and bottom of sill.

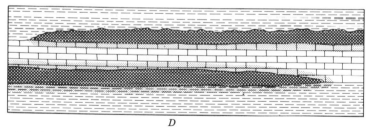

C

Lava flow extruded on limestone. Note alteration of limestone at base of lava flow.

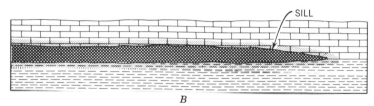

D

Shale deposited on top of lava flow. Note absence of alteration at shale-flow contact.

Figure 3-7. Sequence of cross-sectional diagrams showing the difference between a sill and a lava flow. The sill is intrusive into pre-existing rocks, but the flow is extrusive onto an older surface.

rock fragments blown out of volcanoes during eruptions. They are classified according to size and include *volcanic bombs* (Fig. 3-8) *cinders,* and *volcanic ash.* Some volcanic cones consist almost wholly of volcanic ash, as for example, Paracutin in Mexico (Fig. 3-9).

SEDIMENTARY ROCKS. Sediment is material that settles out of some medium, generally air or water. A pail of water containing silt and sand will clear as the individual particles settle to the bottom. Sedimentary rocks form in similar fashion. The settling basin may be a lake,

Figure 3-8. This volcanic bomb was a molten mass of lava ejected from a volcano during eruption. While still aloft and spinning the mass solidified into the typical shape shown here. (Photograph by Robert Logan.)

solubility of the precipitate are important factors in this process. Other sedimentary rocks consist almost wholly of the remains of plants and animal fragments. The process of sedimentation, although more susceptible to direct observation than the formation of intrusive igneous rocks, is exceedingly complex. A systematic approach to the study of sedimentation is to consider a simplified classification of sedimentary rocks. This classification cannot possibly include all the many different kinds of sedimentary rocks, but it will suffice to show what major categories exist and how they differ in terms of origin.

By volume, sedimentary rocks are about one-tenth as abundant as igneous rocks in the earth's crust; but when it comes to the rocks exposed at the earth's surface, sedimentary rocks or sediments, as they are sometimes called, cover nearly three-fourths of the land surface. A knowledge of the extent and character of individual layers of sediment provides the geologist with a means of determining the existence and extent of shallow salt water seas which formerly covered parts of the present dry land areas.

river bed, or the sea floor, and the sedimentary particles range in size from microscopic to large rock fragments. Some sediment forms by chemical action called *precipitation*, the process whereby solid particles form from a liquid solution. The temperature of the solution and the

Many of the sedimentary rock layers have undergone some change in physical

Figure 3-9. Paracutin Volcano, Mexico, 1946. The cone is mostly volcanic cinder and ash although lava was extruded from the side of the cone after initial eruption. Volcanic ash is seen billowing from the crater. (Photograph by Herbert S. Zumberge.)

Table 3-d. Size Range of Particles According to the Wentworth Scale*

NAME OF PARTICLE	DIAMETER	
	mm	*inches (approx.)*
Boulder	larger than 256	larger than 10
Cobble	64–256	2.5–10
Pebble	4–64	0.15–2.5
Granule	2–4	0.07–0.15
Sand	$\frac{1}{16}$–2	0.0025–0.07
Silt	$\frac{1}{256}$–$\frac{1}{16}$	0.00015–0.00025
Clay	smaller than $\frac{1}{256}$	smaller than 0.00015

* After C. K. Wentworth, 1922, A scale of grade and class terms for clastic sediments, *The Journal of Geology,* **30,** 381.

character, either during the process of sedimentation or shortly thereafter. Chief among such changes is *lithification,* the process whereby sedimentary rock-forming materials are changed from the loose or soft state into a hard rock. Lithification is commonly accomplished by *cementation* of the individual particles. For example, loose sand grains will be lithified to sandstone when the individual sand particles are bonded together by some mineral material such as calcium carbonate, (calcite) or iron oxide (limonite).

Three major categories of sedimentary rocks are recognized—*clastic, chemical,* and *organic.*

CLASTIC SEDIMENTS. The word clastic means fragmental. Clastic sediments are derived from fragments or individual minerals of other rocks. The size of the constituent fragments, or *texture,* is related to the conditions under which the sediment accumulated. Textural terms such as sand, silt, and clay are commonplace in the vocabularies of civil engineers and soil scientists. In geology, these terms have definite meanings in terms of the size of particles in various clastic sediments. Even the term pebble denotes a

definite size. Table 3-*d* shows the terms used in geology for the size ranges of the various particles found in sediments.

The three major kinds of clastic rocks are, in order of decreasing size of constituent particles, *conglomerate, sandstone,* and *shale.* Conglomerates contain particles of sand and larger particles. Sandstones consist of cemented sand grains which range from very fine to very coarse (Fig. 3-10). Shale is compacted silt and clay, and is the most abundant of all sedimentary rocks. Examples of clastic sedimentary rocks are displayed in Plate III-*A* through *G.*

Arkose is a coarse clastic sedimentary rock with a texture intermediate between sandstone and conglomerate. Its major mineralogic constituents are fragments of quartz and feldspar, a fact which suggests that arkoses were derived from granites.

Breccia is a coarse clastic in which the individual particles are angular in shape rather than rounded like the pebbles of a conglomerate. The differences lie in the fact that the pebbles in a conglomerate were rounded by rolling on a stream bed or by wave agitation on a sea coast. The sharp edges of the coarse fragments in a breccia imply that no such rounding

Figure 3-10. Sandstone. The ripple marks suggest a shallow water origin. (Ward's Natural Science Establishment, Rochester, New York.)

process was involved and that the fragments, however derived, must have become incorporated in a fine grain matrix without an intervening stage of wear and abrasion.

CHEMICAL SEDIMENTS. Material precipitated from bodies of fresh or salt water account for the bulk of chemically derived sedimentary rocks. These include *limestone, dolomite, rock gypsum,* and *rock salt.*

True limestones consist predominantly of the mineral calcite, $CaCO_3$, but impurities in the form of SiO_2 (chert) or $MgCO_3$ may be present (Fig. 3-11). The precipitation of calcium carbonate from sea water is most likely to occur where the carbon dioxide is decreased, thereby reducing the amount of $CaCO_3$ that can be kept in solution. Some limestones are clastics because they consist of fragments of other limestones. Some limestones are also derived from organisms, and this group is considered under organic sediments.

Dolomite is the name of a mineral or rock that contains magnesium carbonate and calcium carbonate. No satisfactory explanation exists for the origin of magnesium carbonate, because at the present time dolomite is not known to form directly from sea water. Very likely, limestones are altered to dolomite, but just how and when the transformation takes place is not known.

Rock gypsum, $CaSO_4 \cdot 2H_2O$ and rock salt, $NaCl$, belong to a special class of sediments known as evaporites. The name stems from the concept that sediments of this type develop by evaporation of sea water, or in special cases, salt water lakes. Restricted bays or arms of the seas in past geologic time were sites of the deposition of hundreds of feet of evaporites. Widespread deposits of rock salt in New York and Michigan are mined extensively for their salt content, and deposits of gypsum occur in Texas, New York, and Michigan. Examples of chemical sediments are shown on Plate III, *I* through *L.*

ORGANIC SEDIMENTS. Limestone and coal make up the bulk of organic sediments. They are derived from plant or animal fragments cemented or compacted into rock layers. Organic limestones are formed through the secretion of calcium carbonate by coral reef builders which inhabit the warm shallow seas. Coral reefs survive in clear water in a depth not greater than 150 feet. The atolls of the southern Pacific Ocean are fine examples of organic limestones in the process of formation. Some organic limestones consist of calcareous (rich in calcite) shell fragments which accumulate on the sea floor and become cemented together by calcite. Most coral reefs contain not only the main coral mass in place, but also the broken fragments of coral and sea shells washed in by wave action.

Coal represents the accumulation of vegetation that originated in a swamp environment. The original organic material is transformed to coal by increase in pressure, which expels the moisture and gaseous constituents, and increases the percentage of fixed carbon. Peat, lignite, bituminous (soft coal), and anthracite (hard coal) are varieties of coal that contain respectively higher percentages of fixed carbon.

FOSSILS. A fossil is any evidence of past life. Fossils occur most commonly in sandstone, shale, and limestone. Rocks containing conspicuous shells, shell fragments, bones, teeth, or other animal or plant remains are *fossiliferous*. A fossiliferous sandstone is shown in Plate III-*C*,

Figure 3-11. Bedded layers of limestone, Culbertson County, Texas. (Photograph by P. B. King, U.S. Geological Survey.)

and a fossiliferous limestone in Plate III-*H*. The general subject of fossils and their geologic significance is treated more fully in Chapter twelve. The study of fossils is called *paleontology*.

OCCURRENCE OF SEDIMENTARY ROCKS. All sedimentary rocks occur in nature as layers called *strata* or *beds*. Most strata were deposited in a nearly horizontal position. Later, earth movements moved the strata so that the original flat position was altered in one way or another. Some strata are simply uplifted (elevated) with no change in their horizontal position. Other sedimentary beds are warped or folded in broad flexures so that any part of the original horizontal layer is tilted or inclined. These distorted strata are referred to as *structures* and are treated in greater detail later in this chapter.

■ METAMORPHIC ROCKS. Probably the most complex of all rock types is classed as metamorphic, which literally means "change in form." Metamorphic rocks are formed by the alteration of other rocks under conditions of high pressure and temperature associated with depths several thousand feet beneath the surface. Also, the formation of metamorphic rocks takes place in the *solid state,* although some kind of metamorphic processes take place in the presence of hot liquids and gases.

Metamorphism of sedimentary or igneous rocks may produce changes that are either physical, chemical, or both. Physical changes are manifested in the texture of the metamorphic rock, whereas chemical changes during metamorphism cause the formation of new minerals, many of which are produced only during metamorphism. The metamorphric derivatives of some common sedimentary rocks are shown in Table 3-*e*.

Textural changes usually involve the process of *recrystallization,* which simply means that the original minerals undergo

Table 3-e. Metamorphic Equivalents of Some Common Sedimentary Rocks

ORIGINAL ROCK	METAMORPHIC EQUIVALENT
Shale	Slate, schist, gneiss
Sandstone	Quartzite
Conglomerate	Quartzite conglomerate
Limestone	Marble

a structural change. Recrystallization can result in the growth of new mineral crystals at the expense of the crystals in the original rock, or the original minerals may recrystallize into larger individual crystals.

Chemical changes during metamorphism arise from the exchange of elements and compounds. For instance, during the course of igneous activity, magma comes in contact with the solid rock it intrudes. The reaction that takes place is called *contact metamorphism,* a process usually involving the addition of such elements as silicon and iron. Also, the heat of the magma causes reactions to take place in the invaded rock that would not develop under temperatures normal at or near the earth's surface.

The intense heat and extremely high pressures attending metamorphism give rise to the formation of minerals that are compatible or stable in such an environment. After the metamorphic process is completed and the altered rock is exposed at the earth's surface through uplift and erosion, the metamorphic minerals are again altered or changed to new minerals that are stable under conditions of temperatures and pressures at the earth's surface. These changes are not considered metamorphic since no high pressures or temperatures are involved, and they are considered in more detail in Chapter six.

CLASSIFICATION OF METAMORPHIC ROCKS. Metamorphic rocks are classified on the basis of *texture* and *composition*. Two main textural classes of metamorphic rocks are the *foliated* and the *nonfoliated* groups.

Foliation is a physical condition in metamorphic rocks exemplified by the parallel or subparallel arrangement of certain platy minerals such as the micas, or needle-like crystals such as hornblende. Three grades of foliation are common in foliated metamorphics.

A *banded* type of foliation consists of separate bands or folia containing coarse mineral grains such as quartz or feldspar. Usually each band has only a single mineral species. The banded appearance of these rocks is produced by alternating bands of light and dark minerals. A banded metamorphic rock is called a *gneiss* (pronounced nīce) (Plate IV-*A, B, C*).

A *schistose* texture is characterized by thinner folia than that found in gneisses. The folia commonly consist of platy minerals such as the micas (muscovite, biotite). A rock with a schistose texture is called a *schist,* (Plate IV-*E, F, G, H, I*).

Slate is the third kind of foliated metamorphic rock. It is essentially a metamorphosed shale in which the clay minerals have been rearranged into parallel planes. Hence it possesses *slaty cleavage*, a characteristic property of all slates (Plate IV-*J, K, L*). This cleavage is not caused by the same conditions that produce cleavage in minerals, but is the result of the parallel arrangement of the flakes of microscopically small clay or micaceous minerals.

Many of the species of foliated metamorphic rocks contain conspicuous crystals of certain minerals embedded in the rock. These are called *metacrysts,* and they literally grow in place during the process of metamorphism. Two very common minerals that often occur as metacrysts are garnet and magnetite, but others are also abundant (Plate IV-*G, H, I*).

The name nonfoliated rock is self-explanatory and implies that the constituent minerals are more or less equidimensional so far as their shapes are concerned. Two common examples of nonfoliated metamorphic rocks are *quartzite*, a recrystallized sandstone (Plate IV-*D*), and *marble*, a metamorphosed limestone or dolomite. Marble occurs in many different colors because of small traces of iron and other elements in the original carbonate rock, but all marbles are predominantly composed of the relatively soft carbonate minerals (Plate IV-*M* through *R*).

OCCURRENCE OF METAMORPHIC ROCK. Metamorphic rock units tend to retain the characteristic shape of the rock body from which they were originally formed. In cases of severe deformation involving several episodes of metamorphic action, however, the original rock body may suffer such great distortion that the original structural elements cannot be reconstructed. The *metasediments* (metamorphosed sediments) occur mostly in folds, some of which are highly contorted. The foliation of a metamorphic rock is related to the deforming forces and not the original bedding planes. The slaty cleavage usually cuts across the original bedding planes, thereby proving that the metamorphism postdated the original sedimentary features.

FUNDAMENTALS OF STRUCTURAL GEOLOGY

In the broadest sense the structure of the earth's crust may be described as the granitic continental blocks resting on the basaltic layer (Fig. 2-8). In a narrower sense, however, the term structure is applied to the geometric shape and mutual relationships of rock masses which are much smaller than continental proportions. Structural geologists are also concerned with the mechanics of rock deformation. Still another use of the word structure, in the geological sense, refers to the arrangement and orientation of mineral grains in a rock.

The geometric or structural relationships of adjacent rock masses is basic to the understanding of the origin and age of the various rock units. These relationships are not always apparent from the visual examination of isolated patches of rock which crop out at the earth's surface or are exposed on the walls of a canyon. Most rock units such as a layer of sandstone or an igneous dike have two of its three dimensions measurable in thousands of feet. Some rock layers are identifiable as discrete units over the area of a large state.

To portray the relationships of such widely out-cropping rock units, the geologist constructs a *geologic map*. Just as a political map shows the boundaries of different states, provinces, and countries, so a geologic map shows the boundaries between different rock masses. These rock boundaries are called *contacts*. The construction of geologic maps as well as the interpretation of geologic maps made by others is a function of the trained geologist. Relationships between rock units that are difficult and unnecessarily wordy when described in prose become unambiguous and lucid when portrayed on a map.

The geologic map has one important additional use besides the delineation of contacts between rock units. It can be used to decipher *subsurface* geologic conditions in the upper part of the earth's crust. This is made possible by the fact that a geologic map is merely a two-dimensional view of a three-dimensional situation. In this respect, a geologic map has some of the virtues of a house plan. Both are drawn on a flat piece of paper, and both are scale representations of a three-dimensional structure. One does not have to be a professional architect to visualize what a house

might look like from floor plans, nor does one have to be a professional geologist to appreciate and visualize the shape of rock units depicted on a geologic map.

There is a further analogy between architectural drawings and a geologic map. The designer of a house may wish to illustrate the view of the structure from the front, side, or back instead of only the floor plan or *plan view* as it is called. To do this he draws elevations of all sides of the house. The geologist does the same thing with his rock structures, only he calls a vertical view of the rock units a *cross section* instead of an elevation. The vertical wall of a canyon is a natural cross section of the earth's crust, but because canyons or deep chasms are not always available or accessible for visual inspection, the geologist must be able to construct a geologic cross section from a geologic map. By combining the geologic map with a cross section, a three-dimensional perspective drawing known as a *block diagram* can be sketched. These are very useful in depicting the geometric relationships of the geologic units and the terrain which they underly.

This section deals mainly with the geometric shapes of rock units, their portrayal on a geologic map, and their appearance on geologic cross sections and block diagrams. Some basic definitions and concepts are treated first, after which a few simple geologic maps are introduced.

■ GEOLOGIC CONTACTS. A contact is the boundary between two adjacent rock units. On a map or cross section a contact appears as a line, but in nature, a contact is a plane. Two books standing on a book shelf are in contact along the plane of their covers which are touching. Yet, the observer sees only the line between the two books since he is looking at the edge of the plane which separates them.

Geologic contacts may be very regular; the contact between two flat-lying sedimentary rock layers may be traced as a nearly straight line for many miles along the walls of a canyon, or the contact of an igneous dike may extend across the landscape in a single direction for thousands of yards. On the other hand, some contacts are extremely complex and very irregular.

The geometry of a contact is dependent not only on the shape of the two rock units in contact with each other, but also on the configuration of the terrain which characterizes the area in question. Note the influence of the topography on the contacts between the three horizontal rock layers of Fig. 3-12 and the vertical dike of Fig. 3-13. In both cases the geometry of the rock units remains the same. Only the surface topography is different in *A, B,* and *C* of both figures.

■ ATTITUDE. Many rock units occur as layers or beds. These beds are rarely visible in their entirety over large areas because parts of them have been destroyed by erosion or are buried beneath the soil. In other cases the beds or layers are severely contorted so that the geometry of the whole rock mass is not immediately recognizable from a single vantage point. In such circumstances the geologist must decipher the geometry of the rock unit piecemeal, until he has enough observations and measurements on isolated parts of the structure to reconstruct the gross geometry of the whole rock unit.

At most outcrops where a contact is visible, the position of the contact in space is called the *attitude*. The attitude con-

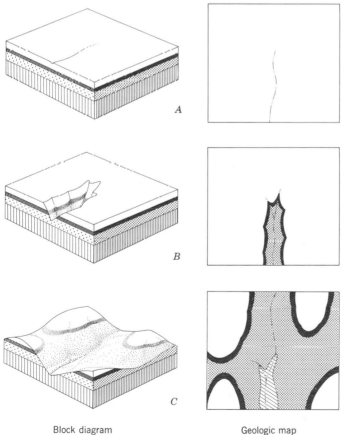

A

B

C

Block diagram   Geologic map

Figure 3-12. The geologic maps, *A, B,* and *C,* all represent identical structural situations in which the sedimentary beds are horizontal. The three maps are different because of the different topography illustrated in the block diagram adjacent to each.

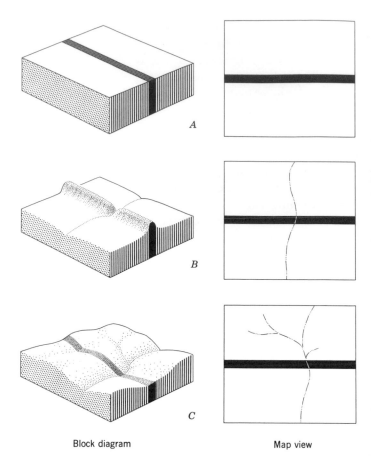

Figure 3-13. The block diagrams, *A, B,* and *C,* depict three different topographic situations in which a vertical dike crops out at the surface. The corresponding geological maps are identical.

Block diagram   Map view

sists of two parts, the *strike* and *dip*. The strike is a horizontal line in the plane of the contact. It is drawn as a line on the map and recorded as a direction (e.g., north-south). The dip is a measure of the inclination of the plane in question. It consists of the angle between the plane to be measured and a horizontal reference plane parallel to sea level (Fig. 3-14). The strike and dip notation may be applied to any geologic plane such as a bedding plane or discrete layers in a single formation.

TYPES OF GEOLOGIC STRUCTURES

■ LAYERED ROCKS. All sedimentary rocks or *strata* occur in layers. Three general types of layered structures are recognized:

(1) horizontal, (2) monoclinal, and (3) folded. Figure 3-12 is a geologic map of an area underlain by horizontal beds. Figure 3-15*A* is a block diagram showing a group of inclined beds dipping in the same direction. This is a monoclinal structure. Folded beds are shown in Figure 3-15*B* and *C* as they appear in a block diagram. Folds are of two geometric types, *anticlines* and *synclines*.

■ PARTS OF A FOLD. The two sides of an anticline or a syncline are the *limbs* of the fold (Fig. 3-16). An anticline and an adjacent syncline share a common limb between them. An imaginary plane separating the two limbs of a fold is called the *axial plane,* which, on a geologic map, appears as a line called the *fold axis.* If the axial plane has a vertical attitude, the

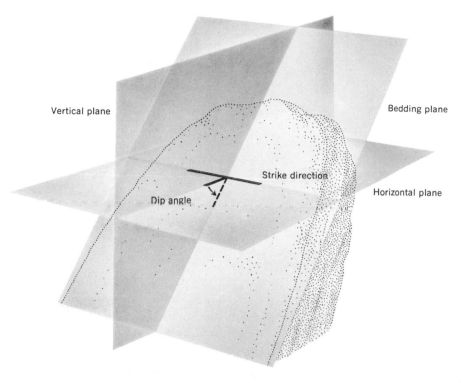

Figure 3-14. Three-dimensional view of a rock exposure in which the attitude of a bedding plane is measured with respect to a vertical and horizontal plane. The strike and dip symbol is a notation universally used by geologists.

fold is said to be symmetrical. If the axial plane is tilted so that the one limb is inclined more steeply than the other, the fold is *asymmetrical*. A fold in which the axial plane is nearly horizontal is an *overturned* fold. Both limbs of an overturned fold dip in the same direction.

Figure 3-17 shows a series of folded sedimentary strata in which three different types of folds occur. Note that the strike of the axial plane is parallel to the strike of the beds in the limbs of the fold.

■ PLUNGING FOLDS. A further complication of folds occurs when the folding is

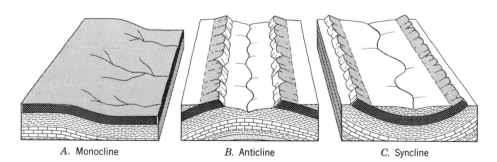

A. Monocline   *B.* Anticline   *C.* Syncline

Figure 3-15. Block diagrams of three types of folds in sedimentary strata.

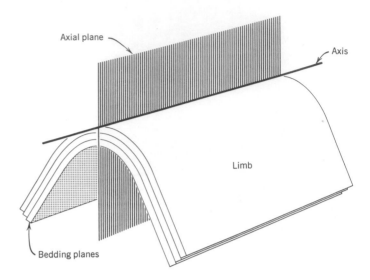

Figure 3-16. Schematic diagram showing terminology employed in describing folded strata.

not uniformly developed along the axial plane. In this circumstance the strike of the beds forming the limbs of the fold is not parallel to the strike of the axial plane of the fold (Fig. 3-18). A fold of this type is a *plunging fold*. A geologic map or aerial photograph of a plunging fold shows a diagnostic outcrop pattern (Fig. 3-19).

■ STRUCTURAL DOMES AND BASINS. A sequence of sedimentary rock layers in which the individual beds form a roughly circular or elliptical banded outcrop pattern is a *structural dome* or *basin*. The term basin or dome in a structural sense does not refer to the shape or the surface

topography, but rather, to the configuration of sedimentary layers. In Fig. 3-20 it is seen that the outcrop pattern of a structural dome is produced by beds dipping outward from the central area. A similar appearing outcrop pattern will result from beds that are dipping toward the center of the circular pattern in which case the geometrical shape of the beds is a structural basin. One of the best known structural basins in the United States is the Michigan Basin shown in Fig. 3-21.

■ FAULTS. A break or fracture in the earth's crust along which movement of the rocks on either side has occurred is a

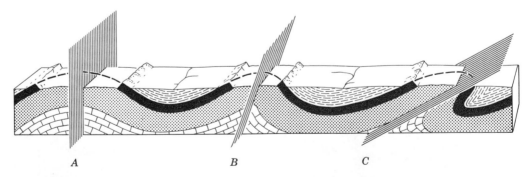

Figure 3-17. Block diagram in which three variations of folds are shown. *A*, symmetrical anticline. *B*, asymmetrical anticline. *C*, overturned anticline. Note the difference in attitude of the three axial planes.

Figure 3-18. Plunging anticline, Washington County, Maryland. (Photograph by C. D. Walcott, U.S. Geological Survey.)

fault. A *fault* is a planar feature; the actual break or fracture is called the *fault plane*. Its attitude may be determined and recorded on a map by the use of strike and dip symbols.

Faults are found in all kinds of rock masses. Rocks on opposite sides of a fault plane may be displaced or offset a matter of a few inches or feet (Fig. 5-2) or, as in the case of the great San Andreas fault of California or the large fault of South Island, New Zealand, the movement of rocks along the fault plane may have been more than 100 miles.

It is a generally accepted fact that the energy released during faulting is the

Figure 3-19. Aerial photograph of a plunging syncline near Herb Lake, Manitoba, Canada. Aerial photographs are useful in the making of geologic maps. The reader may wish to sketch a map of this photo in which the axis of the fold and strike and dip of the beds of each limb is shown. (Courtesy of the Royal Canadian Air Force.)

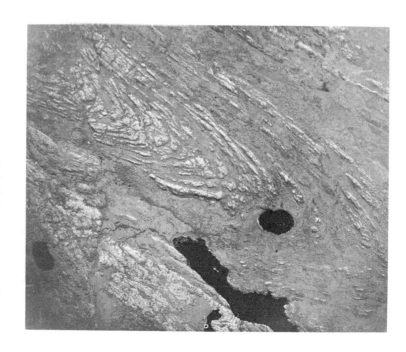

Figure 3-20. Aerial photograph of a structural dome in Wyoming. Note the pattern of strike and dip symbols. (U.S. Geological Survey.)

cause of earthquakes. This subject is treated in more detail in Chapter five. We are more concerned here with faults as geologic structures. Although a great number of faults are known and mapped on all continents, only a relatively small percentage are actually in an active state. Reoccurring movement along the San Andreas and related faults in California was responsible for many of the devastating earthquakes in that state during historical times.

The majority of known faults are inactive, however. They usually are recognizable because the geologic structure is interrupted by the fault itself. Parts of any inactive fault plane surface are rarely visible in outcrops. Usually, a fault is inferred from field evidence because of discontinuities in structural trends or outcrop patterns. Note the fault in the southeastern part of the Michigan basin (Fig. 3-21) and its effect on the outcrop pattern.

Faults may be classified according to any one of a number of systems, but here it is sufficient to consider only three general types, normal, reverse, and strike-slip. All three are defined on the basis of the relative movement on either side of the fault plane. If we consider the simple geologic situation in Fig. 3-22*A*, it is obvious that the fault plane strikes east-west and dips south. The block on the underside of the inclined fault plane is termed the *foot wall* and the block on the upper side is the *hanging wall*. These terms are derived from old mining terminology and relate to the underground mining tunnels constructed along or across a fault plane.

A *normal fault* is one in which the

hanging wall has moved down with respect to the foot wall. A *reverse fault* is one in which the hanging wall has moved up with respect to the foot wall. A *thrust fault* is a reverse fault in which the dip of the fault plane is very low—say 5 to 10 degrees.

In some faults, the hanging wall has not moved either up or down relative to the foot wall. Instead, the two blocks have moved in a horizontal direction parallel to the strike of the fault plane. Such a fault is a *strike-slip fault* (Fig. 3-22*C*).

SUMMARY

Elements combine in nature to produce minerals, the fundamental unit of the inorganic world. A mineral is a naturally occurring inorganic substance with a chemical composition fixed within definite limits, and with definite physical properties determined by the kind and internal arrangement of the constituent atoms.

The common minerals can be classified according to their chemical composition. The major chemical groups are the oxides, sulfides, sulfates, carbonates, haloids, and silicates. The silicate minerals are further subdivided on the basis of the internal structure revealed by X ray studies, with special reference to the SiO_4 tetrahedron. Quartz, although chemically an oxide, is structurally a silicate. Other members of the silicate family include the pyroxene, amphibole, mica, and feldspar groups. The feldspars are represented by orthoclase (potash feldspar) and plagioclase, an isomorphous series combining albite (sodium feldspar) and anorthite (calcium feldspar) in various proportions.

Rocks are aggregates of minerals.

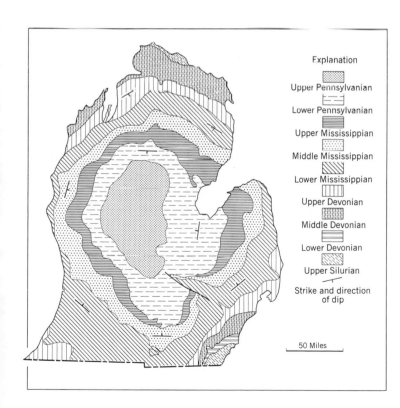

Explanation

Upper Pennsylvanian

Lower Pennsylvanian

Upper Mississippian

Middle Mississippian

Lower Mississippian

Upper Devonian

Middle Devonian

Lower Devonian

Upper Silurian

Strike and direction of dip

50 Miles

Figure 3-21. Geological map of the Michigan Basin. Note the pattern of the strike and dip symbols. (After the Geologic Map of North America, Geological Society of America.)

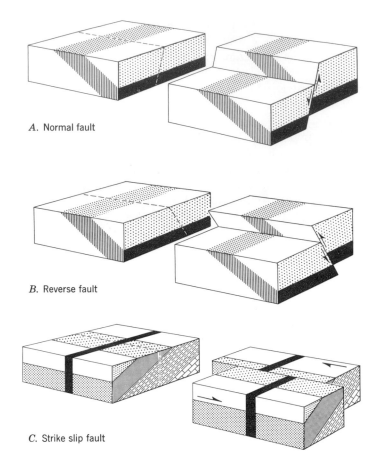

Figure 3-22. Types of faults: *A*. Normal fault in which the hanging wall has moved down with respect to the foot wall. *B*. Reverse fault in which the hanging wall has moved up with respect to the foot wall. *C*. Strike-slip fault in which the movement has been in a horizontal direction only, parallel to the strike of the fault plane. To illustrate the dislocation of strata due to faulting, the reader may wish to draw a third block diagram of series *A* and *B* in which the up-throw side of the fault block is reduced to the same level as the down-throw side. (North is toward the upper right side of each block.)

A. Normal fault

B. Reverse fault

C. Strike slip fault

Three major rock types exist: igneous, sedimentary, and metamorphic. Each major rock category is further subdivided according to texture and composition (mineral content).

Igneous rocks are intrusive or extrusive in origin. Their origin is revealed by texture, composition, and field relationships. Geologists are not in agreement as to the major mechanism involved in the origin of granite. Some favor the processes of intrusion of magma whereas others argue for granitization.

Sedimentary rocks occur in layers that are either in a horizontal position or in some other geometric form such as a monocline, anticline, or syncline.

Metamorphic rocks are produced by the alteration of some previous rock type by heat and pressure. Textural and chemical changes result. Metamorphism takes place while the rocks are in the solid state, thereby involving plastic deformation. Evidence of this deformation is displayed in the parallel arrangement of platy minerals in the foliated rocks such as gneisses, schists, and slates. Recrystallization occurs during formation of quartzite from sandstone, marble from limestone, and the growth of metacrysts in foliated rocks. Metasediments usually occur in intensely deformed layers. Overturned folds, disrupted and broken strata, and severely contorted rock layers are the natural result of the metamorphic processes.

Structural geology is a special phase of geology concerned with the geometry of rock masses and the mechanism by which rock layers of the earth's crust are deformed.

REFERENCES

Billings, Marland P., 1959, *Structural Geology,* 2nd ed., Prentice-Hall, New York.

Dana, E. S., and W. E. Ford, 1932, *A textbook of mineralogy,* 4th ed. John Wiley and Sons, New York.

deSitter, L. V., 1956, *Structural Geology,* McGraw-Hill Book Co., New York.

Heinrich, E. W., 1956, *Microscopic petrography,* McGraw-Hill Book Co., New York.

Kuiper, G. P., (ed.), 1954, *The solar system,* Vol. II, *The earth as a planet,* Chicago, University of Chicago Press. Chapter 4. The development and structure of the crust.

Poldevaart, A., 1956, *The crust of the earth,* Geological Society of America, Special Paper 62.

Walton, M., 1960, Granite problems, *Science,* **131,** 635–645.

Geologic Forces

Observe always that everything is the result of change,
and get used to thinking that there is nothing
Nature loves so well as to change existing forms
and to make new ones like them.

Marcus Aurelius

We do not have to study geology very long to arrive at the conclusion that our earth is a dynamic body. In its four or five billion years of history it has undergone much change. Mountains have been built and eroded away, glaciers have come and gone, and the oceans have transgressed the dry land. Today the dynamic aspects of the earth are manifest in erupting volcanoes, retreating glaciers, and violent earthquakes. What is the cause? Where does all the energy come from?

These questions have been asked by geologists of past generations and modern geologists are still looking for the answers. This does not mean, however, that we have not made progress toward a better understanding of the forces which keep the earth "wound up." On the contrary, new facts have come to light on which new theories and new ideas are based. In this chapter some ideas on the origin of geologic forces will be presented and some of the older concepts will be reviewed.

WHAT FORCES ARE INVOLVED

The earth's surface is a battlefield between two opposing sets of forces. One set, which we shall call the *internal forces,* originates beneath the surface. Another set originates above the surface, and these are the *external forces.*

In a broad sense, the interaction of these two groups of forces determines what the configuration of the earth's surface will be at any one time and at any one place. However, it is well to keep in mind the fact that the kinds of forces as well as their intensities vary with space and time. That is, different parts of the earth are dominated by certain forces during one segment of geologic time and by other forces at other times. Hence any intelligent study of the earth as it is today or as it was in the past must involve some idea of the forces acting both from within and without. First we will consider the internal forces which generally produce mountains.

INTERNAL FORCES

The devastating consequences of an earthquake or the explosive violence of a volcano is convincing evidence that powerful forces are at work beneath the earth's surface. But no less spectacular in the minds of geologists are the lofty mountain ranges that were once submerged and are now high above sea level. Our problem is to account for the forces that can uplift a mountain range or cause a volcano to "blow its top."

■ EARTH MOVEMENTS. As we look at the present distribution of sedimentary rocks which originally were deposited in ancient seas, we find them in various positions *above sea level.* Some of these rock layers, such as those along the Atlantic and Gulf coastal plains of the United States, are only a few tens of feet above sea level. Others have been uplifted a mile or more although the individual rock layers are still in a nearly horizontal position. Vertical uplift of the earth's surface is called *epeirogenic movement.*

In great contrast to the vertically uplifted or downwarped crustal segments are the belts of folded and distorted sedimentary rocks comprising the magnificent mountain chains of the earth. Not only have these mountainous areas been elevated high above sea level, but they have been subjected to strong lateral compressive forces acting more or less parallel to the earth's surface. Such rock-folding forces produce *orogenic movements.* Both epeirogenic and orogenic movements cause a building up of parts of the continents.

But there is still another way in which the earth's surface may be built up. As magma rises to the earth's surface it flows out and accumulates in layer after layer of lava, eventually building a high plateau such as the Columbia Plateau of the northwestern United States. Also, volcanic peaks such as Mt. Vesuvius, Mt.

Rainier, or the Hawaiian Islands represent built-up parts of the earth's surface.

Furthermore, even if the rising magma does not reach the surface, it may force the surface upward when great intrusive masses such as batholiths are formed. In fact, orogenies are invariably accompanied by the rise of magma which invades and further distorts or alters the sediments.

Orogeny, epeirogeny, vulcanism, and intrusion are all manifestations of some force acting beneath the surface. A major consideration is whether all of these *effects* are *caused* by different forces, or whether they all can be explained by a single underlying force. For a possible answer to this moot question, let us now turn to some theories on the cause of earth movements.

THE CONTRACTION THEORY. The idea of a shrinking earth was postulated more than a hundred years ago. Today the idea is still vigorously supported by many, even though some serious defects have been pointed out. The root of the contraction theory is the basic assumption that the earth was once entirely molten, an assumption accepted by most geologists, even those who oppose the contraction theory. After the earth's crust solidified because of cooling, heat loss from the still molten interior caused the globe to contract. Shrinking of the inner sphere set up compressional stresses in the crust, resulting in crumpling and folding of some of the crustal segments, much like the wrinkling of the skin of an apple when its interior shrinks while drying. But, unlike the skin of the apple which is uniformly wrinkled, the earth's "skin" contains only a few major wrinkles with vast areas of unwrinkled areas in between (Fig. 4-1). This, the contractionists argue, is because the original "skin" of the earth possessed certain zones of weakness marginal to the more rigid continental blocks. The weak zones represent the belts of folded mountains lying along the

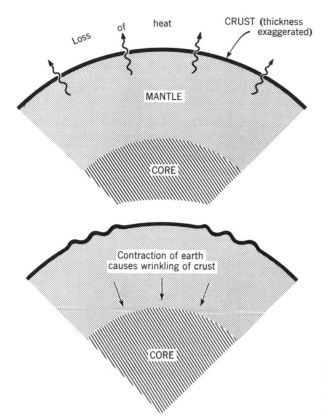

Figure 4-1. Cross section of part of the earth illustrating the contraction hypothesis as an explanation of the forces which cause crustal deformation.

margins of the continents, for example, the Rockies and Coast Ranges of western United States and the Appalachians of eastern North America. The theory was later modified to include periods of no compressional stress during which large blocks of crustal material collapsed or subsided, thereby explaining vertical crustal movements as well.

The one major objection to this scheme is the very real possibility that the earth's crust is being heated by radioactivity just as fast or faster than it is losing heat. If this is true, the whole contraction theory is untenable, because the earth would not be losing any heat and therefore is not shrinking.

THE EXPANSION HYPOTHESIS. This idea claims to explain a number of major features of the crust. The hypothesis begins with an earth having a diameter less than half the present diameter. The sialic crust uniformly covered the entire planet. Expansion caused the crust to fracture into large blocks that are the present continents. As expansion continued the blocks were separated more and more so that the space between them became the ocean basins. The upwelling of magma from the mantle broke through the rift between continental blocks during the early phase of expansion. The Mid-Atlantic ridge is visualized as the original rift between Africa-Europe and North and South America. The depression or trough along the crest of the Mid-Atlantic Ridge represents continued crusted expansion which is still going on today, as evidenced by the coincidence of an active earthquake belt with the Mid-Ocean Ridges.

CONTINENTAL DRIFT. In 1929 Alfred

Wegener, a German, proposed his theory of drifting continents. The concept originated because the east coast of South America fits like a jigsaw puzzle into the west coast of Africa. According to the theory, these continents plus Australia, Antarctica, and Asia were all part of one protocontinent called Gondwanaland that existed through most of geologic time, but for some unknown reason broke into separate blocks and "drifted" through the plastic subcrustal material to their present positions (Fig. 4-2).

One of the reasons why Wegener and his followers considered this hypothesis was that it explained the mountain belts as a result of crumpling of the various continental blocks due to friction of the underlying plastic "sea." Hence, the driftists could account for the belts of

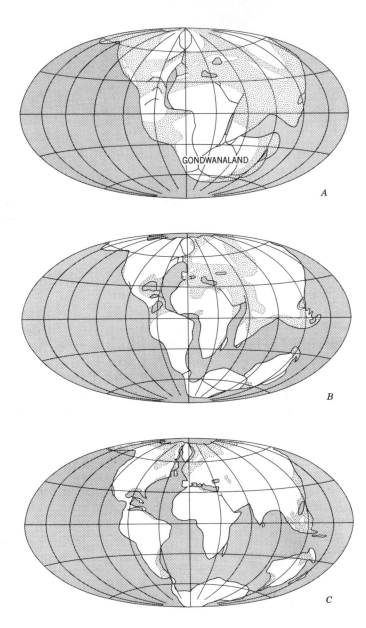

Figure 4-2. The hypothesis of drifting continents according to Wegener. Gondwanaland existed through most of geologic time (*A*), but later broke into segments (*B*) which "drifted" to their present positions (*C*). Dotted areas on continents were formerly covered with shallow seas. (After A. Wegener, from a drawing in A. L. du Toit, 1937, *Our Wandering Continents,* Edinburgh, Oliver and Boyd.)

folded mountains on the continents even though they could not explain the forces that caused the initial break-up of the original master continent.

Some geologists of Europe, Africa, and South America still adhere strongly to the idea of drifting continents because, to them, it is an attractive way of explaining many geological similarities on both sides of the Atlantic Ocean. When initially proposed, the idea never had many ardent supporters in North America because it created more problems than it solved. Not the least of these is that continental drift explains only the origin of the most recently formed mountain ranges, but leaves out entirely the older folded mountain systems.

Actually, the "drift hypothesis" was practically abandoned until a new field of earth science resurrected it and gained new support for it, even in America. The new field is *paleomagnetism* which means, "early magnetism." It refers to the history of the earth's magnetic field and is based on relict magnetism in certain rock types. A short digression into the principles of paleomagnetism is apropos here because of the growing importance of this phase of earth science and its bearing on the question of continental drift.

The earth is essentially a large dipole magnet and it is assumed that throughout geological time the north and south poles of this huge magnet have been more or less coincident with the poles of the earth's axis of rotation. We know, of course, that the earth's two poles are not exactly coincident with the magnetic poles today, but the deviation is such that when considered over a period of 1000 to 10,000 years, the earth behaves as a uniformly magnetized sphere whose axis, called the *geomagnetic axis,* is coincident with the axis of spin. The positions of the *geomagnetic poles* can be determined from relict magnetism in certain kinds of rocks.

Rocks owe their magnetic properties to the presence of small particles of iron-bearing minerals such as magnetite or hematite. These minerals, which occur in lava flows or sandstones, become oriented in the earth's magnetic field at the time that the lava cooled or the sandstone was deposited. These magnetic minerals impart to the rock containing them a magnetism parallel to the earth's magnetic field. Even though the force of magnetism in such rocks is minute, the measurements of the orientation of the magnetic field in ancient rocks permits the establishment of the position of the geomagnetic poles during past geologic time.

The most important fact which comes from paleomagnetic studies is that the earth's magnetic poles have not always occupied their present positions. If the north pole positions for each successive geologic period are plotted on a map and connected with a line, the line defines a path of *polar wandering.* The interesting thing is that a plot of polar wandering lines based on paleomagnetic data from different continents do not coincide. This discrepancy can be resolved only when it is assumed that the positions of the continents were changing relative to each other during the time that the poles were shifting. Paleomagnetic data thus seems to add strong support to the hypothesis of continental drift.

THE CONVECTION HYPOTHESIS. An ingenious explanation for all the earth's mountain belts as well as many other seemingly unrelated features of the globe is the more recent convection hypothesis championed by a number of American geologists as well as some Europeans.

Essentially, the proponents of this hypothesis conceive of some source of great heat in the mantle, such as centers of intense radioactivity, which generates movement in the form of giant convection cells. The mantle, being at a high temperature, would react like a very viscous material, and would exert a frictional drag on the crust. Velocities of rock flowage in the mantle would be of the order of a few inches per year according to reasonable estimates. Moreover, if such convection cells were operating in cyclic fashion over a period of tens of millions of years, they would not only provide a plausible explanation for folded mountains, but would also suggest that magma is generated during orogeny when some of the crustal material is dragged down into zones of high temperature. Figure 4-3 is a diagrammatic sketch showing various steps in the development of the convection currents and their effect on the crust.

This theory is attractive because it ties together many geological phenomena. Presumably, convection currents moving in directions *opposite* to those shown by the arrows in Figure 4-3 would cause parts of the crust to rise, as appears to be the case for the Mid-Atlantic Ridge. Rising convection currents should bring heat from the interior of the earth to the surface of the crust. This prediction was verified when heat-flow measurements on the Mid-Atlantic Ridge showed a faster flow of heat there in comparison with other parts of the ocean basins and the continents.

Convection currents provide a force capable of deforming the earth's crust without the necessity of having the force transmitted by the crust. A serious objection to ideas that require the crust to transmit its own force of deformation is the possibility that the crust is too weak to do so. This is one reason why the con-

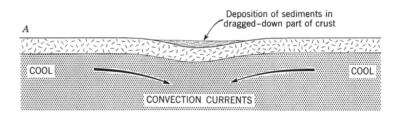

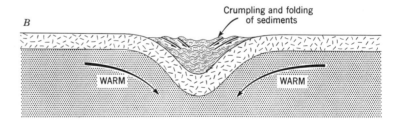

Figure 4-3. Sequence of diagrams showing the way in which convection currents deform the earth's crust and cause folded mountains. (After David Griggs, 1939, A Theory of mountain-building, *Amer. Jour. Sci.*, **237**, 611–650.)

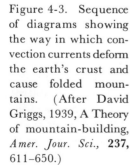
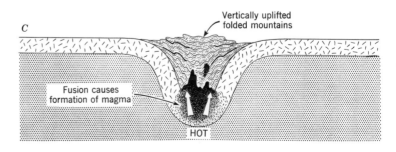

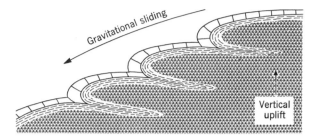

Vertical
uplift

Figure 4-4. According to the hypothesis of gravitational sliding, rock layers become distorted and folded as they slowly flow and spread out from an uplifted segment of the crust. Structures such as these can be seen in the Alps and Himalayas.

vection theory is preferred to the contraction hypothesis by many

THE ROLE OF GRAVITY. The force of gravity is considered by many students of geology to be the essential cause of many deformed features of the earth's crust. This hypothesis embodies the concept of *gravitational sliding*, a process which first requires large segments of the earth's crust to be uplifted by one means or another. Then, the hypothesis continues, gravity causes the uplifted mass to flow or creep slowly until gravitational equilibrium is restored (Fig. 4-4). It is well known, for instance, that some rocks may be deformed under their own weight if sufficient time elapses. Support for this hypothesis comes essentially from the complicated folds revealed in the Alps and Himalayas. The Alps have long attracted both European and American geologists because of their unusual structural features.

One rather comprehensive hypothesis based on some ingenious laboratory experiments by Bucher invokes, first, the contraction of the earth to provide crustal shortening by compressing weakened portions of the crust into lofty "welts"; and second, the flattening of these uplifted welts when they rise to elevations greater than can be supported by the strength of the rocks which comprise them. Gravity is, of course, the force which produces the flattening and sliding movements of the plastic crustal material.

This very brief account of some causes of mountain building is intended to point out the difficulties involved in formulating an all-inclusive hypothesis that will provide the answers to many unsolved mysteries of the forces originating within the earth's crust. The lack of firsthand observation of what goes on far beneath the surface is obvious, and it is for this reason, if for no other, that knowledge of the cause or causes of mountain building will probably always be based on indirect evidence, deductive reasoning, and intelligent speculation.

EXTERNAL FORCES

However they were formed, the uplifted segments of the earth's crust do not stand forever, nor do volcanic peaks exist for all eternity. All mountains, no matter how lofty, eventually succumb to the relentless forces acting on the earth's surface. These forces act in opposition to the forces from within, and hence tend to lower the uplifted parts of the continents to sea level.

What are these forces that can reduce lofty mountain ranges to low-lying hills, or cut deep gashes into high plateaus? We see them in action every day but they are so commonplace that many people fail to recognize them for what they are.

■ THE HYDROLOGIC CYCLE. Water, covering about 70 per cent of the earth's surface, fills the oceans more than brim full. Were it not for the sun's rays, the water would be confined to the ocean basins and would never fall as rain on the dry land. Because of solar heating, water from the sea is evaporated and carried inland as clouds of water vapor. Precipitation in the form of rain or snow releases the water from the atmosphere and places it on the surface of the ground. Then a second mighty influence, the earth's gravitational field, comes into full play. The water goes back to the sea, sometimes directly, often indirectly. But whatever path the water takes from mountain top to ocean basin, it expends energy along the way. And it is this energy that wears away the land. Throughout the entire history of the earth, the hydrologic cycle, driven by solar energy and the force of gravity, has drastically altered the face of the earth.

■ ELEMENTS OF THE HYDROLOGIC CYCLE. The path taken by a water particle from the time it is evaporated from the sun until it is again returned to the oceanic reservoir may be extremely short or incredibly long. Let us examine the many facets of the hydrologic cycle (Fig. 4-5) in some detail, for in them we find the reasons for many land forms which occupy the earth's surface.

Consider first the precipitation which falls on the continents as rain. Some of it collects in natural surface water courses and flows directly back to the sea; this fraction is called *runoff*. The geologic work done by running water accounts for most of the erosive features on the earth's surface.

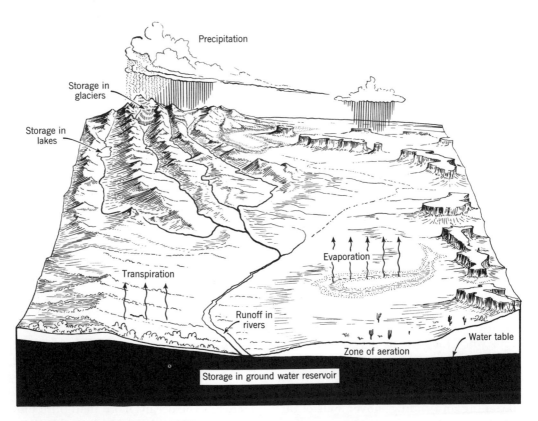

Figure 4-5. Diagram showing the major elements of the hydrologic cycle on land. Precipitation originates from the ocean. Water falling on land eventually returns to the oceans via direct or indirect routes. See text for details.

Some of the rain collects in lakes where it is temporarily stored before being re-evaporated into the atmosphere or discharged into a surface water course via the lake's outlet. Another portion of the rainfall soaks into the ground and infiltrates the pores of soil and rock where it remains temporarily stored as *ground water.* This underground water dissolves some rock material and eventually returns to the sea carrying a huge load of dissolved mineral material with it.

Plants, which use soil moisture in their life processes, return water to the atmosphere through the process of *transpiration.*

Precipitation falling as snow may accumulate during the winter but will be set free during the spring breakup. But in the polar regions and in high mountainous areas the snow builds up year after year to form *glaciers.* Some glaciers move as rivers of ice and carve deep valleys. Others, in the form of great ice sheets thousands of feet thick, slowly creep over areas of continental proportions, scraping, grinding, and wearing away the land surface in general.

The hydrologic cycle, then, is the unifying thread that binds the geologic agents together. The geologic work accomplished by each agent will be considered in more detail in chapters to follow. But for the moment, keep in mind that the geologic agents of running water, moving glaciers, ground water, and others, operating over fantastically long periods of time, can reduce mountains to hills, and hills to plains. The work accomplished by these agents is called *erosion.*

Unlike the forces from within, the external forces lend themselves to direct observational study. Even with this advantage we still have much to learn about these geologic agents and the way they operate. We know enough about the workings of each to permit us to interpret past geologic events in the light

of the hydrologic cycle, however, because it is through the study and understanding of the hydrologic cycle of today that we provide ourselves with the necessary information for the understanding and interpretation of the geologic past.

INTERACTION OF UPLIFT AND EROSION

Throughout past geologic time various parts of the earth have been subjected to spasms of uplift, whatever the cause, and each time the upraised portions have been worn down by agents of erosion operating through the hydrologic cycle. A significant feature of this uplift followed by erosion is the redistribution of materials on the earth's surface. Shifting the load on top of the crust upsets the gravitational balance. To correct this imbalance certain adjustments take place within the crust and in the upper part of the mantle.

For example, suppose that a mountain range is eroded and the sediments derived from it are transported to an adjacent basin of deposition (Fig. 4-6). Evidence from earthquake waves (discussed in Chapter five) indicates that the light crustal material beneath the mountains extends deeper into the mantle than does the crustal material beneath lower-lying continental segments, just as icebergs standing 50 feet above sea level must extend to a greater depth below sea level than icebergs rising only 25 feet. When material is removed from the top of the mountain range by erosion, the crust below rises for exactly the same reason that the base of an iceberg will rise if its top is melted away. Conversely, as the sediments derived from the mountain accumulate in a depositional basin, the basin is depressed because of the additional weight imposed on it.

This tendency for various blocks of the earth's crust to be restored to gravitational equilibrium is known as *isostasy*. Isostasy is neither a force nor a process, but is simply either a condition of balance between crustal segments of different thickness, or a tendency toward restoration of balance once it has been disturbed by some other mechanism. For example, Greenland is now in isostatic balance, but should the thick ice cap melt, the result would be a gradual rise of the land mass (Fig. 4-7).

If one segment of the crust is rising and another is sinking, a logical conclusion is that a very slow subcrustal transfer of material from the sinking area to the rising area must take place, as shown diagrammatically in Fig. 4-6.

The main thing to keep in mind about isostatic adjustment is that it essentially involves vertical movements of the crust. Isostasy, therefore, cannot be invoked to explain horizontal compression in the crust. In other words, isostasy does not account for the folded rock layers in mountain ranges, nor can isostasy explain crustal thickening in the mountainous regions. The origin of the forces causing those phenomena must lie elsewhere.

SUMMARY

The configuration of the earth's surface is determined by the interplay of two opposing forces or sets of forces; those that work from within and tend to uplift the crust, and those that work from without and wear the crust down.

The ultimate origin of the internal forces is unknown, but various hypotheses have been proposed to explain orogeny and epeirogeny during past geologic time. The contraction theory postulates a shrinking earth due to continuous heat loss since its beginning as a molten globe. The expansion hypothesis proposes that the earth has expanded over 1000 miles in diameter, thereby causing the ocean basins to be the result of the enlargement of the original cracks in the sialic crust. The Mid-Ocean Ridge system as exemplified by the Mid-Atlantic Ridge is the original rift system of the crust through which magma flowed as expansion progressed. The expansion is still in progress. Continental drift explains deformed belts as the result of the crumpling of the edges of continental blocks as they "skidded" to a stop by friction with subcrustal material, through which they floated like massive icebergs. The reason the original protocontinent broke into smaller units or the force which caused them to start moving is not explained by the driftists. Evidence from paleomagnetism tends to support the theory of continental drift.

The convection theory explains orogeny, epeirogeny, vulcanism, and igneous intrusion as a result of slow-moving convection currents produced by localized

Figure 4-6. A continental land mass rises as material is eroded from its top, just as an iceberg rises as material is melted from its surface. (After C. R. Longwell and R. F. Flint, 1962, *Introduction to physical geology*, John Wiley and Sons, New York.)

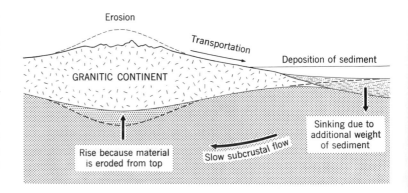

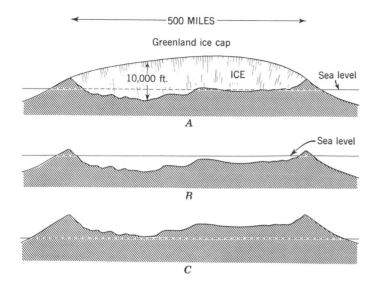

<- 500 MILES ->

Greenland ice cap

10,000 ft.   ICE   Sea level

A

Sea level

B

C

Figure 4-7. *A.* The land beneath Greenland is depressed below sea level because of the weight of overlying ice. *B.* If the ice melted, the crust would begin to rise, but would lag behind the rise in sea level caused by the return of melted glacier ice to the hydrologic cycle. *C.* Final isostatic balance, reached long after the ice melted, would raise the entire land surface above sea level.

radioactive heating near the earth's core. The crust is dragged into great downfolds when two opposing convection currents flow toward each other beneath the crust. This stage is followed by a squeezing of the sediments deposited in the downfolded area (geosyncline), the production of magma by fusion of the sediments, and rise of the magma to form volcanic extrusions or batholithic intrusions. The final stage involves the uplifting of the now thickened crust as isostatic adjustment takes over when the convection currents have died out.

Isostasy is neither a force nor a process, but rather, a tendency toward gravitational balance between crustal blocks of different thicknesses. Isostatic adjustment involves vertical movements initiated when crustal materials are shifted from one part of the earth's surface to another through the action of the hydrologic cycle.

The hydrologic cycle involves the path of moisture from a starting point in the ocean to the land surface, and back to the sea. The hydrologic cycle is driven by solar radiation and gravity. The energy contained in the cycle is expended by water flowing over the land, by glaciers grinding away on rocks, by winds attack-

ing loose soil, by ground water dissolving soluble rocks, or by waves wearing back the shores of lakes and oceans. All these happenings are external geologic processes with respect to the earth's surface. Combined or alone, they work continuously toward reducing the uplifted crustal segments to sea level.

REFERENCES

Bucher, W. H., 1956, Role of Gravity in orogenesis, *Bull. Geol. Soc. Amer.*, **67**, 1295–1318.

Carey, S. Warren, and others, 1958, *Continental drift, a symposium,* Geology Department, University of Tasmania, Hobart.

de Sitter, L. U., 1956, *Structural geology,* McGraw-Hill Book Co., New York.

Heezen, B. D., 1960, *The rift in the ocean floor, Scientific American,* October issue.

Paige, Sidney, 1955, Sources of energy responsible for the transformation and deformation of the earth's crust. In: A. Poldevaart, *The crust of the earth,* Geological Society of America, Special Paper 62, pp. 221–342.

Runcorn, S. K., ed., 1962, *Continental drift,* Academic Press, New York and London.

Umbgrove, J. H. F., 1947, *The pulse of the earth,* 2nd ed., The Hague, Martimus Hijhoff.

Van Hilten, D., 1962, *Presentation of paleomagnetic data, polar wandering, and continental drift,* Am. Jour. Sci., **260**, 401–426.

Earthquakes, Volcanoes, and the Earth's Interior

*The human mind is not satisfied with observing
and studying any natural occurrence alone,
but takes pleasure in connecting every natural
fact with what has gone before it, and with
what is to come after it.*

John Tyndall

Fifty years ago earthquakes and volcanoes were viewed mainly in the light of the frightful human experiences associated with them. In more recent years, however, geologists have learned to regard the physical phenomena resulting from earthquakes and volcanoes as some of the most important sources of information about the earth's interior. Some of the conclusions about the interior of the earth have been previewed in the previous chapters. This chapter will be concerned with the facts about earthquakes and volcanoes on which deductions about the physical conditions beneath the earth's crust are based. The way in which earthquake waves travel through the earth provides clues to the physical properties of the earth's interior, and the study of lava tells us about the nature of magma, the material from which igneous rocks are formed.

The study of earthquakes is called *seismology*, and the science of volcanoes is known as *volcanology*.

The fact that man has found some academic use for earthquakes and volcanoes does not reduce the effect of a quake or an eruption on a heavily populated area, nor is it much comfort to those who live in areas threatened by these fearful events that, with all of their modern instruments, the experts still are unable to predict accurately the time or place of the next severe shock or eruption on the earth's surface. Although it is extremely doubtful whether geophysicists will ever be able to predict the time of an earthquake to the nearest day or week, it is not beyond the realm of possibility that they eventually may be able to predict the time of occurrence to the nearest year or so. The prediction of volcanic eruptions is closer to reality, however, particularly if the volcanologists can install and monitor certain instruments on a volcano's flank, such as has been done on the island of Hawaii.

SEISMOLOGY: FACTS ABOUT EARTHQUAKES

An earthquake is a natural vibration of the ground produced by the rupturing of large masses of rock beneath the surface. The intensities of earthquakes vary over a wide range from those barely perceptible to people near by to those which create widespread destruction of life and property. The energy released during the largest shocks is roughly equivalent to 10,000 of the original atom bombs dropped on Hiroshima late in World War II.

The place beneath the earth's surface where an earthquake originates is called the *focus,* and the point on the earth's surface immediately above the focus is the *epicenter.* Earthquake foci are distributed in three general depth ranges. Shallow earthquakes originate within 40 miles of the surface. Intermediate earthquakes have foci between 40 and 200 miles down, and the deep focus earthquakes originate at depths between 200 and 400 miles. The deepest focus ever recorded was 435 miles. Most of the million earthquakes a year are shallow. These also have the greatest energy.

■ DISTRIBUTION OF EARTHQUAKES. The greatest belt of earthquake activity is concentrated in what is known as the circum-Pacific belt. Earthquakes in this area affect Alaska, the Aleutian Islands, Japan, the Philippines, New Guinea, New Zealand, and the west coasts of North and South America (Fig. 5-1). Another belt extends from the Mediterranean eastward through Asia and eventually joins the Pacific belt in the East Indies.

Theoretically, no place on the earth's surface is entirely safe from earthquakes. However, 80 to 90 per cent of the shallow and intermediate shocks and almost all the deep focus quakes are concentrated in the circum-Pacific belt. Nearly all of the remainder of shallow and intermediate earthquakes occur in the Mediterranean-Asiatic belt. A few major shocks and a number of minor ones occur along the Mid-Atlantic Ridge as well as in the Arctic and Indian Oceans.

In the eastern United States earthquakes of varying intensities have occurred in Boston (1775), Missouri (1811), South Carolina (1886), Maine (1904), New York City (1937), and Chicago (1938). Eastern Canada has also experienced several shocks within the last hundred years.

The California-Nevada region has had about five thousand earthquakes a year since the first human record of a California quake in 1769. This amounts to about $2\frac{1}{2}$ per cent of all quakes felt in the entire world, and almost 90 per cent of all shocks felt in the United States exclusive of the Hawaiian Islands and Alaska. VanderHoof estimates that an earthquake of sufficient intensity to be felt by a person somewhere in the California-Nevada region occurs on the average of once every hour and three-quarters. It is for this reason that the science of *seismology,* the scientific study of earthquakes, made its North American debut in California when the first earthquake recording instrument, a *seismograph,* was set up at Berkeley in 1887. We thus turn to California for much of our knowledge about the causes and effects of earthquakes.

THE SAN FRANCISCO EARTHQUAKE OF 1906

On April 18, 1906, San Francisco was partially destroyed by a severe earthquake. To this day it is probably one of the best documented quakes of California history. Oddly enough, direct damage

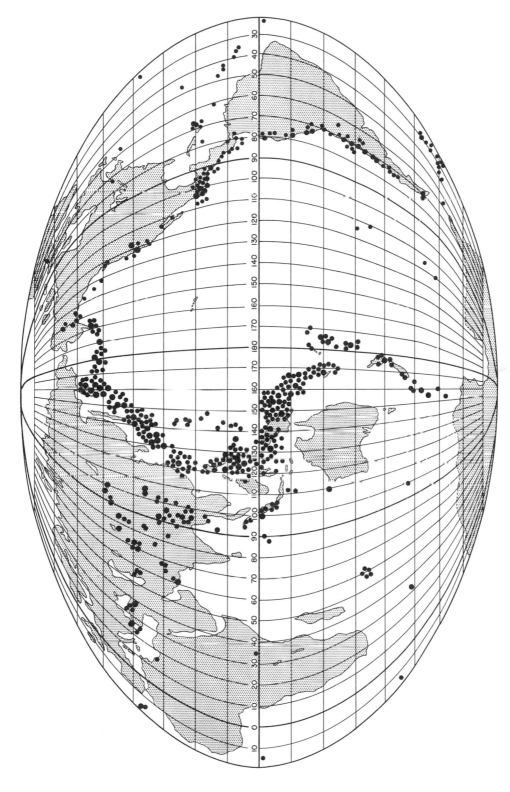

Figure 5-1. Map showing the distribution of large earthquakes. (After H. Benioff and B. Gutenberg, 1955, *Earthquakes in Kern County, California during 1952*, California Department of Natural Resources, Division of Mines, Bulletin 171.)

by the quake to buildings and property on that fateful day amounted to only about 5 per cent of the total damage. Most of the havoc was caused by fire which broke out after the quake. The quake itself lasted only about 40 seconds, but water mains, disrupted by the shock, reduced the fire-fighting capacity of the city to nil. The quake's intensity has been exceeded many times elsewhere, but the geologic circumstances surrounding it make the San Francisco quake one of the most valuable examples of the way in which an earthquake is produced. A more recent example of a well-documented earthquake is the Hebgen Lake earthquake which occurred in Montana in 1959. Both of these earthquakes are discussed in some detail later in this chapter.

CAUSES OF EARTHQUAKES

Aristotle (384–322 B.C.) explained earthquakes as the result of entrapped air escaping from the earth's interior. No less fanciful were the writings of some theologians two thousand years later who taught that earthquakes were manifestations of God's wrath.

Modern earthquake theory is based on factual data rather than the musings of philosophers and theologians. Earthquakes are produced by the slippage of rock masses along a rupture or break called a *fault*. Where such faults intersect the earth's surface, a *fault trace* is produced (Fig. 5-2).

One of the most intensely studied and best-known faults in the earth's crust is the San Andreas fault of California which passes near San Francisco. The surface trace of this great fault extends from a point off the Oregon coast to the lower reaches of the Gulf of California (Fig. 5-3), a total distance of over 1800 miles. Not only is the trace of the San Andreas fault visible on the ground but its trend beneath the ocean has been established by the positions of many earthquake epicenters. The total movement along the fault since its origin in the geologic past is estimated by some geologists at 350 miles, the west side having moved to the north. Sporadic movements along this fault resulted in many earthquakes including the San Francisco quakes of 1906 and 1957. Displacement along the fault

Figure 5-2. Fault scrap associated with the Fairview Peak, Nevada earthquake of December 16, 1954. (Photograph by James T. Wilson.)

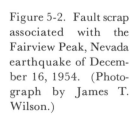

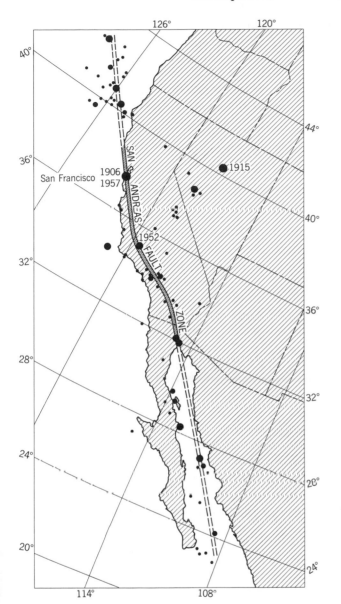

Figure 5-3. The black dots show the distribution of earthquakes in California and Nevada. Most of them are related to the San Andreas fault zone. (After H. Benioff and B. Gutenberg, 1955, *Earthquakes in Kern County, California during 1952,* California Department of Natural Resources, Division of Mines, Bulletin 171.)

zone in 1906 was practically all in a horizontal direction and amounted to 21 feet. Why did the slippage take place on that early morning in April 1906?

The answer to this question lies in the *elastic rebound theory,* a widely accepted idea advanced by seismologists to explain the mechanism of faulting. This theory does not account for the force which produced faulting, however, but only the

manner in which the rocks yield to these forces. Ultimately, the forces which cause faulting are the same as those which produce the mountains and other structural features of the crust.

■ THE ELASTIC REBOUND THEORY. When a solid is squeezed (by compression) or stretched (by tension) it deforms according to certain physical laws which depend on the inherent properties of the solid itself.   The squeezing or stretching force on a unit is called a *stress,* and the deformation of the solid yielding to the stress is called *strain.*

Elastic materials are those in which the stress is proportional to the strain.   For example, to increase the length of a rubber band to twice its unstretched length, a certain pull is required.   If the amount of stretching is doubled, twice the pull must be exerted, and if the stretching is tripled, three times the original pull is required.   But the band cannot be stretched indefinitely because eventually it will break.

The same analysis can be applied to a stick of wood bent across the knee.   Up to a certain point the stick can be deformed without breaking.   If the bending stress is released, the stick returns to its original unstressed shape, but if the stress continues to increase, the stick snaps.   At that instant the stress returns to zero.

Some materials are elastic up to a certain stress value.   When the stress exceeds a certain point, the solid continues to deform *without the addition of more stress.* Such deformation is called *plastic deformation,* and the stress value where the deformation changes from elastic to plastic is called the *yield point.*   Another factor involved in this matter is the rate at which the stress is applied.   For some solids it has been shown experimentally that if the stress is applied very slowly, the material will deform plastically at stress values far below the "normal" yield point.   But when the stress is built up rapidly, the material ruptures or breaks shortly after the yield point is reached without much plastic deformation.   This important experimental evidence may explain why rocks will be folded under certain conditions and faulted under others.

In rock masses where the stress is building up rapidly, faulting occurs, and when rupturing takes place an earthquake is born.   Hence the elastic rebound theory requires that the stresses build up rapidly to the point where rupture takes place. Some breaking may occur before the principal shock in the form of *foreshocks,* and adjustments along the fault zone after the principal shock produce *aftershocks* (Fig. 5-4).

After the principal shock occurs, most of the strain in the rocks is released. However, the ruptured zone is a plane of weakness along which further movement will take place when the stress becomes large enough to overcome the friction which holds the two sides of the ruptured rock mass together.   Hence recurrent movements along faults like the San Andreas are to be expected.

EARTHQUAKE WAVES

The energy released during movement along a fault plane is transmitted away from the focus in the form of earthquake waves.   The seismograph is an instrument which automatically records the various kinds of earthquake waves and their exact time of arrival even at recording stations so far from the epicenter that the waves cannot be felt by humans.

A network of seismograph stations is absolutely necessary for the study of earthquakes.   Several hundred stations are in operation all over the world, especially in Japan, New Zealand, central Europe, and North America.   California alone has more than twenty permanent stations.

The seismograph consists essentially of a weight suspended from a rigid frame. The frame vibrates when earthquake waves arrive, and the suspended weight tends to remain at rest because of its own inertia.   By measuring the magnified movement of the frame with respect to the

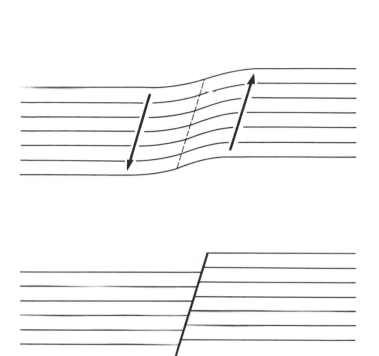

Figure 5-4. Diagram showing the development of an earthquake by faulting, according to the elastic rebound theory. (After H. Benioff and B. Gutenberg, 1955, *Earthquakes in Kern County, California during 1952*, California Department of Natural Resources, Division of Mines, Bulletin 171.)

suspended mass, the traces of earthquake waves are recorded. A mechanism is also attached to the seismograph which accurately places time marks on the record sheet so that the exact time of arrival of each vibration can be determined. The graphic record produced by a seismograph is a seismogram (Fig. 5-5).

■ TYPES OF EARTHQUAKE WAVES. The energy released during faulting produces two classes of waves. One group, known as *body waves,* travels deep within the earth. The second group, known as *surface waves,* travels along the surface. Body waves consist of longitudinal waves (*P* waves) and transverse waves (*S* waves). The terms transverse and longitudinal refer to the vibration direction in relation to the direction of propagation of the wave (Fig. 5-6). The *P* waves travel faster than the *S* waves and therefore arrive at the seismograph station before the *S* waves.

Seismologists have been able to construct travel-time graphs for earthquake waves (Fig. 5-7). Such graphs show that the difference in time of arrival of *P* and *S* waves at a seismograph station is a function of the distance between the station and the epicenter of the quake. The farther away the station is from the epicenter, the greater will be the time lapse between the *P* and *S* waves. The seismographs indicate the distance but not the

Figure 5-5. Seismogram of an earthquake recorded at Victoria, B. C. on May 24, 1944. The dashes along the lower margin give the time in minutes at the recording station. The epicenter of this quake was located at 2.5° South Latitude, 152° East Longitude, near New Ireland. The time of the shock was fixed at 12:58 Greenwich Civil Time. (Courtesy of James T. Wilson, University of Michigan.)

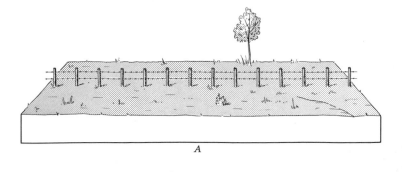

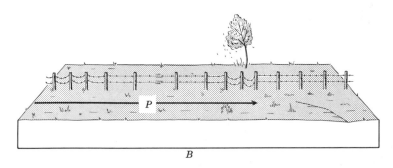

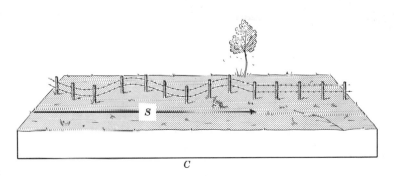

Figure 5-6. Earthquake waves are vibrations of the ground. The above diagrams show the effect *P* and *S* waves would have on a straight fence if the waves were greatly exaggerated. The arrow shows the direction of propagation of the waves.

direction of the epicenter; therefore, seismograms from a minimum of three stations are necessary to locate it accurately.

■ EARTHQUAKE INTENSITY. The energy released during an earthquake is a difficult thing to measure. The forces released during the explosion of a thermonuclear device are reported in terms of the equivalent explosion of tons of TNT. A similar quantitative reporting of earthquakes is highly desirable. A scale of earthquake intensities based on the energy at the focus has actually been de-

vised. It is known as the *Richter scale,* after the California seismologist who developed it. The Richter scale is based on seismograms and is the most scientific of the various scales.

Two other scales used to show earthquake intensity are the *Rossi-Forel* scale and the *Mercalli* scale. Both are qualitative in that they are based on human reaction to the quake and on damage to man-made structures. The Rossi-Forel scale is named after M. S. de Rossi, an Italian, and F. A. Forel, a Swiss, both of

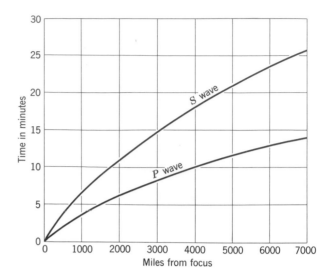

Figure 5-7. Graph of time versus distance traveled by *P* and *S* waves. (Based on data in K. E. Bullen, 1954, *Seismology,* Metheum and Co., London, p. 95.)

whom were seismologists in the late nineteenth century. The modified Mercalli scale (Table 5-*a*) is still used in situations where insufficient seismographs do not permit the more analytical approach to intensity determinations at varying distances from the epicenter of the earthquake.

An earthquake intensity map shows the diminishing intensity of an earthquake at increasing distances from the place of origin of the shock. Lines connecting points of equal intensity are called *iso-seismal* lines, and they are plotted on a map of the area affected by the earthquake. A good example of such a map is the one shown in Figure 5-8, constructed on the basis of the Hebgen Lake earthquake of 1959.

In the area of the epicenter of the earthquake near the Montana-Wyoming border, an intensity of X on the modified Mercalli scale was assigned to it. The limits of the "felt" area extended more than 500 miles from the epicenter. The quake was actually felt by persons as far away as Regina, Saskatchewan; Calgary, Alberta; Seattle, Washington; Salt Lake City, Utah; and Dickenson, North Dakota.

The Hebgen Lake earthquake caused considerable damage and loss of life. The quake was clearly caused by movement along a fault. Offsets along the fault plane were measured at 10 feet in a horizontal direction and 15 to 20 feet in a vertical direction. The most spectacular and disastrous effect of the earthquake was the dislocation of a great mass of rock and soil which cascaded from the south wall of the Madison River Canyon. The debris roared down the steep canyon slope from a zone 1300 feet above the canyon floor and formed a barrier across the Madison River, thereby creating a lake 175 feet deep and nearly 7 miles long. Most of the people killed as a result of the earthquake were engulfed in the Madison Canyon slide.

The main shock occurred on August 17, 1959, but aftershocks continued almost daily until the end of the year.

THE EARTH'S INTERIOR AS DEDUCED FROM EARTHQUAKE WAVES

In an earlier chapter the major subdivisions of the earth were defined as the crust, mantle, and core. The reader may

Table 5-a. Modified Mercalli Earthquake Intensity Scale (Abridged) *

I.   Not felt except by a very few under specially favorable circumstances. (I Rossi-Forel scale.)

II. Felt only by a few persons at rest, especially on upper floors of buildings. Delicately suspended objects may swing. (I to II Rossi-Forel scale.)

III. Felt quite noticeably indoors, especially on upper floors of buildings, but many people do not recognize it as an earthquake. Standing motorcars may rock slightly. Vibration like passing of truck. Duration estimated. (III Rossi-Forel scale.)

IV. During the day felt indoors by many, outdoors by few. At night some awakened. Dishes, windows, doors disturbed; walls make creaking sound. Sensation like heavy truck striking building. Standing motorcars rocked noticeably. (IV to V Rossi-Forel scale.)

V.   Felt by nearly everyone, many awakened. Some dishes, windows, etc., broken; a few instances of cracked plaster; unstable objects overturned. Disturbances of trees, poles, and other tall objects sometimes noticed. Pendulum clocks may stop. (V to VI Rossi-Forel scale.)

VI. Felt by all, many frightened and run outdoors. Some heavy furniture moved; a few instances of fallen plaster or damaged chimneys. Damage slight. (VI to VII Rossi-Forel scale.)

VII. Everybody runs outdoors. Damage **negligible** in buildings of good design and construction; **slight** to moderate in well-built ordinary structures; **considerable** in poorly built or badly designed structures; some chimneys broken. Noticed by persons driving motorcars. (VIII Rossi-Forel scale.)

VIII. Damage **slight** in specially designed structures; **considerable** in ordinary substantial buildings with partial collapse; **great** in poorly built structures. Panel walls thrown out of frame structures. Fall of chimneys, factory stacks, columns, monuments, walls. Heavy furniture overturned. Sand and mud ejected in small amounts. Changes in well water. Persons driving motorcars disturbed. (VIII+ to IX− Rossi-Forel scale.)

IX. Damage **considerable** in specially designed structures; well-designed frame structures thrown out of plumb; **great** in substantial buildings, with partial collapse. Buildings shifted off foundations. Ground cracked conspicuously. Underground pipes broken. (IX+ Rossi-Forel scale.)

X.   Some well-built wooden structures destroyed; most masonry and frame structures destroyed with foundations; ground badly cracked. Rails bent. Landslides considerable from river banks and steep slopes. Shifted sand and mud. Water splashed (slopped) over banks. (X Rossi-Forel scale.)

XI. Few, if any, (masonry) structures remain standing. Bridges destroyed. Broad fissures in ground. Underground pipelines completely out of service. Earth slumps and land slips in soft ground. Rails bent greatly.

XII. Damage total. Waves seen on ground surfaces. Lines of sight and level distorted. Objects thrown upward into air.

---

* Modified Mercalli Intensity Scale of 1931. Harry O. Wood and Frank Neumann, *Bulletin of the Seismological Society of America, vol. 12, No. 4, December 1931.*

wonder how such positive statements can be made about parts of the earth that have never been observed directly. The answer lies in the tremendous strides made by seismologists in the interpretation of earthquake waves. The knowledge gained from earthquake waves used in conjunction with laboratory experi-

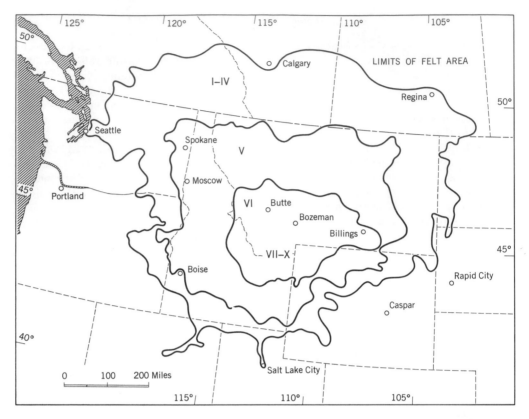

Figure 5-8.   Earthquake intensity map of the Hebgen Lake Earthquake, August 17, 1959.   Roman numerals indicate intensities according to the Modified Mercalli Scale.   Table 5-*a* describes the intensity characteristics of each of the zones.   (After R. A. Eppley and W. K. Cloud, 1961, *United States Earthquakes, 1959,* U.S. Coast Guard and Geodetic Survey.)

ments has revealed much about the earth as a planet.

Theoretical considerations confirmed by laboratory experiments reveal that vibrations travel faster as the elasticity of the transmitting medium is increased. (Elasticity is simply an expression of the ratio of stress to strain.)   It is also known that velocity decreases as density increases.   Seismologists have learned that the velocities of body waves increase as they penetrate the deeper portions of the earth, at least to a depth of 1800 miles (Fig. 5-9).   Hence, the deduction is that the elasticity of the earth increases more rapidly than the density with depth. The question is, however, does the earth consist of a number of concentric shells, each of which permits waves to travel at a higher velocity than the shell immediately surrounding it, or is the increase in the velocity of earthquake waves gradual so that no sharp boundaries exist?   Actually, the evidence points to both conditions, some definite boundaries (discontinuities) do exist, but between these the increase in velocity is gradual.

THE CRUST

The base of the crust is marked by a sharp boundary known as the Mohorovičić discontinuity or Moho (Fig. 5-9).

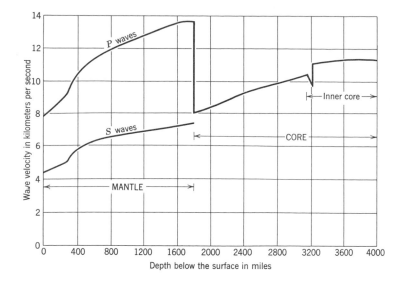

Figure 5-9. Graph showing the change in velocity of *P* and *S* waves at different depths below the earth's surface. (Based on a diagram by P. Byerly, 1942, *Seismology,* Prentice-Hall, New York.)

At this depth, 20 to 30 miles below the surface of continents the velocities of both *P* and *S* waves increase abruptly. The speed of *P* waves increases from a velocity of about $6\frac{1}{2}$ kilometers per second (4 miles per second) to about 8 kilometers per second (5 miles per second) as they cross the M discontinuity at the base of the crust.

The depth of the Moho is greater beneath the continents than beneath the ocean basins (Fig. 2-8), and is deeper beneath mountains than lowlands (Fig. 5-10). Also, some seismic evidence sug-

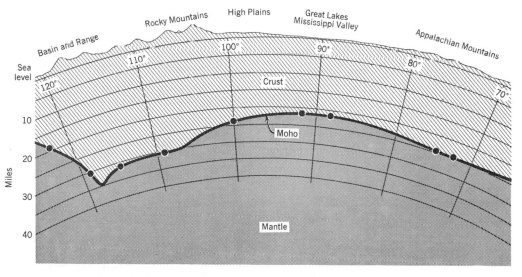

Figure 5-10. Cross section of North America showing the variation in crustal thickness as determined by seismic means. The black dots are points at which the base of the crust were actually established by seismic records. The vertical scale of the topography and crustal depths is exaggerated 20 times. The numbers at the top are degrees of longitude. (After Jack Oliver, 1959, Long earthquake waves. *Scientific American,* March.)

gests the presence of an intermediate layer lying above the Moho but below the granitic continental crust. This zone is denser than granite, a fact which suggests that it is probably equivalent to the basaltic material which characterizes the oceanic crust. The upper limit of this intermediate "layer" is not well defined, however.

The long surface earthquake waves travel faster in oceanic crustal material than they do in continental crustal rocks. This fact gives added support to the concept of light granitic continents "floating" in a sea of basalt.

THE MANTLE

From the M discontinuity to a depth of 1800 miles, the velocity of both P and S waves increases gradually (Fig. 5-9). About 300 miles down there is an increase in the *rate* of velocity increase. The experts are not in agreement as to the significance of this flexure in the velocity-depth curve, but the geophysicist, Birch, believes that it indicates a boundary between materials of different composition rather than a boundary between two phases of the same material. About 500 miles down the rate of velocity increase falls off somewhat.

From 500 miles to 1800 miles the mantle is apparently quite uniform in composition but increases in density. The most pronounced discontinuity below the crust is the core boundary which not only indicates a change in density and composition, but a change in state as well.

THE CORE

Earthquake waves that reach depths of 1800 miles or more are drastically affected. The P wave arrives several minutes "late" after it passes through the core, and S waves are lost entirely. S waves are transverse and therefore cannot be transmitted through a material that lacks rigidity. Liquids and gases have no rigidity, but in view of the high density the materials at the earth's core must have, it is not probable they are in the gaseous state.

This leaves us with the concept that the earth's core consists of an extremely dense liquid, dense because the earth as a whole has a density of 5.52 whereas the crustal rocks have densities of about 2.7 to 3.0, and the difference must be made up in the deeper earth materials. The density of the core is probably 12 or more, but its exact composition is not known. Some favor an iron-nickel composition whereas others support the idea of iron-silicate core.

An abrupt velocity increase of P waves at 1360 miles below the core boundary (3160 miles below the earth's surface) suggests an inner core (Fig. 5-11). This may mean a change from the liquid to the solid state, but this is not a well-established fact.

Modern views concerning the origin of the earth's magnetic field attribute it to electric currents generated by the motion of the liquid core. This is possible because the core is thought to be metallic and therefore a good conductor.

A diagrammatic wedge of the earth is shown in Fig. 5-11, and Table 5-b summarizes the physical properties of the different zones of the earth.

VOLCANOLOGY

Of all nature's violence the eruption of a volcano is the most spectacular. The early Greeks and Romans identified volcanic eruptions with the activities of certain of their gods. Vulcan, the Roman god of fire, forged arrows for Apollo, a shield for Achilles, and the armoured

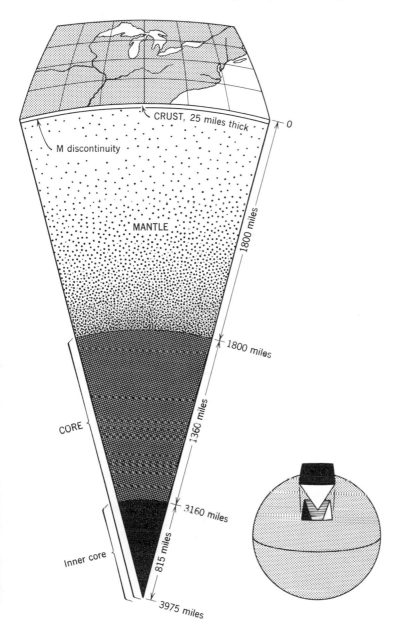

CRUST, 25 miles thick

M discontinuity

MANTLE

1800 miles

0

1800 miles

1360 miles

CORE

3160 miles

Inner core

815 miles

3975 miles

Figure 5-11. Diagram of a wedge of the earth showing the major zones and boundaries. For a summary of the physical properties of each see Table 5-*b*.

breast plate of Hercules. The eastern Mediterranean region, the seat of western civilization, provided a number of active volcanoes such as Vesuvius, Etna, and Stromboli, on which the early writers could direct their imaginations.

The Aztecs of Mexico, the Polynesians of the Pacific, and the Japanese of Honshu all had rituals related to fire gods who dwelt in the volcanoes of their lands. Even today, superstitious worship of volcanoes is known among some highly educated and prominent citizens of Hawaii. In 1955 during an eruption of Kilauea on the island of Hawaii in the Puna District, inhabitants of the village of Kapoho made

Table 5-b. Summary of the Physical Properties of Various Parts of the Earth

UNIT	DEPTH (MILES)	DESCRIPTION
	0	Surface of the earth
Crust		Sedimentary, igneous, and metamorphic rocks in the upper few miles. Granitic continents, basaltic ocean basins. Gradual increase in density with depth. Possible intermediate zone between base of granite and Moho. (See Fig. 2-8)
	20–25	Moho (base of the crust)
Mantle		Rapid increase of velocity with depth between 100 and 500 miles. At about 300 miles there may be a compositional change. Rate of velocity increase slacks off between 500 and 1800 miles down.
	1800	Core boundary
Core		Material of the core lacks rigidity and is probably liquid. Density is 12 or more. Inner core begins 3160 miles down where P waves increase in velocity, indicating a possible change back to the solid state. Both solid and liquid portions of the core may be of iron-nickel or iron-silicate composition.
	3975	Center of the earth

pilgrimages to the edge of the lava flow where they performed rituals involving chants and offered gifts of breadfruit, bananas, pork, and tobacco to the mythical Hawaiian Volcano Goddess, Pele.

Not far from Kapoho on the flanks of the same volcano to which the Hawaiians paid homage stands the Hawaiian Volcano Observatory of the United States Geological Survey. From that laboratory, studies have been made and experiments have been performed that provide an ever increasing store of knowledge which, someday, will dispel the lingering beliefs of people such as the Kapohoans.

Another laboratory dedicated to the same end is the Vesuvius Volcano Laboratory situated on a hill of lava in the shadow of Mt. Vesuvius overlooking the beautiful Bay of Naples. Scientists associated with these two installations are making considerable progress in the interpretation, understanding, and prediction of volcanic events. The paragraphs that follow are based mainly on their writings.

FACTS ABOUT VOLCANOES

■ DISTRIBUTION. Nearly 500 active volcanoes exist on earth. They are concentrated along the borders of the Pacific Ocean in a belt which roughly coincides with the circum-Pacific earthquake girdle. Another volcanic belt is coincident with the Alpine-Himalayan mountain system which stretches from the Mediterranean through Asia Minor to the East Indies Archipelago. Finally, active volcanoes rise from the floors of the Pacific, and Indian Oceans.

Volcanoes of the circum-Pacific belt are near the continental margins or are situated on the island arcs (p. 23), the convex sides of which are always toward the Pacific Ocean basin. The circum-Pacific volcanoes and those which lie along the Alpine-Himalaya trend are part of an actively growing mountain system.

The volcanoes of the Atlantic Ocean occur along the Mid-Atlantic Ridge and form the islands of the Azores, Cape

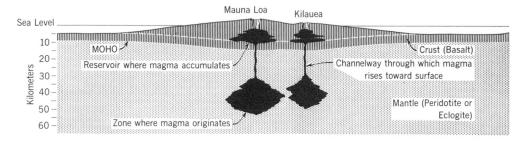

Figure 5-12. Cross-sectional diagram across the island of Hawaii. The distance from the crest of Mauna Loa to the crest of Kilauea is about 30 kilometers. (After Gordon A. Macdonald, 1961, Volcanology, *Science*, **133**, 677.)

Verde Islands, St. Paul Rock, and Iceland. Generally speaking, the continental borders marginal to the Atlantic Ocean contain no active volcanoes and are also relatively free of earthquakes. However, the Lesser Antilles (West Indies) is a volcanic island arc system separating the Caribbean Sea from the Atlantic Ocean.

■ THE ORIGIN AND SOURCE OF VOLCANIC MATERIALS. A volcano is an opening in the earth's crust from which molten rock, solid rock fragments, and gases are liberated. The rocks of volcanic origin were treated briefly in Chapter three where they were designated as lava or pyroclastic. Lava is molten rock derived from some place beneath the surface of the earth and is the nearest thing to magma that a geologist will ever see. In fact, lava in the molten state *is* magma that has reached the earth's surface where it immediately loses some of its most important constituents, notably gases. Since the general structure of the earth has already been considered in a previous chapter, and because the reader is now familiar with the geologic meaning of such terms as peridotite, basalt, andesite, granite, mantle, crust, sial, sima, ocean basin, continental block, he can now proceed one step further and consider some of the ideas set forth by some leading geologists

to account for the origin of magma, the ultimate source of volcanic materials.

Geologists who have studied the Hawaiian volcanoes over the past years believe that the magma which feeds the Hawaiian volcanoes comes from a zone about 40 kilometers below the summit of Mauna Loa. This would place the magma-generating zone about 35 kilometers below the Moho in that region (Fig. 5-12). The occurrence of volcanic tremors at about the same depth is regarded by some geophysicists as a confirmation of the 40-kilometer depth of magma generation.

Earlier in this chapter it was demonstrated on the basis of earthquake waves that the mantle was solid down to 1800 miles (2900 km). The temperature at 40 kilometers below the crust is not known but all calculations from various sources put it well *below* or *cooler* than the measured temperatures of molten Hawaiian lavas of 1100 to 1200°C. This means that the surface temperature of molten lava at eruption time is hotter than the rocks in the mantle at 40 kilometers beneath the surface in a nonvolcanic area. Obviously, then, magma must be generated from the solid mantle by the addition of *local* heat.

The question of how the local heat is generated is still largely unanswered. Radioactivity produces heat, and some geologists would have localized radioactive "hot spots" provide the heat for melting the mantle into magma. Checks of active hot lava flows and volcanic clouds with a Geiger counter fail to show any increase in radioactivity over the normal background count. Another possible source of the heat is from deeper in the mantle where rising convection currents bring hotter mantle upward toward the Moho. No one really knows the answer to the question, how is volcanic magma, or any magma, for that matter, generated? About all that can be said is that the heat of a volcanic eruption is brought up from depth with the rising magma. Where the magma obtained the heat for its formation is simply not known.

The composition of lava is another point on which we might dwell briefly in order to compare it with the composition generally attributed to the mantle. Lava ranges in composition between the light-colored felsites (rhyolites) and the dark-colored andesites and basalts. Generally, the lavas containing more than about two-thirds SiO_2 by weight are the "acid" rocks of which rhyolite is the best example (Plate II-*H, I*). Those containing between one-half and two-thirds SiO_2 are the intermediate lavas known as andesite (Plate II-*J*), whereas the lavas with less than half their composition composed of SiO_2* are the basalts (Plate II-*K*).

---

* The conventional way of reporting the chemical analysis of a rock is to list the various oxides rather than the mineral content. Thus we would find the following oxides listed: SiO_2, Al_2O_3, FeO, MgO, CaO, Na_2O, K_2O, TiO_2, and MnO. These do not represent individual mineral species in the rock, but rather represent a convenient way in which the chemical constituents of a rock can be presented in a standardized form. Thus, SiO_2 in this case is not all quartz, but rather the amount of silicon dioxide that would exist in the rock if all the silicon were combined with oxygen. Actually, some of the silicon may occur in quartz, but it may equally well occur in feldspar, olivine, or any other silicate mineral found in an igneous rock (Table 3-*c*).

By far the greatest volume of lava is basaltic in composition. The great Hawaiian chain has a volume approaching 100,000 cubic miles. The Deccan region of India and the Columbia River Plateau (Fig. 16-5), both of which are more than a million years old, have volumes of basaltic lava of the same order of magnitude. It is, therefore, apparent that large volumes of basaltic magma of rather uniform composition were generated in past geologic time.

Basaltic magma is supposed to originate in the upper mantle. No one has sampled the mantle, although both the United States and the Soviet Union intend to do so by actually drilling through the earth's crust to the Moho. Until this is accomplished, however, the actual composition of the mantle is still open to question. Earthquake waves indicate a sharp difference between the crustal rocks and the mantle. This "contact" between crust and mantle is the well-known M discontinuity or Moho. Earthquake waves also require the mantle to have a certain density. This density is met by an ultra-basic rock called *peridotite*, which contains much less SiO_2 than basalt; many geologists believe that basaltic magma is produced by fractional melting of peridotite. The proponents of this view hold that the Moho represents a *compositional* change between crustal sima and the mantle.

Another group of geologists argue that the Moho represents a *phase* change rather than a compositional difference between the sima and upper mantle. According to this hypothesis, the chemical composition of the upper mantle is the same as the basalt of the sima, but the minerals normally found in basalt of the crust cannot exist below the Moho because of the high pressure. The name of the "mantle basalt" is *eclogite;* it has the chemical composition of basalt but the density of peridotite, supposedly because the high pressures in the mantle produce a closer-packed arrangement of the atoms in the constituent minerals.

Basalt magma could be generated from either peridotite or eclogite. In the case of the former, the melting would have to be only partial because peridotite, like any rock composed of different minerals, does not have a finite melting point but a melting range of several hundred degrees. Presumably, partial melting of peridotite would produce a basaltic magma which would migrate upward into a chamber that feeds a volcano. In the case of eclogite, the entire mantle would melt locally and then migrate surfaceward toward the volcanic vent.

■ VOLCANIC GASES. During a volcanic eruption many gases are liberated into the atmosphere. While the magma is still confined in its chamber under enormous pressure, these gases are dissolved in the liquid melt. As the magma rises, however, the gases expand, causing the lava to froth into a highly porous rock. The basaltic lavas are quite fluid (low viscosity) so the expanding gases can escape fairly quickly as the lava reaches the surface. The more acidic lavas such as rhyolite are highly viscous (sticky), a condition which keeps the gases entrapped for a longer time. When they do finally burst forth, they do so with terrific explosive violence. Blasts from such volcanoes are destructive to life and property. The escape of gases from a volcano is very similar to the effervescing of a bottle of warm beer or champagne after the cap or cork has been removed.

The collecting of gases from an erupting volcano is a difficult and somewhat dangerous task. Table 5-c gives the typical composition of gases emitted from Hawaiian volcanoes. The gaseous products of other volcanoes vary to some extent in their percentages of the lesser gases but all show a high proportion of water vapor. This fact compelled W. W.

*Table 5-c. Composition of Volcanic Gases from Hawaii**

GAS	COMPOSITION	PER CENT BY VOLUME
Steam	H_2O	70.75
Carbon dioxide	CO_2	14.07
Sulfur dioxide	SO_2	6.40
Nitrogen	N_2	5.45
Sulfur trioxide	SO_3	1.92
Carbon monoxide	CO	0.40
Hydrogen	H_2	0.33
Argon	A	0.18
Sulfur	S_2	0.10
Chlorine	Cl_2	0.05

* Data from Jaggar, T. A., (1940) Magmatic gases, *Am. J. Sci.*, Vol. 238.

Rubey, an American Geologist, to propose the hypothesis that the water in all the oceans of the world was derived from water produced by volcanic eruptions throughout the entire span of earth history.

TYPES OF VOLCANIC ERUPTIONS

Some volcanologists recognize five or six different kinds of volcanic eruptions, but in this book only two will be considered. Actually, the other types are variations of these two which will be called the Hawaiian and Vesuvian types.

■ HAWAIIAN TYPE. This kind of an eruption is characterized by the enormous outpouring of basaltic lava that builds up a broad-based, convex-upward cone of enormous height. Because the lava has a relatively high fluidity (low viscosity), the associated gases are liberated rather quickly with very little explosive violence, although *lava fountains* are sometimes projected upward to heights of 1000 feet or more as they are squirted out of fissures on the volcano's flank (Figs. 5-13, 5-14).

Mauna Loa, the world's largest active volcano, is the most magnificent example

Figure 5-13. Lava fountain formed during the eruption of Kilauea Volcano on the island of Hawaii, December 5, 1959. The wavy lines in the foreground are cracks in the crust of the lava lake through which molten lava radiates an incandescent glow. The lava lake is over 360 feet deep and covers about 135 acres. (Photograph by E. J. Britten, courtesy of *Science*.)

of the Hawaiian type (Fig. 5-15). It rises 13,680 feet above sea level and about 30,000 feet above its base on the ocean floor. It has been built by thousands of individual lava flows which average about 10 feet thick. Since 1832 it has erupted lava intermittently for a total of more than 1300 days from the summit

Figure 5-14. Lava fountain, 1000 feet high, spouting from the eastern rift zone of Kilauea Volcano during the eruption of January 19, 1960 near Kapoho, Hawaii. Frothy pumice ejected into the air cools into dust which is blown over the country side. The road (lower right) through the sugar cane field ends in a rough *aa* lava flow. (Photograph by Wayne Ault, Hawaiian Volcano Observatory, Hawaii National Park.)

Figure 5-15. Mauna Loa, the largest active volcano in the world, rises to an elevation of 13,680 feet above sea level as a broad shield cone. Rounded boulders in the foreground were transported by glaciers in earlier geologic time on the slopes of Mauna Kea from where this photograph was taken. The notch at the crest of Mauna Loa is the summit caldera. The long black band (right center) is a 1935 lava flow. Other flows, which are also visible, originated from the summit caldera and a rift zone on the left flank. Basaltic lava is highly fluid, a property which allows it to flow down gentle slopes over a distance of 20 miles to the ocean. (Photograph by Wayne Ault, Hawaiian Volcano Observatory, Hawaii National Park.)

crater and a similar length of time from fissures on its flanks. This has resulted in the accumulation of an estimated 4 billion cubic yards of lava. The longest recorded eruption began on April 20, 1873 and lasted for about $1\frac{1}{2}$ years.

Mauna Loa is one of five great volcanoes on the island of Hawaii (Fig. 5-16). It is also the most active. On its summit is an oval depression, named Mokuaweoweo, 4 miles long, $1\frac{3}{4}$ miles wide, and nearly 600 feet deep. The form of Mauna Loa is described as a *shield cone*. Although it rises to a height of 30,000 feet above its base, its slopes are nowhere steeper than about 12 degrees.

A typical eruption begins with the opening of a fissure or fissures several miles long. In the initial stages, lava fountains squirt from these fissures. These lava geysers increase in intensity until a maximum height of several hundred feet is reached. A yellowish-brown gas cloud rises several thousand feet above the fountains as lava continues to pour out and flow down the volcano's flanks. Eventually the fountains cease to play because of the cessation of gaseous emanations, and a short period of lava outpouring ends the eruptive sequence.

Some of the volcanic materials formed during an Hawaiian eruption consist of pumice and Pele's hair (natural spun glass) which rain down on the countryside during the lava fountain stage. The lava itself is an *olivine basalt,* the chief

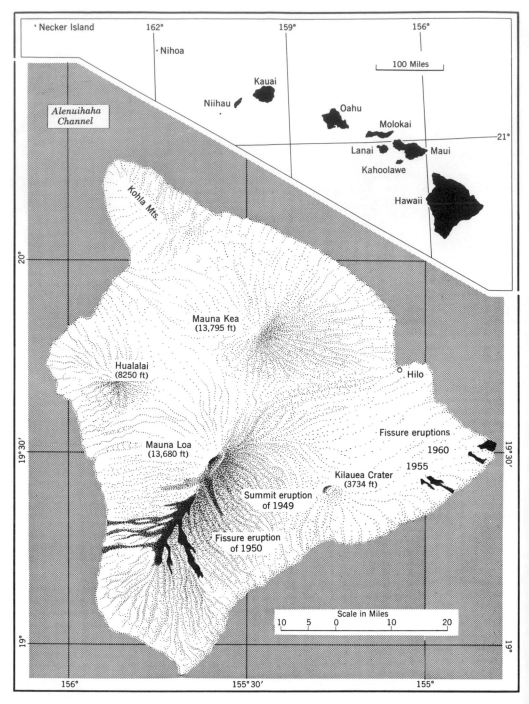

Figure 5-16.   Map of the island of Hawaii.   (Based on G. A. Macdonald and D. H. Hubbard, 1961, *Volcanoes of the national parks of Hawaii,* Hawaii Natural History Association.)

Figure 5-17. Lava flows on the flank of Mauna Loa, Hawaii. The *aa* lava in the background partially covers the ropy or pahoehoe lava in the foreground.

mineral constituents of which are plagioclase feldspar, magnetite, and olivine. The olivine crystals are generally bottle-green or brownish-green in color and occur up to a half-inch in size. Some of them are of gem quality and are known in the jewelry trade as "peridot."

Two principal types of lava flows are derived from Hawaiian type eruptions, the *aa* and pahoehoe (Fig. 5-17). *Aa* lava is also called blocky lava and is characterized by a very rough jagged surface. Pahoehoe lava is also known as ropy lava because of its appearance as a series of parallel strands of twisted rope (Fig. 5-18). Both *aa* and pahoehoe lavas have identical composition. Their different physical appearance results largely from the state of enclosed gas at the time of solidification of the lava.

Similar to the Hawaiian type of eruption is the *fissure* type which builds huge lava plateaus or "flood lavas" as they are sometimes called. The type of basalt is similar, too, being very fluid in order to allow vast lateral spreading of the flows. The main difference between the Hawaiian type and the fissure type is that the

Figure 5-18. Pahoehoe or ropy lava on Mauna Loa, Hawaii.

fissures from which the Hawaiian lavas are ejected are more or less fixed, whereas in the building of lava plateaus, the fissures shift from place to place. The only place where modern fissure flows are active is Iceland which lies on the Mid-Atlantic Ridge. Iceland is one of the few places in the world where volcanic activity is in progress adjacent to large glaciers. Subglacial lava eruptions produce enormous quantities of meltwater which floods the surrounding area with destructive consequences of considerable magnitude.

■ VESUVIAN TYPE. The chief characteristic of the Vesuvian-type eruption is that considerable amounts of volcanic ash, cinder, and bombs are explosively ejected during some stage of the eruption. During other phases of the eruptive activity lava is extruded from the crater or from fissures on the flanks. The initial explosion of a Vesuvian type may actually disrupt the volcanic cone.

Vesuvius, a volcanic peak near Naples, Italy, is cited as the chief example of this type, but other subtypes in the Aeolian Islands of the Tyrrhenian Sea between Sicily and Italy are included for the sake of simplicity. These are Stromboli, Vulcano, and Etna. The inclusion of these other examples would not be accepted by all volcanologists, but the reader must recognize that, of necessity, some oversimplification must be adopted in a text of this scope.

Mount Vesuvius is a well-known volcano, not only to Europeans but to the entire world (Fig. 5-19). The Vesuvian Volcano Observatory was established in 1845, but records of eruptive activity go back to the beginning of the Christian Era when, in A.D. 79, Vesuvius erupted with such violence that it destroyed the cities of Pompeii and Herculaneum. An eyewitness account of this eruption was recorded by Pliny the Younger, the nephew of Pliny the Elder, an important Roman who, at the time of the eruption was in command of the Roman fleet near Naples. Pliny the Elder lost his life during the eruption while directing the evacuation of refugees fleeing from the holocaust. Although the nephew believed his uncle's death resulted from ". . . some gross and noxious vapor," it is more likely that death was caused by a coronary.

Vesuvius killed a lot of people in Pompeii during the A.D. 79 eruption. The city was completely buried by pumice and ash and lay undiscovered for nearly fifteen centuries before the digging of a well and the excavation of a canal in the sixteenth century uncovered clues which eventually led to a systematic exhuming of this ancient city. Today, a visit to the ruins of Pompeii is an exciting experience for any traveler in the Bay of Naples area.

Stromboli is another Mediterranean volcano that rises from the blue waters of the Tyrrhenian Sea. It has been in more or less continuous eruptive activity for more than 2500 years and consists of a twin-peaked cone, whose crest rises 3000 feet above sea level and the base of which rests on the sea floor 7000 feet below sea level. Like Vesuvius, Stromboli ejects both ash and lava, but its distinguishing feature is a dense white cloud of steam which rises from the crater from time to time. The whiteness is attributed to the lack of ash content during this phase of the eruption.

Vulcano is only 50 miles from Stromboli. Its name is the basis for the word volcano itself. It is further distinguished among volcanoes because the Italian government appointed a special commission to study the 1888–1890 eruption. The report resulting therefrom described the Vulcanian type of eruption as one in which a central crater plug was blasted skyward in the form of volcanic bombs, ash, and scoria. No lava was produced. Most of the material thrown out of Vul-

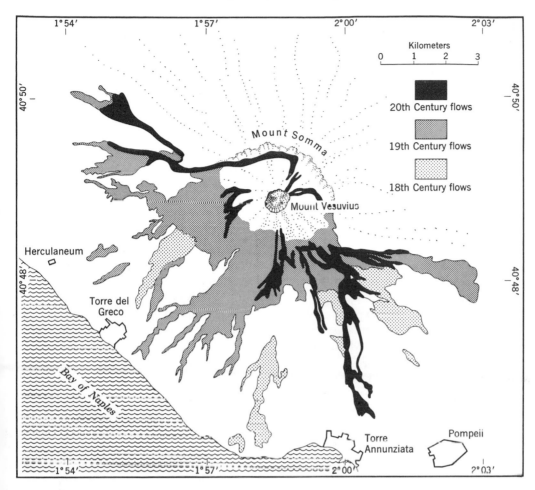

Figure 5-19. Map of Mount Vesuvius and vicinity showing the distribution of lava flows of three centuries. Pompeii and Herculaneum were destroyed by ash falls during the eruption of A.D. 79. (After Fred M. Bullard, *Volcanoes in history, in theory, in eruption,* 1962, University of Texas Press, Austin.)

cano consists of white ash (pumice) and other incandescent bombs which create a bright glow over the volcano during night time eruptions. The analysis of some of the ejected material showed an SiO_2 content ranging from 62 to 67 per cent. This lava is an example of the acidic type.

■ NUÉE ARDENTE. On the northern end of the island of Martinique in the Lesser Antilles of the West Indies there exists a roughly circular volcanic cone known as Mount Pelée. On May 8, 1902 a sudden eruption of Mount Pelée resulted in the death of all except two inhabitants of

the city of St. Pierre, a seaport city 5 miles south of the crest of the volcano. Nearly 30,000 people were annihilated in a matter of minutes by a dense cloud of ashes ejected with explosive violence from the crater. The cloud was so dense that only part of it was disseminated in the atmosphere. The rest literally swept down the mountainside as a huge avalanche of hot gas, dust, and ashes. The velocity of this roaring mass as it swept toward the city of St. Pierre was on the order of 100 miles per hour, a speed comparable to that of a hurricane. This hot, glowing mass of volcanic ejectamata is called a *nuée ardente* ("glowing cloud").

The inhabitants of St. Pierre were killed by the inhalation of hot gases, suffocation through lack of oxygen, or from burns. The temperature of the cloud, based on the effect it had on various objects such as glass and wood, is estimated at several hundred degrees. One of the survivors was a prisoner confined to a dungeon during the blast. The other was a shoemaker who miraculously escaped the blast in his own house although he was severely burned. Eyewitness accounts from these two plus interviews of a few survivors aboard two ships in the harbor helped greatly to recast the details of the horrible scene.

Five months after the expulsion of the *nuée ardente,* a stiff mass of lava was extruded from the crater of Mount Pelée. It rose like a gigantic tower or spine from the throat of the crater and eventually reached a height of more than 1000 feet above the crater floor. The spine continued to rise until August 1903, after-which it disintegrated into a stump standing in its own rubble.

SUMMARY

Earthquakes are produced by slippage along fault planes. Deep focus earthquakes originate at depths from 200 to 400 miles, intermediate quakes have foci at depths ranging from 40 to 200 miles, and shallow earthquakes originate within 40 miles of the earth's surface.

The majority of earthquakes are shallow and are distributed around the rim of the Pacific Ocean and from the Mediterranean eastward through Asia.

The elastic rebound theory provides a logical explanation of the mechanism of faulting but does not reveal the ultimate forces which cause the buildup of the stresses beyond the breaking point of rocks. An analysis of the different kinds of earthquake waves, especially the velocities of the P and S waves (body waves) provides a reasonable picture of the earth's internal features. The crust consists of two kinds of crystalline materials, granite beneath the continents, and basalt beneath the ocean basins. The base of the crust is marked by a major boundary known as the M discontinuity or Moho which lies 20 to 25 miles down. Both P and S waves increase their velocities abruptly at this boundary.

From the M discontinuity to a depth of 1800 miles a denser material exists, known as the mantle. The core boundary marks the base of the solid mantle and the top of the liquid core. The core lacks rigidity as indicated by its failure to transmit S waves and its slowing-down effect on P waves. An inner core between 3160 miles and the center of the earth (3975 miles) may be solid owing to extremely high pressure. The core's density is 12 or more and its composition might well be iron–nickel or iron–silicate (Table 5-*b*).

Volcanoes are vents in the earth's crust from which lava is extruded and pyroclastics and gases are ejected. They are distributed around the earth in belts roughly coincident with the earthquakes of the world. Lavas range in composition from basic (basalt) through intermediate (andesite) to acidic (rhyolite). Lava is generated in the upper mantle which may be either peridotite or eclogite.

Hawaiian-type eruptions are characterized by immense outpourings of olivine basalt of the *aa* or pahoehoe type. Violent explosions are rare although lava fountains are common during the initial stages.

Vesuvian types of eruptions are characterized by the explosive expulsion of ash, cinders, and bombs which may be followed in later stages by lava erupting from the central crater or flank fissures.

Nuée ardentes are hot dense ash clouds that retain contact with the ground as they rush down the flanks of the volcano at hurricane velocities.

REFERENCES

Benioff, H., and B. Gutenberg, 1955, *Earthquakes in Kern County, California during 1952,* California Department of Natural Resources, Division of Mines, Bulletin 171.

Bullard, Fred M., 1962, *Volcanoes in History, in Theory, in Eruption,* University of Texas Press, Austin, 441 pp.

Bullen, K. E., 1954, *Seismology,* Methuen and Co., London.

Eaton, J. P., and K. J. Murata, 1960, How Volcanoes Grow, *Science,* **132,** 925–938.

Eppley, R. A., and W. K. Cloud, 1961, *United States Earthquakes 1959,* U.S. Department of Commerce, Coast and Geodetic Survey, Government Printing Office, Washington, D.C.

Kuiper, G. P. (ed.), 1954, *The solar system,* vol. II. *The Earth as a planet,* University of Chicago Press, Chicago. Chapter 5, Distribution of density within the earth, by Sir Harold Spencer Jones.

Leet, L. Don, 1948, *Causes of catastrophe,* McGraw-Hill Book Co., New York.

Macdonald, Gordon A., and Douglass H. Hubbard, 1961, *Volcanoes of the National Parks in Hawaii,* Hawaii, Natural History Association.

Macdonald, Gordon A., 1961, Volcanology, *Science,* **133,** 673–679.

Poldervaart, A., 1955, *The crust of the earth.* Geological Society of America, Special Paper 62.

Wood, H. O., and N. H. Heck, 1961 *Earthquake History of the United States. Part II* (Revised Edition through 1960), U.S. Department of Commerce, Coast and Geodetic Survey, Government Printing Office, Washington, D.C.

VI

Rock Weathering and Soil Formation

. . . do you not see that stones even are conquered by time,
that tall turrets do fall and rocks do crumble . . . ?

Lucretius

Weathering is really one of the first steps in a long chain of events that may cause an entire landscape to be changed drastically over a period of geologic time. Rock weathering includes the various processes whereby the minerals in rocks at or near the earth's surface become physically or chemically altered under normal conditions of temperature and pressure. In a sense, weathering is the result of the interaction between the atmosphere and the rocks exposed at the earth's surface. This interaction may be physical or chemical, but in either case, the result is a softened or weakened rock, which, under certain conditions appear as grotesque forms (Fig. 6-1).

Weathering proceeds at widely different rates. The rock type and general climatic conditions determine, to a large extent, the type and intensity of the weathering process. Vegetation, which is also a function of climate, influences the weathering of rocks. Topography determines the rate at which the products of weathering will be removed. In some circumstances the weathered debris is removed by some geologic agent such as wind or water as fast as it is produced, but weathering products which accumulate *in situ* are the basic materials on which a soil is developed.

WHY ROCKS WEATHER

Some rocks form deep beneath the earth's crust whereas others originate as sediment on the sea floor. In either case the minerals in many rocks develop under conditions different from those at the earth's surface. If the environment of formation remains constant, the minerals will remain in a stable state, that is, they will be in equilibrium with their surroundings. However, when the environment is altered or changed, the minerals respond to this change by weathering.

■ BEDROCK, MANTLE, AND SOIL. The material any place at the earth's surface can be classified as bedrock, mantle, or soil (Fig. 6-2). Bedrock is any consolidated

Figure 6-1. Weathered sandstone in the Black Hills of South Dakota. Because of the steep slopes the weathered debris is removed by rain and does not accumulate *in situ*. Weathering proceeds at a faster rate along joints. The spires and vertical rock projections seen here are formed by differential weathering along intersecting vertical joint planes in the sandstone.

rock that lies in a position more or less undisturbed by surface agents. Bedrock may exist right at the surface or it may be hundreds of feet beneath the ground.

The mantle* always lies on top of the bedrock and may be *residual* or *transported*. The former is simply weathered bedrock, the latter is a surficial deposit moved onto a bedrock surface by one of the geologic transporting agents. The upper part of the mantle contains the soil, the natural medium for plant growth. Both mantle and soil are products of weathering.

PHYSICAL WEATHERING

Physical weathering involves a physical breakdown or disruption of the rock mantle, or soil, in place. The two most common types of physical weathering are frost action and the action of plants and animals.

■ FROST ACTION. Freezing and thawing is a common daily event in many regions of the earth. When water is present in the pores and cracks of rock and soil, the

* Not to be confused with mantle as used for the outer 1800 miles of the earth.

freeze-thaw cycle exerts pressures greatly exceeding the strength of the natural material. The breaking or shattering of rocks is the result of water expanding as it changes to ice. This process is called *frost wedging*.

The most favorable conditions for maximum frost action is the daily (diurnal) crossing of the freezing point. These conditions are most commonly found in the polar regions and in mountainous regions above the tree line. Thawing by day allows water from melting snow to seep into the natural openings in rocks. Freezing by night causes expansion of the entrapped water, which in turn forces the crack open a little more, thus making more room for more water when melting starts the following day. The freeze-thaw cycle may be repeated many times in a single year, and each time it makes the crack in the rock a little larger. Eventually the rock may be disrupted completely owing to a large number of freeze-thaw cycles.

TALUS AND BLOCKFIELDS. A conspicuous product of frost wedging is the accumulation of blocks of broken rock at the foot of a steep bedrock cliff. This jumble of angular rock fragments, ranging in size from a few inches to a few feet, is called *talus* or sliderock (Fig. 6-3). Talus slopes are steep and unstable during their growth, but may be stabilized eventually by vegetation if frost wedging ceases because of a permanent warming of the climate.

On high plateaus and in arctic regions where bedrock crops out at the surface, the angular blocks produced by frost wedging form *blockfields*. They become inactivated when frost action ceases, but even then they are difficult to traverse on foot or horseback, and they are almost impassable by conventional field motor vehicles.

FROST HEAVING. Frost heaving is the process of expansion of unconsolidated sediment due to the freezing of the water contained in the pores. Excessive mois-

ture is necessary for the frost heaving process to take place. Laboratory experiments show that soils with a high silt content are the most liable to excessive expansion upon freezing because of their capacity to draw free water from the lower, nonfrozen part of the soil. This has been verified many times during the course of field investigations for highway routes, and highway engineers now recommend that all silt zones in areas of first-class highway construction be excavated and the silt replaced by gravel. The gravel cannot retain sufficient water to cause excessive heaving when freezing occurs.

PERMAFROST. In polar regions a peculiar configuration of the ground surface is produced by intense frost action. In an

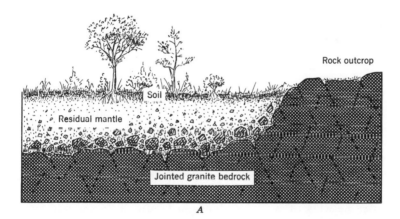

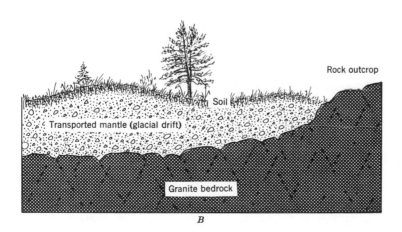

Figure 6-2. Residual (*A*) and transported (*B*) mantles.

Figure 6-3.   Talus cones accumulated on the lower slope of these mountains near Mt. Antero in Chaffee County, Colorado, are derived chiefly from frost action at higher elevations.   The central valley contains a transported mantle deposited by a glacier which occupied the valley during a previous geological epoch.   (Photograph by D. B. Sterrett, U.S. Geological Survey.)

unconsolidated mantle consisting of a heterogeneous mixture of fine and coarse debris, the coarse particles are separated from the fine.   The result is a kind of systematic arrangement of the coarser fragments into a network of ridges.   These ridges outline polygonal tracts of ground ranging from a few feet to many tens of feet in diameter.   The entire network of ridges and intervening areas is referred to as *patterned ground* or *polygonal ground*.

Beneath the surface of the polygonal ground lies a zone of perenially frozen ground called permafrost.   Only the upper part of the permafrost zone is subjected to the freeze-thaw cycle, and this zone is called the *active layer*.   Beneath the active layer, which may range from a few inches to many feet thick, there is no frost action because of the absence of the freeze-thaw cycles.   Figure 6-4 shows polygonal ground in the Arctic.

■ PLANT AND ANIMAL ACTIVITY.   Tree roots penetrate the ground for several feet and dislodge or disrupt the soil particles. Trees blown over by wind disrupt wide areas of soil, causing loosening of the particles if nothing else.

Burrowing animals may also churn up soil, and earthworms, especially, may dislocate tons of earth over a period of years. As agents of physical weathering, however, plants and animals do not equal the effectiveness of other specific types of weathering, except in local areas under rather restricted conditions.

CHEMICAL WEATHERING

■ OXIDATION.   The atmosphere contains many substances, but about 20 per cent of it is free oxygen, which is the chief constituent provided by the atmosphere for chemical reaction with rocks and soil. *Oxidation* is thus one of the main types of chemical change produced in rocks by chemical weathering.   Minerals like pyrite

(FeS_2) are especially susceptible to oxidation because iron has a high affinity for oxygen. When pyrite is oxidized, limonite ($Fe_2O_3 \cdot nH_2O$) is formed and the liberated sulfur combines with water to produce a weak solution of sulfuric acid. This solution in itself is a powerful chemical agent and greatly accelerates the rate of chemical decomposition of a pyrite-rich rock. A surface zone of oxidized sulfide minerals is often a clue to important sulfide ore deposits at greater depth.

The iron oxides are a very common by-product of oxidation, not only of pyrite but of other iron-bearing minerals. Iron oxides in varying amounts impart the red and yellow colors to soils.

■ LEACHING. The atmosphere also provides moisture for rocks and soils. Water is called "the universal solvent" because of its ability to dissolve various compounds and elements, although the natural solvent action of water is more effective on some rocks than on others. *Leaching* is the process whereby water dissolves mineral and rock material, that is, minerals actu-

ally go into solution just as table salt is dissolved in water. Limestone, dolomite, rock salt, and rock gypsum are particularly susceptible to leaching.

The leaching of limestone is more rapid if carbon dioxide (CO_2) is present in the water. Together they form carbonic acid (H_2CO_3) which is a potent chemical agent on minerals such as calcite ($CaCO_3$). The reaction between carbonic acid and calcite or limestone can be expressed as follows:

$$CaCO_3 + H_2CO_3 \rightarrow Ca(HCO_3)_2$$

calcite + carbonic acid → calcium bicarbonate

The calcium bicarbonate is soluble and is therefore removed in solution, a process which is very prominent along joints in limestone occurring in humid regions (Fig. 6-5).

■ HYDRATION. Another weathering phenomenon involving water is *hydration,* the process whereby water molecules combine chemically with a compound to produce a new compound. A good example of this is the change produced when anhy-

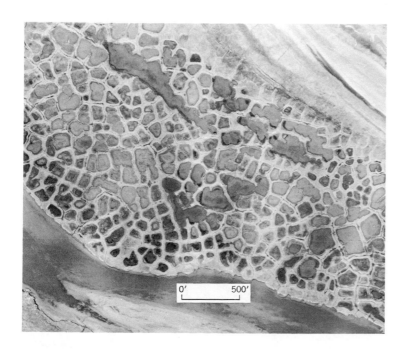

Figure 6-4. Aerial photograph of patterned ground 60 miles southeast of Pt. Barrow, Alaska, July 20, 1957. The area is underlain by permafrost. (Photograph by Robert F. Black.)

drite (CaSO$_4$) is hydrated to gypsum (CaSO$_4 \cdot 2H_2O$). It is important to note that although hydration is a chemical reaction, there is an important attending *physical* change as well. This change is a swelling or increase in volume. All minerals expand to some extent when hydrated, and the force of expansion exerted on adjacent minerals results in a spalling or flaking off of the outer layers of the rock surface. This process of shelling off of concentric rock slabs due to hydration is called *exfoliation* (Fig. 6-6). If an outcrop of jointed rock is reduced to a series of rounded knobs by exfoliation, the process is called spheroidal weathering.

Another important phase of chemical weathering is the transformation of feldspars into clay minerals. Water again plays an important part in this chemical reaction which also produces rock expansion, and hence exfoliation. One clay mineral produced by the weathering of feldspar is called kaolinite, a hydrated aluminum silicate. So commonplace is this process in nature that it bears the special name of kaolinization.

■ ORGANIC MATERIAL. No discussion of chemical weathering would be complete without some mention of the role of organic material, especially decayed plant material. Decayed vegetable matter or humus goes into the making of humic acid, which, like other acids, greatly accelerates the decomposition of rock and soil. Furthermore, humus is the home of a great variety of bacteria, and experiments have shown that direct bacterial attack on rock fragments accelerates the process of chemical weathering.

■ STABILITY OF MINERALS DURING WEATHERING. Not all minerals react in the same way when exposed to weathering under identical chemical environments. Some decompose more readily than others. The order of stability for common minerals of igneous rocks with respect to chemical weathering is as follows: quartz (most stable), muscovite, orthoclase, biotite, amphibole, pyroxene, plagioclase, and olivine (least stable). We may deduce from this stability series that, in a given environment and over the same period of time, a granite with its characteristically high quartz and orthoclase content will be more resistant to chemical decay than a gabbro in which the predominant minerals are pyroxene and plagioclase.

The explanation behind the stability series is based on the chemical composition of the minerals of the series and their

Figure 6-5. Leached joints in limestone, Hastings County, Ontario. (Photograph by M. E. Wilson, Geological Survey of Canada.)

Figure 6-6.   Exfoliation in granite near Royal Arch Lake, Yosemite Quadrangle, California. (Photograph by H. W. Turner, U.S. Geological Survey.)

structure.   Furthermore, the stability series is the reverse order in which the same minerals crystallize from a magma (see page 38).   That is, olivine and plagioclase are the least stable minerals and are among the first to crystallize from the melt, and quartz and muscovite, both chemically stable insofar as weathering is concerned, are the last minerals to crystallize from the magma.

SOILS

Soil is one of our most valuable resources and is a product, in part, of the weathering processes.   Its origin is intimately associated with the interaction of climate and organisms on the mantle of weathered materials at the earth's surface.   *Pedology* is the science of soils.   Soil, in a pedological sense, is a ". . . collection

of nautral bodies on the earth's surface, containing living matter, and supporting or capable of supporting plants."* Construction or highway engineers, on the other hand, define soil in a broader sense to include all unconsolidated earthy materials, even those at considerable depth (Fig. 6-7).   In this discussion, the pedological rather than the engineering definition will be used.

The dynamic characteristics of soil were not recognized until the late nineteenth century when the work of Dokuchaiev, a Russian geologist, was published. He recognized that soil formation is an integrated process dependent on five factors: (1) parent material, (2) climate, (3) organisms, (4) topography, and (5) time. Collectively, these five factors determine

* *Seventh Approximation,* U.S. Soil Conservation Service, 1960, p. 1.

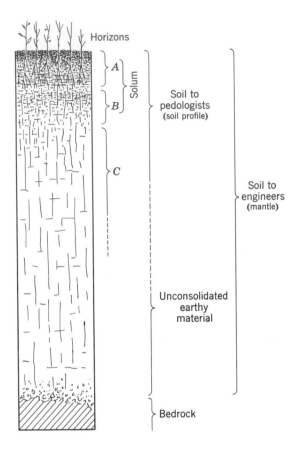

Figure 6-7. Generalized soil profile show-ing the various morphological units. (From A. C. Orvedal, 1952, *Frost action in soils,* Washington, D.C., National Acad-emy of Sciences, National Research Coun-cil, Highway Research Board, Special Report 2.)

what a particular soil will look like, or, as a scientist would say, what its *morphology* will be. Dokuchaiev argued that the morphology of each kind of soil reflects the combined effects of the particular set of genetic factors responsible for its develop-ment. The classification system based on this concept presupposed that a compe-tent soil scientist could decipher soil genesis from soil morphology. Before we proceed, however, with a discussion of soil classification, some aspects of soil mor-phology and nomenclature must be intro-duced at this point.

■ SOIL MORPHOLOGY.

THE SOIL PROFILE AND SOLUM. The depth to which the soil-forming processes affect rocks or unconsolidated material determines the layers of the *soil profile* (Fig. 6-7). They are not layers in the

sense that one was laid down on top of another. Actually, the horizontal zonation in the profile is produced *in situ* by the soil-forming processes. The tech-nical term for the "layers" is *horizons*. Three main horizons are normally pres-ent in mature soil profiles. They are designated *A, B,* and *C* from the surface downward.

A soil horizon is usually differentiated from those adjacent to it by character-istics that are observable in the field. Some of these characteristics are color, texture, and the presence or absence of carbonates. Color is determined by comparing the soil to a standard color chart. Texture (the amount of sand, silt, and clay) can be ascertained roughly by feel, and the presence of carbonate can be detected by an effervescent reaction which occurs when a small amount of dilute hydrochloric acid (HCl) is applied to the part of the soil in question.

The A and B horizons, together, constitute the *solum,* which is the part of the soil profile that has been developed owing to the combined effects of climate and organisms over a period of time under certain conditions of relief on a given parent material. Some of the original constituents of the A horizon are usually depleted by the leaching process. Also, clay particles of extremely small size are mechanically washed out of the A horizon by rain water infiltrating the ground. The B horizon is enriched by compounds and clay particles washed out of the A horizon (Fig. 6-7). Development of a B horizon through the movement of soluble materials and clay particles from the overlying A horizon implies a downward movement of water through the solum. However, in some desert or even semi-desert areas the rate of evaporation or *upward* movement of water through the solum is greater than the downward percolation. This results in a lesser degree of differentiation between the A and B horizons and a more even distribution of soluble constituents throughout the solum.

The C horizon is weathered parent material that is unaltered by the process of soil formation. It is a mineral horizon or layer roughly equivalent to the part of a residual or transported mantle that has been little affected by soil forming processes, and lacks properties diagnostic of the A or B horizons. Some immature soils contain only the A and C horizons because of insufficient time for full development of the solum. All three horizons can be subdivided further if the nature of the solum requires it, but these additional complexities need not be considered in an elementary discussion.

■ SOIL CLASSIFICATION. Dokuchaiev revolutionized soil science when he proposed in 1870 that soils were independent natural bodies, each with a unique morphology resulting from a unique combination of climate, living organisms, parent material, topography, and time. He designed a classification that, in part, reflected this point of view. His highest categories were called soil types and were differentiated mainly on the basis of climatic and vegetational factors.

Following the original work of Dokuchaiev, American soil scientists used his basic plan with further modifications. The difficulty with most of the modifications involved the belief that soil genesis (the cause) could be deduced from soil morphology (the effect). Theoretically, this belief is in keeping with sound scientific reasoning, but the science of pedology was not ready for this level of sophistication in Dokuchaiev's time, nor indeed is it ready now.

One of the main stumbling blocks which stood in the way of a clear-cut relationship between soil morphology and soil genesis was the inability of the pedologists to evaluate the element of time. The passage of time alone can produce profound changes in the morphologic character of the solum. Neither Dokuchaiev nor his successors were able to recognize these changes with any degree of success, quantitatively. Another problem involved the soils brought under cultivation by man. Soil profiles developed under natural conditions are *virgin soils.* Cultivated soils, under any of the old classification schemes, were classified on the basis of properties that they are *presumed* to have had when virgin. Still another classification problem arose because climatic change during the life history of a soil introduced another variable in the soil-forming processes which could not be related accurately to the morphology of the profile. Such *polygenetic* soils have always posed a problem under any of the previous schemes of classification.

In recognition of the need for a new

Figure 6-8.   Examples of soil profiles belonging to four different orders of the United States Department of Agriculture soil classification system: *A.* Spodosol.   The *A* horizon consists of a dark upper A_1 horizon about 12 inches thick, and a light gray lower A_2 horizon about 6 inches thick.   The *B* horizon is about 12 inches thick and rests on the *C* horizon, 6 inches of which is visible in the photograph.   The parent material is loess.   *B.*   Mollisol.   The *A* horizon is 18 inches thick

and consists of rather soft material high in organic matter. The soil is typical of the Corn Belt of western Iowa. Numbers on the scale are feet. *C.* Aridisol. This profile was developed on a parent material of gravel in Utah. The white material is a calcic horizon which is commonly called caliche and is formed under semiarid conditions. Black marks on the scale are 6 inches apart. *D.* Oxidol. A red soil of the lower Congo in Africa formed under a tropical rain forest. Note the lack of visible horizons. Scale is 6 feet long. (Photographs A and B by Roy W. Simonson; C by W. M. Johnson; and D by Charles Kellog.)

approach to soil classification, the soil survey staff of the United States Department of Agriculture in 1952 began the bold task of devising a new system of soil classification. One of their basic assumptions was the belief that a natural classification should be based on the properties of the objects classified. A natural system based on observable soil properties was devised and presented to the Seventh International Congress of Soil Science in 1960. The published document containing the new classification system is called the *7th Approximation* because it represents the seventh revision of the first draft outlined in 1952 for the first time.

The new scheme discards many of the names used in older systems and introduces a new nomenclature consisting of coined terms in which Latin and Greek roots are largely used. The new system consists of six ranks or levels of classification. The highest category is the order, followed by suborders, great groups, subgroups, families, and series. Ten different orders are recognized. They correspond in a rough way to the soil types defined by Dokuchaiev although they are by no means identical. Nevertheless, the close relationship between the orders of the 7th Approximation and Dokuchaiev's types shows that climate is still a fundamental basis for differentiating the highest soil categories. Below the rank of order, however, climatic influence in the classification is of less importance, and it is at the lower levels where the new scheme differs most markedly from the older ones.

Full definitions of all ten orders will not be given here, but the principal dif-ferentiae for six of them will serve to illustrate the broader differences between soils. The six orders herein considered are the *entisols, aridisols, histosols, mollisols, spodosols,* and *oxisols.*

The entisols are mineral soils with little or no horizonation, either because of a lack of time or because of unfavorable conditions for development of the solum. Alluvium on an active flood plain or soils of the permafrost zone in polar regions belong in this order.

The aridisols form in desert regions in which the water table lies deep below the surface. They often show a concentration of calcium carbonate somewhere in the profile (Fig. 6-8C) which is called a *calcic horizon* or *caliche.*

Histosols are soils with a high content of organic matter. Common names for such soils are peat and muck.

Mollisols are mineral soils characteristic of the Great Plains in the United States and the grasslands of Russia. They have a diagnostic *A* horizon which is black (Fig. 6-8B), and they are almost always developed in a semiarid to subhumid climate under a vegetational cover of native grasses. These soils are highly fertile and among the most productive in the world. The original Russian term for these soils was *Chernozem.*

The *spodosols* are mineral soils developed in cool, humid regions, and they exhibit a well-developed solum (Fig. 6-8A). The lower part of the *A* horizon is very light colored, and the *B* or *spodic* horizon is characterized by an accumulation of organic material, iron, and aluminum washed down from the *A* horizon. The spodosols are generally formed under a coniferous forest cover and occur extensively in eastern Canada, New England, the states around the Great Lakes, and northern Russia. These soils were among the first to be studied in detail by Russian scientists, probably because of the strong development of horizons. These soils were called *podzols* in the older classifications.

Oxisols are restricted in occurrence to the tropical and subtropical regions of the world. They were formerly called *laterites* or *latosols* and are distinctive because of their red color. The solum is very deep, poorly differentiated, and contains a high percentage of clay (Fig. 6-8*D*). Oxisols commonly occur on old land surfaces and are thought to be the end product of chemical weathering of long duration.

SUMMARY

Weathering is the physical and chemical change induced in minerals and rocks as they react with constituents of the atmosphere under normal conditions of temperature and pressure. Physical weathering produces polygonal ground, talus, and blockfields. Chemical weathering is accomplished by oxidation, leaching hydration, and kaolinization. Exfoliation is a physical change induced by hydration and kaolinization.

The relative resistance of some common minerals is expressed in the stability series in which quartz, the most resistant to chemical weathering, is followed in order by muscovite, orthoclase, biotite, amphibole, pyroxene, plagioclase, and olivine.

Soil is a product of weathering controlled by the factors of climate, parent material, organisms, relief, and time. The solum consists of the A and B horizons, which, when permitted to reach mature development, will reflect the influence of climate and organisms under certain conditions of relief.

The chief basis of soil classification is climate, although it probably has been overemphasized at the expense of equally important geological factors, especially parent material. The 7th Approximation is a newly devised classification system that displaces previous ones in which too much emphasis was placed on soil genesis as inferred from soil morphology. Ten major orders are defined in the new system which uses as its basis the natural properties of the soils.

REFERENCES

Goldich, S. S., 1938, *A study in rock weathering, Jour. Geology,* **46.**

Keller, W. D., 1955, *Principles of chemical weathering,* Lucas Bros, Co., Columbia, Missouri.

Kellogg, Charles E., 1951, *The soils that support us,* The Macmillan Co., New York.

Orvedal, A. C., *et al.,* 1952, *Frost action in soils,* Washington, D.C., National Academy of Sciences, National Research Council, Highway Research Board, Special Report 2.

Simonson, Roy W., 1962, *Soil classification in the United States, Science,* **137,** 1027–1034.

Soil Survey Staff, 1960, *Soil classification, a comprehensive system—7th Approximation,* U.S. Department of Agriculture Soil Conservation Service, Washington, D.C.

U.S. Department of Agriculture, 1951, *Soil survey manual,* Washington, D.C., Agriculture Handbook 18.

VII

The Force of the Wind

The seasons change, the winds they shift and veer . . .

Sir William Watson

Wind is a geologic agent that is able to produce profound changes on the earth's surface. Although no part of the earth's surface is completely free from the force of strong winds, a common misconception exists as to just what they can accomplish. This chapter will cover the geologic work of the wind. It will not include the role of wind in the generation of water waves which in turn modify the shores of lakes and oceans. This will be considered in a later chapter.

WIND: MOVEMENT OF THE ATMOSPHERE

The earth is surrounded by an envelope of gases called the atmosphere. The movement of the atmosphere in a direction parallel to the earth's surface is *wind,* whereas vertical movements of the atmosphere are referred to as air currents.

The causes of atmospheric circulation are considered in the science of *meteorology.* The geologist is more concerned with the effects of wind on the surface materials of the earth than with winds themselves. A few basic concepts of wind movement will suffice.

■ WIND VELOCITIES. The speed of the wind ranges from dead calm to over one hundred miles per hour. The fierceness of hurricanes and the havoc produced by them along the Gulf and eastern coasts of the United States can hardly be exaggerated. The widespread destruction of man-made structures is well known. On the other hand, the more moderate winds of 20 to 30 miles per hour are capable of accomplishing a great deal of geologic work, not only by transporting quantities of soil and dust particles but also by the direct impact of sand blown against rock outcrops and man-made objects.

■ WIND DIRECTION. The pattern of atmospheric circulation has been quite well established for most of the earth. Recently established weather stations in the Arctic and Antarctic regions are adding much to the general knowledge of atmospheric circulation, and the Tiros weather satellites are providing broad coverage of large portions of the earth's surface in terms of all types of weather phenomena. *Prevailing winds* for any given locality are those which come from one direction for the longest period of time during the year. They are not necessarily the strongest winds because local variations in the circulation of the atmosphere can produce winds of shorter duration but of greater velocity. Hence geologic features related to wind action are produced by prevailing winds as well as by local storm winds.

MECHANICS OF WIND ACTION

Wind action can be divided into three categories: *erosion, transportation,* and *deposition.* All three are interrelated and depend on wind velocity, the nature of materials at the earth's surface, and vegetational cover.

The load of material moved by the wind falls into two categories, *bed load* and *suspended load.* The bed load consists of particles too large or too heavy to be lifted more than a few feet above the ground. The wind moves this part of its load by a process known as *saltation,* a kind of a jumping motion in which sand grains are dislodged from a position of rest and momentarily lifted above the ground. During the brief time aloft, the particles are bodily carried down wind before falling back to the ground (Fig. 7-1). As a particle strikes the ground, it in turn dislodges another particle so that the process continues as long as the wind velocity is sufficiently high to keep the sand particles moving. Experimental work in wind tunnels indicates that a wind velocity of 11 miles per hour is necessary for fine dune sand, 0.25 millimeter in diameter, to be moved.

The suspended load consists of particles small enough that they can be kept constantly in suspension by the turbulence of the wind. The size of the fragments which comprise the suspended load ranges from 0.02 millimeter to extremely small dust particles. Finely disseminated dust originating from volcanic eruptions may remain in suspension for months, thousands of feet above the ground; and top soil, unprotected by vegetation, is born aloft for days and weeks before it eventually settles back to earth.

WIND EROSION

Two types of erosive action of the wind are *deflation* and *abrasion.*

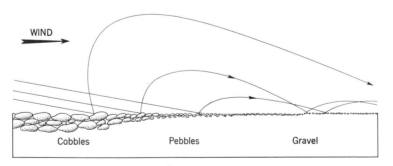

Figure 7-1. Paths of sand grains driven along the ground by the wind. Particles moved in this manner constitute the bed load of wind-borne sediments. (After R. P. Sharp, 1949, Pleistocene ventifacts east of the Big Horn Mountains, Wyoming, *Jour. Geol.,* 57, p. 175–195; and R. A. Bagnold, 1941, *The physics of blown sand and desert dunes,* Methuen and Co., London.)

■ DEFLATION. This process involves the removal of loose particles from an area, and leaves a denuded surface consisting of coarse material too large for wind transport. Eventually, the residual cover of coarse gravel and stones becomes so concentrated that it prevents any further removal of fine-grained particles. Such a surface is called a *lag gravel,* and it may involve several hundred square miles or only a few acres.

The deflation process is impeded greatly by patches of vegetation, the roots of which tend to bind the soil particles together so they cannot be dislodged by the wind. Where the surface materials contain no coarse particles of gravel or stones, the deflation process may continue until a depression is formed. Such features are called *blowouts* and occur where dry sand deposits are attacked by the wind. Blowouts are not normally much deeper than a few feet, but occasionally they attain depths of ten or fifteen feet and are several acres in extent. Some blowouts are filled with water when a climatic change brings more rainfall.

Deflation, of course, is the major process in denuding agricultural lands during extended periods of drought. The infamous "dust bowls" of Kansas, Oklahoma, and adjoining states during the 1930's and the 1950's resulted when crops failed to grow because of the lack of rainfall. The bare top soil, deprived of its vegetational cover, was thus easy prey even for moderate winds.

Such disasters probably cannot be prevented entirely, but they may be averted in part by a more widespread use of strip farming. This method involves tilling parallel strips of land with intervening tracts of equal area planted to grass, thereby creating a surface only partially vulnerable to attack by the wind. Planting rows of trees along field boundaries also materially reduces wind velocity.

■ ABRASION. Even though the particles of the bed load do not move great distances during a single "jump," they are tools impelled by the wind against natural or artificial objects lying in its path. Hard grains of quartz sand driven by the wind sandblast telephone poles, fence posts, stones, and rock outcrops, causing wearing or abrasive action on these objects. Because the bed load is concentrated within a few feet of the ground, wind abrasion is not a very potent process on the parts of obstructions projecting high above the ground level.

Stones and boulders subjected to wind abrasion are smoothed and polished if they are fine grained, and pitted or etched if they consist of coarse crystals of unequal hardness. Such wind abraded stones are known as *ventifacts,* and they usually occur in association with lag gravels (Fig. 7-2).

A common misconception is that wind abrasion produces "wind caves," indentations along bedrock cliffs in arid regions. Although such features occur in regions subject to strong winds, their origin is more likely the result of concentrated physical or chemical weathering due to the local concentration of moisture. At most, abrasion by wind only exerts a modifying influence on such features. Some "wind caves" may develop through deflation of a sandstone whose grains have been loosened by weathering or were not strongly cemented during lithifaction. Generally speaking, however, there are no large land forms produced solely by wind abrasion.

DEPOSITION BY WIND

Bed load and suspended load materials eventually settle out of the atmosphere. Where bed load particles accumulate, *sand dunes* are formed. Suspended load deposits are more widespread and may form blanket deposits covering hundreds of thousands of square miles.

Figure 7-2. Wind-facetted pebbles (ventifacts) from Rock Springs, Wyoming. The longest dimension of the largest stone is about 4 inches. (Photograph by M. R. Campbell, U.S. Geological Survey.)

■ SAND DUNES. It is difficult to dispel the commonly-held notion that sand dunes exist only in the desert regions of the world. This idea is greatly nourished through popular articles, books, and movies which portray the chieftain sheik riding his faithful camel over endless miles of desert waste, the exclusive realm of sand dunes. Perhaps the main reason this mistaken idea persists is because of the failure to distinguish between sand dunes of two different categories, the *active* dunes and the inactive or *stabilized* dunes. The active dunes are those which are actively in the process of formation and occur mostly in true desert regions. These dunes change their shapes and positions on the ground.

The stabilized dunes are those whose shape and position become fixed because of a vegetational cover. Stabilized dunes might reflect a change from an arid climate to one in which grass or even trees could become established on the dune surface because of increased rainfall.

■ SHAPES OF DUNES. Sand dunes occur in a variety of shapes and sizes. Dune shape is a function of wind direction and degree of stabilization by vegetation. The shapes of active dunes are generally different from the forms of the stabilized group. From this fact we deduce that vegetation plays an important part in the configuration of a dune during the transitional stages of development between the active and stabilized states.

Active dunes include (1) *barchans,* or crescent-shaped dunes with the convex side facing toward the wind; (2) *transverse* dunes, or dune ridges extending at right angles to the wind direction; (3) *longitudinal* dunes, or sand ridges elongated parallel to the wind direction; and (4) *complex* dunes of irregular shapes. The barchans and transverse dunes are both strongly asymmetrical in cross section with the steep side facing away from the wind direction and inclined at an angle of about 30–33 degrees with the horizontal.

The most common form of stabilized

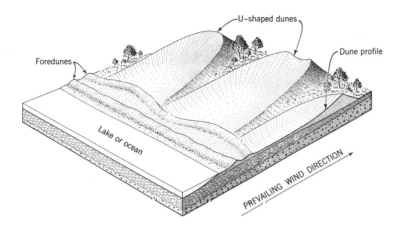

Figure 7-3. U-shaped dunes are characteristic of the eastern shore of Lake Michigan. They are generally stabilized by vegetation and do not migrate.

dune is the U-shaped dune, often called a *parabolic* dune (Fig. 7-3). Unlike the barchans, the U-shaped dunes have the open end facing toward the wind, and the steep lee slope of the convex side facing in a down wind direction.

Some coastal dunes are U-shaped owing to the formation of blowouts on the windward side of pre-existing dune forms. Vegetation holds the rest of the dune in place while the central blowout zone is further eroded by wind. A study of dunes along the southeastern shore of Lake Michigan suggests that a regular evolutionary sequence of dune shapes develops, beginning with the original transverse dunes, passing through a parabolic stage, and finally ending with longitudinal dunes (Fig. 7-3).

DISTRIBUTION OF DUNE SAND IN THE UNITED STATES

Deposits of wind-blown sand in the United States are more extensive than most people realize. The largest area of active sand dunes lies in northeastern Arizona, (Fig. 7-4), where barchans, longitudinal dunes, and some U-shaped dunes occur. Other extensive areas of active dunes are found in New Mexico, a state well known for its famous white sands near Alamogordo. These sand deposits consist entirely of white gypsum grains derived from local gypsum beds (Fig. 7-5).

The Mojave Desert of southern California as well as Death Valley in that same state have only small isolated areas of active dunes. Most of the surface is covered with bare rock or unconsolidated deposits too coarse for wind transport.

A rather small but interesting occurrence of active sand dunes lies on the west flank of the Sangre de Cristo Mountains in southern Colorado (Fig. 7-6). There the asymetrical shapes of the dune ridges clearly indicate a westerly source of sand. The dunes migrated eastward until they reached the Sangre de Cristos, an imposing barrier which prevent any further eastward migration.

The areas of stabilized or partially stabilized dunes in the United States exceeds by far the areal extent of active dunes. The stabilized dunes are relics of a more arid climate of past geologic time. Some date back only three or four thousand years whereas others are several times as old.

Nebraska has the greatest extent of stabilized dunes in the United States in an area known as the Sand Hills (Fig.

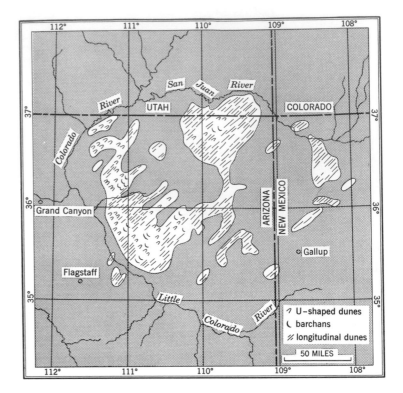

Figure 7-4. Map of northeastern Arizona and parts of adjoining states showing areas of active dunes and types of dune forms. (Based on Map of Pleistocene Deposits of the United States, Alaska, and parts of Canada, published by the Geological Society of America, 1952.)

7-7). Locally, some of these dunes are being modified by deflation, but generally they are covered with grass typical of the Great Plains states. Dune shapes and alignment point to a northwesterly wind direction during the period of dune building. Because the sand dunes are so porous, about 25 per cent of the annual

Figure 7-5. These active sand dunes of the White Sands National Monument in New Mexico are composed of grains of gypsum. (Courtesy of the National Park Service, U.S. Department of the Interior.)

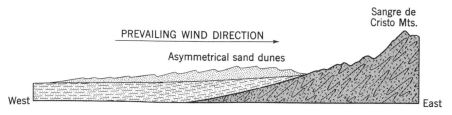

Figure 7-6. Diagrammatic cross section of the sand dunes in Sand Dunes National Monument, Colorado. These active dunes were halted in their eastward migration by the Sangre de Cristo Mountains.

rainfall seeps into the ground where it is stored until man withdraws it by means of water wells, or until it emerges in rivers farther east.

In the Great Lakes region, the largest tract of stabilized dunes is found in northeastern Illinois, northwestern Indiana, and along the eastern shore of Lake Michigan. The sand was derived from vast quantities of river sands released from melting glaciers about 13,000 years ago.

A remarkable display of partially stabilized dunes lies along the eastern coast of Lake Michigan (Fig. 7-8). Some of these dunes rise more than 150 feet above their bases and were derived from beach sand blown inland by prevailing westerly winds. Many of the dunes along the Michigan coast are U-shaped. Some are

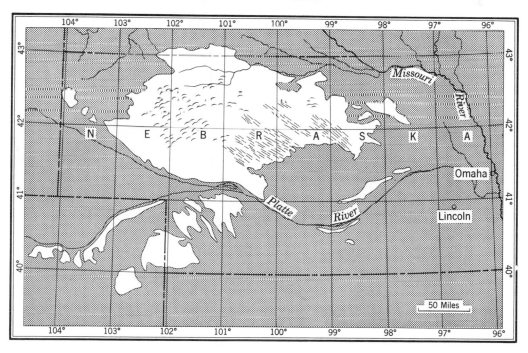

Figure 7-7. Map of the Sand Hills of Nebraska showing stabilized barchans and longitudinal dunes. Wind direction was from the northwest. (From Map of Pleistocene Eolian Deposits of the United States, Alaska, and Parts of Canada, published by the Geological Society of America, 1952.)

Figure 7-8. Partially stabilized dunes along the eastern shore of Lake Michigan. These dunes are currently being modified by blowout action of the wind. View is toward the east. Prevailing winds are from the west. (Hann Photo Service, Hartford, Michigan.)

being modified currently by blowout action of the wind, but by and large most of the dunes became stabilized by vegetation as they migrated inland farther away from the source of beach sand.

GEOLOGIC SIGNIFICANCE OF DUNES

The shapes of dunes are controlled mainly by prevailing winds during the active period of dune formation. Even though some of the active dune shapes are not completely preserved when the dunes become stabilized, it is still possible to decipher the direction of prevailing winds during the period of dune growth. Stabilized dunes constitute another clue for the geologist in reconstructing the physical conditions of the geologic past in certain areas.

Of practical importance is the artificial stabilization or control of active dunes. Civilian and military installations are constantly subjected to invasion by migrating dunes in most deserts and some coastal regions. Oil field derricks and other drilling equipment in desert areas of the Middle East are subject to encroachment and damage by wind-blown sand. Only through a complete understanding of the processes of transportation and deposition by wind can man hope to combat this geologic agent effectively.

LOESS

The suspended load wafted about by winds consists mainly of silt and dust particles. As the suspended load settles out of air suspension, it builds a blanket deposit of silt known as *loess* (lōs, lōes, lŭs, lĕrs, lĕs). These deposits are remarkably uniform in grain size composition, and consist mainly of silt grains, 0.002–0.05 millimeter in diameter.

Loess deposits are derived from unconsolidated surficial materials that are only sparsely vegetated or completely barren of plants. The true deserts of arid lands certainly qualify as a source of material. But also broad river flats (flood plains), replenished yearly with new layers of fine sand and river silt, are excellent sources of silt for suspended load wind transport in humid regions of the world. Figure 7-9 shows a dust storm originating from

the river deposits of the Delta River in central Alaska. Silt of similar origin occurs around Fairbanks, Alaska, as a blanket ranging in thickness from 10 to 100 feet on the hilltops, and over 300 feet in the valleys. The Delta River and others like it in central Alaska are fed by melting glaciers which supply the load of sand and silt to the rivers. This load is deposited along the course of the rivers during flood stages and is later exposed to the wind when the rivers return to their low stages.

This direct observation of river-deposited silt being lifted by the wind has an important bearing on ideas about the origin of loess in the central United States along the Mississippi and Missouri Rivers (Fig. 7-10). Most geologists concur that this loess is definitely eolian in origin and that it was derived from flood plain silts deposited by rivers which originated farther north as glacier meltwater channels.

■ LOESS AND AGRICULTURE. The loessial soils of the central United States, especially Iowa, Illinois, and Indiana, are

Figure 7-9. Dust storms arising from the flood plain of the Delta River in central Alaska. The loess of the central United States may have originated in a similar manner from the flood plains of the Mississippi and Missouri Rivers during the Ice Age or Pleistocene. (Courtesy of Troy Péwé, University of Alaska.)

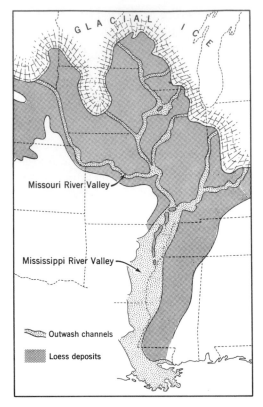

Figure 7-10. Map showing distribution of loess deposits in central United States and their relationship to rivers that carried meltwater during the retreat of the great continental glaciers of the Pleistocene. (Based on a diagram by M. M. Leighton and H. B. Willman, 1950, Loess formation of the Mississippi Valley, *Jour. Geol.* **58,** 604.)

among the most fertile in the world. Their silty texture makes them easy to plow, yet gives them enough cohesion that they have a high capacity for holding moisture. A great variety of minerals in the loess parent material provides an adequate supply of elements for soil fertility. Not the least among these is calcite ($CaCO_3$) which, because of its solubility in water, is readily available for plant use.

■ LOESS AND ENGINEERING. Loess deposits require special treatment when highways or airfields are built on them because of the high susceptibility of silty sediments to frost heaving. Usually the only remedy is to remove the loess to a depth below the level of frost penetration and replace it with a coarser material, thereby preventing the accumulation of ice lenses due to excessive moisture during freezing.

SUMMARY

Wind action is a geologic process involving erosion, transportation, and deposition of particles ranging in size from sand to silt and clay. Sand particles are transported as bed load, and silt and smaller particles are moved as the suspended load.

Erosion by wind consists of abrasion, a sandblasting process whereby the bed load is driven bodily against protruding rock surfaces close to the ground. Abrasion by wind-borne sand is concentrated near the ground level, because sand particles are moved by saltation, a process which operates only within a few feet of the surface. Wind-faceted stones or ventifacts are the chief products of wind erosion. Deflation is another process of wind erosion in which loose grains of sand and smaller particles are evacuated from a local area. Concentrated deflation results in blowouts (shallow depressions) and lag gravels.

Wind-deposited materials consist of sand dunes (bed load) and loess (suspended load). Sand dunes have shapes related to prevailing wind directions. Barchans, transverse dunes, longitudinal dunes, and U-shaped dunes are four of the most commonly observed types. Sand dunes are either active or stabilized, depending mainly on the extent of vegetational cover. Most dunes are steep on the lee (downwind) side and gentle on the windward (upwind) slope.

Loess is generally regarded as a wind-blown (eolian) silt derived from river flood plains in humid regions and desert wastelands in arid regions.   The extensive loess blanket of the central United States was derived from flood plains of rivers fed by melting glaciers.   Loess is an excellent parent material from which many of the fertile soils of the Middle West farm belt were derived, but requires special treatment against frost action in highway and airfield construction.

REFERENCES

Bagnold, R. A., 1941, *The physics of blown sand and desert dunes,* Methuen and Co., London.

Péwé, Troy, 1955, Origin of the upland silt near Fairbanks, Alaska, *Bull. Geol. Soc. Amer.,* **66,** 699–724.

Sharp, R. P., 1949, Pleistocene ventifacts east of the Big Horn Mountains, Wyoming, *Jour. Geology,* **57,** 175–195.

Smith, H. T. U., 1949, Physical effects of Pleistocene climatic changes in nonglaciated areas; eolian phenomena, frost action, and stream terracing, *Bull. Geol. Soc. Amer.,* **60,** 1485–1495.

VIII

Ground Water

. . . he digged the hard rock with iron, and made wells for water.

Ecclesiastes

Ground water is underground water that occurs in a saturated zone of variable thickness and depth below the earth's surface. Cracks and pores in rocks and unconsolidated material make up a large underground reservoir where part of the precipitation is stored. Ground water not only functions as a geologic agent in the role of solvent, carrier, and depositer of minerals, but it also serves as a source of water supply for man. Yet its origin and occurrence are still viewed by many through the eyes of the medievalists who believed in a mysterious source of underground water and the peculiar powers of some people to find it by the use of a forked twig. One purpose of this chapter will be to show that these archaic ideas have no basis in fact.

PRINCIPLES OF GROUND WATER ORIGIN AND OCCURRENCE

■ ORIGIN OF GROUND WATER. We have already seen that the concept of the hydrologic cycle is a principle based on observable and measurable facts. Up until the latter part of the seventeenth century, however, the philosophers or "scientists" of the Old World knew nothing about the occurrence of ground water, much less its origin. They did know of its existence, however, because water could be seen emerging from the ground as springs, and water has been withdrawn from wells for millenniums. The ancients also recognized the fact that many rivers were fed by seepage of water from beneath the ground. But even though astronomers were already versed in the methods of measuring distance and time, the idea of measuring rainfall or runoff was not successfully applied until the late seventeenth century. Two Frenchmen, Pierre Perrault (1608–1680) and Edmé Mariotté (1620–1684) successfully measured the rainfall of a part of the Seine River drainage basin over a three-year period, and also determined the amount of water discharged by the river. They showed that the discharge of the

Seine at a point in Burgundy was only one-sixth of the quantity of water which fell in the basin as snow or rainfall. In other words, the runoff from that part of the Seine River drainage basin was only one-sixth of the rainfall. The other five-sixths was "lost" somewhere between its point of contact with the earth and the discharge measuring point. The dispensation of the "losses" was soon related to *infiltration* (seepage into the ground), *transpiration* (use of water by plants), and *evaporation*. These relationships can be expressed in the form of the general hydrologic equation,

Precipitation = Runoff + Infiltration + Transpiration + Evaporation.

Hydrologic studies since the initial discoveries of Perrault and Mariotté have benefited from more precise measuring techniques, but they have all substantiated this fundamental principle: ground water originates as that fraction of total precipitation which infiltrates the ground and fills the voids in the rock or unconsolidated material. Ground water originating from precipitation is called *meteoric water*. Two very minor sources of ground water are *connate water* (sea water trapped in pores of rocks that originated in shallow seas of the geologic past), and *juvenile water* (water which comes chiefly from volcanic emanations in the form of water vapor). Neither one is significant in terms of the total volume of fresh underground water.

■ OCCURRENCE OF GROUND WATER. The outer portion of the earth's crust is made up of material ranging from dense granite with almost no pores to loose, unconsolidated gravel with many voids between mineral grains. The volume of the pores in a rock or sediment is expressed as a per cent of the total volume of the material, and is known technically as *porosity*. Porosity depends on the shape and packing of the grains plus the degree of sorting (Fig. 8-1).

For example, a 5-gallon pail is filled with coarse, dry sand. To this is added 1 gallon of water which just saturates the sand. The porosity of the sand is quickly established by the relationship,

$$\text{Porosity} = \frac{\text{Volume of voids}}{\text{Total volume}}$$

$$= \frac{1 \text{ gallon}}{5 \text{ gallons}} \times 100 = 20\%$$

All the materials of variable porosity near the upper portion of the earth's crust can be considered as a potential storage place for ground water, and hence might be called the *ground water reservoir*. The total volume of water contained in the ground water reservoir in any localized area is dependent on (1) the porosity

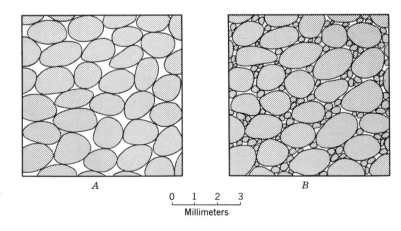

Figure 8-1. Diagrammatic sketch of well-sorted (*A*) and poorly-sorted (*B*) deposits. Porosity of *A* is greater than *B* because the grains of *A* are all about equal in size. In *B*, the smaller grains fill the spaces between the larger grains, thus reducing the volume of void space.

A

B

0 1 2 3
Millimeters

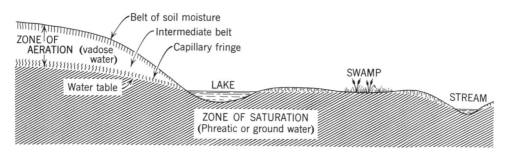

Figure 8-2. Cross-sectional diagram showing the zones of subsurface moisture and the relationships of ground water to surface water. (After O. E. Meinzer, 1923, *Outline of groundwater hydrology*, U.S. Geological Survey, Water Supply Paper 494, p. 23.)

of the rock, (2) the rate at which water is added to it by infiltration, and (3) the rate at which water is lost from it by evaporation, transpiration, seepage to surface water courses, and withdrawal by man.

To understand the conditions of occurrence of ground water, consider the zones penetrated while drilling a hole through a homogeneous and isotropic (i.e., the same in all directions) material such as sand. Within a few feet of the surface the soil might be slightly damp, depending upon the recency of the last rainfall. Below this *belt of soil moisture* a zone of increasing moisture content, *the intermediate belt,* would be encountered, and still deeper the sand might be very wet where it is held by molecular attraction in the *capillary fringe.* These three belts comprise what is known as the *zone of aeration* or *vadose* zone as shown diagrammatically in Fig. 8-2.

Eventually, the hole would penetrate to sand in which all the voids were filled or saturated with water. This is the *zone of saturation* or *phreatic* zone, and the undulating plane separating the vadose zone from the phreatic zone is the *water table.* Under "normal" conditions, the water table is a subdued replica of the land surface. Where the water table lies at or very near the ground surface, swampy conditions exist, and a lake is

merely a surface depression that has a bottom below the water table.

Springs are points at which water escapes from the ground water reservoir and becomes incorporated in the surface drainage system. Springs usually occur along valley walls where downward eroding streams have incised the rock strata below the water table (Fig. 8-3), but wherever the water table intersects the ground surface, a spring occurs. Seasonal fluctuations of the water table also affect the discharge from springs to the extent that many of them "dry up" completely during periods of drought.

The water table fluctuates as the amount of infiltration changes. It is high during the wet seasons and low during periods of drought. If no more moisture were added by infiltration, the water table would eventually flatten out, because the water in the zone of saturation is constantly moving toward lower points on the water table, although such movement may amount to only a small fraction of a foot per day in silts and other fine-grained materials.

■ MOVEMENT OF GROUND WATER. Because the water table has high and low points on it, it is not in equilibrium. In order that equilibrium may be approached, however, water moves from the high points on the water table to points lower down. The rate at which such movement occurs is dependent on two factors: (1) the ability of the porous medium to transmit the water, and (2) the *hydraulic gradient,* usually expressed as the ratio between the difference in elevation of two points on the water table (in the direction of flow) and the distance between them (Fig. 8-4).

The ability of a rock or unconsolidated sediment to transmit ground water is *permeability.* It is not to be confused with porosity since the latter is only an expression of how much void space exists in the rock. The *coefficient of permeability,* on the other hand, is the quantity of water passing through a certain cross-sectional area of the water-bearing material in a definite time under a hydraulic gradient of 1 (i.e., $H/L = 1.00 = 100$ per cent). The United States Geological Survey defines the permeability coefficient, P, as the number of gallons of water transmitted through 1 square foot of an aquifer in 1 day under a hydraulic gradient of 100 per cent. Laboratory and field tests have been devised whereby P can be determined. Values of P range from less than 1 gallon a day per square foot of shale or clay to 10,000 or more gallons a day per square foot of coarse gravel.

In a more general sense, clays and shales are usually classified as relatively impermeable whereas sandstones, sands, and gravels are considered permeable.

The distinction quite obviously explains the fact that permeable materials in the zone of saturation will yield appreciable quantities of water to a well whereas relatively impermeable strata will yield little if any water to a well. Even though a shale may have a porosity equal to that of a sandstone (about 20 per cent), the shale has a low permeability because the size of the openings between the individual mineral grains of the shale are too small to permit easy passage of water through them.

The materials of the earth's crust vary greatly in their coefficients of permeability, and it is this variation that complicates the pattern of ground water movement as well as the occurrence of water available for man's use.

AQUIFERS AND WELLS

A well is a man-made hole or pit in the ground from which water can be withdrawn, and the geologic material which yields the water to the well is an *aquifer.* The amount of water yielded by a well is dependent on many factors, some of which, such as the well diameter, are inherent in the well itself. But all other things being equal, the permeability and thickness of the aquifer are the most important.

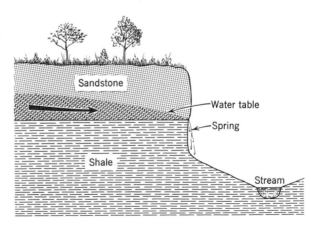

Figure 8-3. The spring is formed by ground water seepage along the contact of the permeable sandstone and relatively impermeable shale. The water table is said to be "perched."

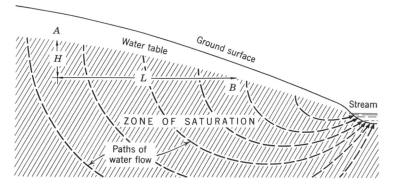

Figure 8-4.   Cross-sectional diagram showing the flow of ground water in a uniformly permeable material.   The difference in elevation between points A and B on the water table is H, and the distance between them is L.   The hydraulic gradient is H/L.   (After M. King Hubbert, 1940, The theory of ground-water motion, *Jour. Geol.*, **48**, 930.)

Aquifers vary in depth, lateral extent, and thickness, but in general all aquifers fall into one of two categories, *unconfined*, and *confined*.   An unconfined aquifer is one in which water table conditions prevail owing to the absence of a layer of relatively impermeable material on top (Fig. 8-5*A*).   Confined aquifers are those which are capped with a relatively impermeable stratum which restricts the movement of the water (Fig. 8-5*B*); the water is thus under pressure and will rise in a well that penetrates it.   Such wells are called *artesian*.

The level to which the water will rise in an artesian well is determined by the highest point on the aquifer.   The water in an artesian well cannot rise to this full height, however, because the friction of the water moving through the aquifer uses up some of the energy.   The flow of water through a confined or artesian aquifer may be likened to the flow of water through an inclined pipe filled with sand (Fig. 8-6).   If no flow existed then the levels in all artesian wells tapping the same aquifer would form a horizontal surface because of the principle, known by all, that water contained in a vessel of any shape will seek a level surface.

The fact that the water level in an artesian well may rise all the way to the surface of the ground is a matter of topographic circumstance rather than an inherent peculiarity of the artesian aquifer beneath that particular well.   If the pressure surface (Fig. 8-5*B*) lies above the ground surface, the wells will be *flowing artesian wells*, but if the pressure surface is below ground level, the wells will be artesian but nonflowing, and will require a pump to bring the water to the surface (Fig. 8-5*B*).

■ PUMPING OF WELLS.   When a well pump is turned on, the water level in the well immediately declines so that a hydraulic gradient is established toward the well forming a *cone of depression* if the aquifer is unconfined, and a *cone of pressure relief* if the aquifer is confined (Fig. 8-7).   The difference between the *static* or nonpumping level of the water in the well and the pumping level is the *drawdown*, and the maximum distance from the pumped well at which the effects of pumping are felt is the *radius of influence*. The drawdown increases and the radius of influence expands until the flow toward the well is balanced by recharge from the aquifer.   In all aquifers, the drawdown

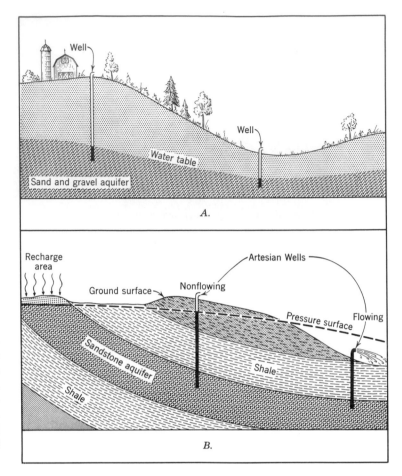

Figure 8-5. Confined and unconfined aquifers. Artesian wells may be flowing or non-flowing, depending on whether the pressure surface is above or below the ground surface. *A*. Wells in an unconfined aquifer. *B*. Artesian wells in a confined aquifer. Compare *B* with Fig. 8-6.

rate decreases with time. The example in Fig. 8-7 illustrates the changes in drawdown and radius of influence with time. Note that the drawdown increased from 20 to 25 feet in 9 hours (drawdown after 10 hours of pumping minus drawdown after 1 hour of pumping). But, to increase the drawdown by another 5 feet, 90 additional hours of pumping was required.

If several closely spaced wells all draw water from the same aquifer, their respective cones of depression overlap so that there is interference between them. This results in greater drawdown in each well, a condition that could result in a general lowering of the water table in the heavily pumped area.

GROUND WATER PROBLEMS

■ PROBLEMS OF SUPPLY. The water requirements of the United States are increasing at a phenomenal rate. The total amount of water used in the United States for an average day in 1960 was in excess of 300 billion gallons. Conservative estimates place this figure at the staggering level of 494 billion gallons per day in 1980!

The reason for this increase derives from two facts: the population increase and the increase in per capita consumption of water. The population of the United States, exclusive of Hawaii and Alaska, in 1960 was 178.5 million people, and by 1980, will reach 230 million. The daily water requirement for the average urban dweller was 150 gallons in 1960 and is expected to increase to about 190 gallons by 1980. Figure 8-8 shows the trend in water use for irrigation, public water utilities, rural domestic, industrial, and steam electric utilities from 1900 to 1980. On the same graph the population growth for the same period is shown.

Not all of this water will have to be of the same quality because the uses to which the water is put provides for a wide range of acceptable standards. Public water for human consumption requires the most rigid regulation in terms of potability, but industrial uses and irrigation needs can be met by water supplies of poorer quality.

Fresh water for any purpose comes from two chief sources, surface water and ground water. Seventeen per cent of the total water supplied for all categories

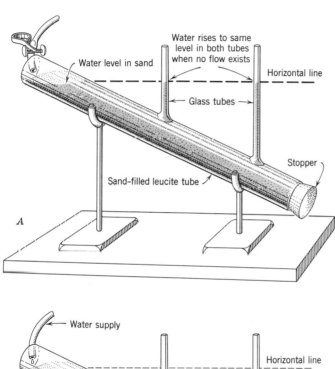

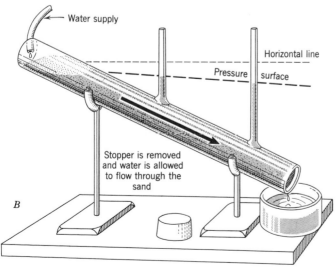

Figure 8-6. Diagram of an experiment in which the principles of artesian flow in aquifers is demonstrated. *A.* A leucite tube filled with permeable sand is saturated with water. The stopper in the lower end of the tube prevents flow. Water in the two glass tubes stands at the same elevation. *B.* The stopper is removed and water is allowed to flow through the sand. The water level in the glass tubes defines the pressure surface. The difference in elevation of the water in the tubes is *H*, and the distance between them is *L*. The hydraulic gradient is *H/L*.

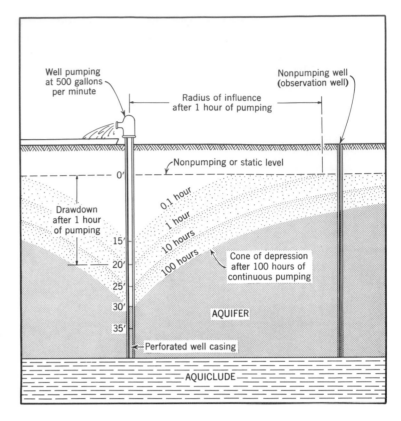

Figure 8-7. Diagram showing the development of a cone of depression around a pumping well drawing water from a homogeneous aquifer. Note the relationships of drawdown to time, and radius of influence to time. See text for details.

shown in Fig. 8-8 is obtained from ground water sources. If the percentage of ground water supplies are to remain more or less constant during the next few decades, the problem of locating important new supplies will pose a continuing challenge for geologists during the years ahead.

In some areas the ground water resources are already overtaxed and in short supply, but other areas undoubtedly exist where the underground water potential has not yet been discovered. In some parts of Texas, for example, the increasing demands on ground water has produced a steady lowering of the water table. The water withdrawn by man simply exceeds the natural recharge by infiltration (Fig. 8-9). In many western states the problem of *overdraft* has become so acute that special steps have been taken by local governmental authorities

to restrict the drilling of new wells and to restore some of the ground water by means of *artificial recharge*. This is usually accomplished by collecting surface water in shallow basins or ponds during certain parts of the year and pumping it back into the ground water reservoir where it is stored for use later in the year.

In localities such as the Los Angeles and Miami metropolitan areas, depletion of the ground water reservoir has reached the point where sea water has infiltrated the coastal aquifers and contaminated the fresh water supply (Fig. 8-10). In the San Joaquin Valley, California, overdraft of the aquifer for irrigation has depressed the water table by more than 100 feet in some places so that pumping levels are becoming uneconomical.

These and countless other examples cannot help but focus man's attention on one of his most precious natural assets, ground water. Conservation of ground water is, therefore, one of the fundamental problems facing many sections of the country today and is destined to pose problems in many other areas in the very near future. The solution can come only through the understanding of the geologic and climatologic conditions which determine the quantity, occurrence, and movement of underground water.

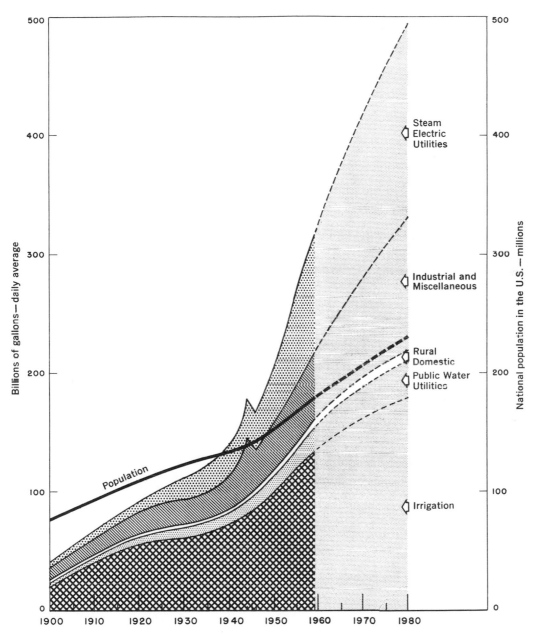

Figure 8-8.   Graph showing trends in water consumption by principal categories of use between 1900 and 1980 in the United States.   (After W. L. Picton, 1960, *Water use in the United States, 1900–1980,* U.S. Department of Commerce.)

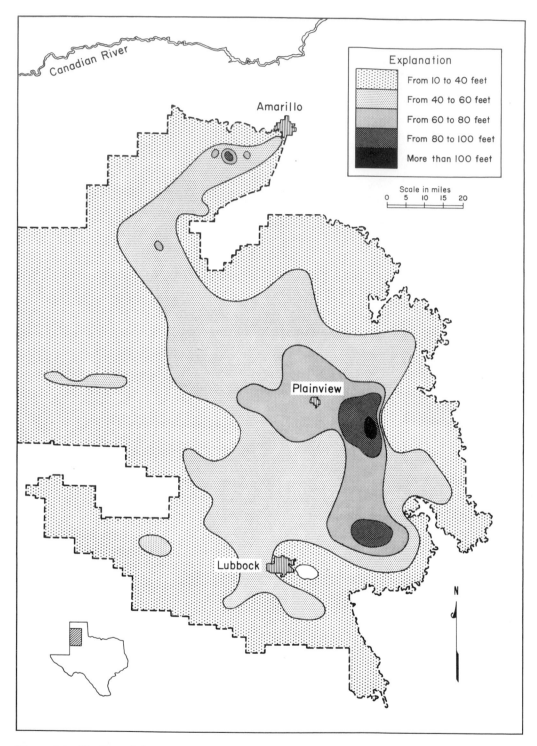

Figure 8-9. Decline of the water table between 1938 and 1962 in a part of northern Texas. (After a map in *The Cross Section,* vol. 8, No. 12, High Plains Underground Water Conservation District No. 1, Lubbock, Texas, 1962.)

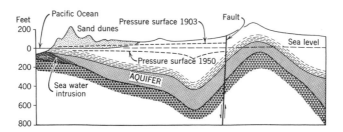

Figure 8-10.   Cross-sectional diagram showing sea water intrusion in the Los Angeles basin area. The slope of the pressure surface of 1903 has been reversed because of overpumping of the aquifer. (From report of the Interior and Insular Affairs Committee, House of Representatives, U.S. Congress, 1953, *The physical and economic foundation of natural resources,* vol. IV, *Subsurface facilities of water management and patterns of suppy-type area studies.*)

■ FINDING NEW SUPPLIES.   Besides making wise use of the water from known aquifers, which is really what conservation means, industries, municipalities, and agriculturalists are pressing the search for additional ground water supplies. Governmental agencies such as Federal and state geological surveys are leading the way in determining the location of heretofore unknown aquifers. They employ the traditional geologic methods which have proved successful in the past. Not that a geologist can see below the grass roots any better than anyone else, but his knowledge of geology qualifies him as an expert in the important search for more ground water.

■ DOWSING.   Opposed to the scientific and systematic methods employed by various geological surveys in the exploration for more ground water are the "water witches," "dowsers," and "diviners." These individuals claim the ability to locate underground water "veins" by using a forked twig, freshly cut sapling, bent wire, pendulum, or other devices of various shapes and sizes. The American Society of Dowsers holds an annual convention during which time the attending members demonstrate their prowess in the ancient and mysterious art of dowsing.

The use of divining rods goes back at least to the mid-fifteenth century according to historical record and there is good reason to believe that some form of dowsing was practiced in the early history of civilization. Agricola (1494–1555) commented on the use of the divining rod in his famous *De re metallica:* "Since this matter remains in dispute and causes much dissension among miners, I consider it ought to be examined on its own merits." Today, even though dowsing has been put to the scientific test dozens of times and has been, as Agricola suggested, "examined on its own merits," there are still thousands of believers that under ground water can be found by a form of medieval "hocus pocus." One is tempted to devote an inordinate amount of space to the subject here, but the interested student is directed to the references at the end of this chapter for further elucidation on the subject. The book by Vogt and Hyman in which the entire subject is treated from the historical, psychological, sociological, and scientific point of view is especially good and quite revealing. Only a few additional comments are apropos here.

A great many diviners are sincere in their belief that water can be found by their methods, but they exhibit a profound lack of knowledge about such basic concepts as the water table, zone of saturation, porosity, and permeability. Much of the mystery surrounding dowsing for water centers around the extraordinary beliefs held by dowsers about the nature and occurrence of ground water. Figure 8-11 illustrates the average dowser's concept of ground water conditions. The main element is the water "dome" which usually occurs underneath a hill. Flowing from the dome are the "veins" which are the main object of the dowser's search.

Since most dowsers have such a distorted view of the rudimentary principles of ground water geology, we might rightfully ask, "Do dowsers actually find water?" The answer is, "Yes," if one considers a well yielding a few gallons a minute proof of dowsing success, for that is about the capacity of most wells located by a forked twig or other dowsing devices. A better question is, "Can a dowser tell where water isn't?" If a dowser actually possesses the extrasensory perception powers that most claim to have, he should be equally successful in locating points where no ground water exists.

The obvious facts presented in this chapter show that ground water is more or less ubiquitous. Its availability is limited only by the depth of the water table under ordinary conditions and the permeability and porosity of the geologic materials in the zone of saturation. Also, the definition of a water well is highly important. A hole in the ground which intersects the water table will yield a few gallons a minute almost anywhere, espe-

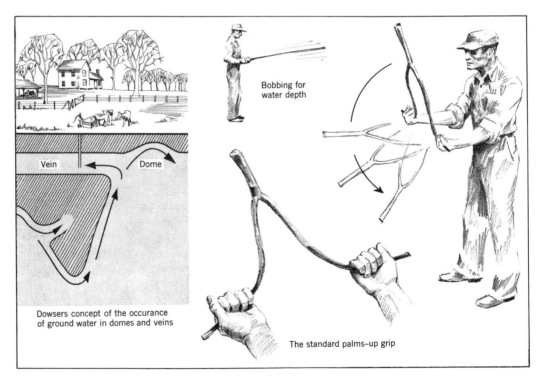

Vein   Dome

Dowsers concept of the occurance
of ground water in domes and veins

Bobbing for
water depth

The standard palms–up grip

Figure 8-11.   Medieval concept of the occurrence of ground water (left) according to beliefs still held by some dowsers. The techniques illustrated on the right are considered by dowsers to be more reliable in the finding of new ground water supplies than the traditional geological methods. (Drawing by Thomas Coates after E. Z. Vogt and R. Hyman, 1959, *Water witching USA,* Chicago, University of Chicago Press.)

cially in the Great Lakes Region and the eastern United States where most dowsers are concentrated, no matter how impermeable the zone of saturation happens to be. The dowser would call this a well but by any other standard it would be a dry hole.

An additional feat claimed by many dowsers is the ability to predict the depth of the "vein" by observing the number of times the rod or forked stick dips or bobs while the dowser stands over the "vein." The number of dips is equal to the depth of the "vein" in *feet*. Interestingly enough, the European dowsers use precisely the same technique with the exception that their forked twigs are calibrated in the metric system so that one dip of the rod equals one *meter* of depth to the "vein"!

There is no use belaboring the point here because many people who have seen dowsers at work are firmly convinced that the dowsers are actually "finding" water. Suffice to say that there is not a shred of *scientific* proof that a forked twig in the hands of a dowser *reacts* in any way to water underground. It is just as absurd to claim that the wand in the hands of a trained magician can put a white rabbit into a black top hat!

GEOLOGIC WORK OF GROUND WATER

Ground water accomplishes geologic work on a large scale. Underground caverns or caves represent the solution action of ground water on soluble sedimentary rocks such as limestone, dolomite, gypsum, and rock salt. In the sense that rock materials are removed during cavern formation, ground water is an erosive agent.

But ground water acts also as an agent of transportation because dissolved mineral matter is carried in solution by the percolating underground water. Finally, under certain conditions, the dissolved

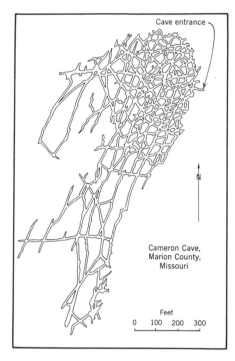

Figure 8-12. The map shows an intersecting network of cave passages which are related to a joint pattern in the limestone. (From J Harlen Bretz, 1956, *Caves of Missouri,* Rolla, Missouri, Missouri Geological Survey and Water Resources Division.)

material carried in ground water solution is redeposited, thereby making ground water an agent of deposition. Ground water erosion, transportation, and deposition thus constitute the three roles played by subsurface water as a geologic agent.

■ LIMESTONE CAVERNS. Underground caves are attractive natural features which provide scenic pleasure for the vacationing public and a source of controversy for the geologist and speleologist.* Caverns are subterranean openings in soluble rock strata. They usually form a three-dimensional network or system of chambers and passageways frequently controlled by the joint system inherent in the original rock (Fig. 8-12). The growth

* One who studies caves; not necessarily a geologist.

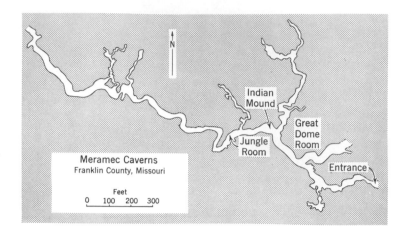

Figure 8-13. This cave has a pattern less obviously controlled by a joint pattern in comparison to Cameron Cave shown in Fig. 8-12. (After J Harlen Bretz, 1956, *Caves of Missouri,* Rolla, Missouri, Missouri Geological Survey and Water Resources Division.)

of some caves is thus directed by the joints and bedding planes in carbonate rocks, but other cave systems are less obviously joint-controlled in that they exhibit a branching linear pattern (Fig. 8-13).

The question of cave origin is an interesting problem. Are caves formed above or below the water table? Although it is true that most of the known caves lie in the zone of aeration (vadose zone), it does not necessarily follow that this has been the case throughout the life history of the cave. As a matter of fact, the most obvious process taking place in known caverns is the *deposition* of calcium carbonate in the form of *stalactites, stalagmites,* and other *dripstone* features (Fig. 8-14).

From a geologic point of view, considerable evidence suggests that caves undergo a two-cycle history. The first cycle involves the dissolving of the rock along joints and bedding planes by circulating ground water in the zone of saturation (Fig. 8-15A). The second cycle begins after the caverns emerge above the water table either by uplift of the land or by lowering of the water table. Once above the water table, the cavern is modified by the action of underground streams which can cause further enlargement by erosion, while at the same time calcium carbonate or other soluble compounds accumulate on the walls, ceiling, and floor of the cave

when vadose water seeps into it (Fig. 8-15B). Although the two-cycle theory is not accepted by all, it can hardly be denied that both phreatic and vadose features are common phenomena of limestone caves.

■ KARST TOPOGRAPHY. The name karst was first applied to the Yugoslavian plateau which is underlain by soluble rocks. In countless other regions of similar geologic nature, the solution action of ground water has dissolved portions of the underlying rock forming caverns and surface depressions called *sinks.* As time progresses, the sinks enlarge and surface streams flow into the underground network of caverns. Karst topography is therefore characterized by the presence of many sinks and a system of underground streams flowing through solution passages in the rock. In the United States, karst topography is well displayed in Florida, southern Indiana, and in Kentucky especially in the vicinity of Mammoth Cave.

■ GEYSERS AND HOT SPRINGS. About once every hour, Old Faithful Geyser in Yellowstone National Park shoots out a column of scalding water nearly 150 feet in the air (Fig. 8-16). Since 1872 when Yellowstone became the first of our national parks, millions of people have witnessed this spectacular display, but it is doubtful whether one in a thousand actually understands the process.

The water spouted from geysers is ground water that has come in contact with igneous rock still in the cooling stage. Ground water collects in irregular tubelike openings and although its temperature at depth may rise above 100°C, boiling does not occur. This is because the weight of the overlying water raises the pressure which, in turn, raises the boiling point. However, the superheated water expands and spills some of the water column over the lip of the tube, causing a reduction of the pressure at depth and hence, a lowering of the boiling point. At the moment the pressure is released, the superheated water flashes into steam which violently drives out the remaining water. After the eruption is over, the process begins anew as more water seeps into the tube and becomes heated.

■ TRAVERTINE. Around the orifices of geysers and especially where hot springs discharge at the surface, calcium carbonate is released from solution and accumulates as a porous or solid mass known as travertine (Fig. 8-17). Impurities of iron and other substances impart variegated colors of red, brown, yellow, and black to some travertines. The carbonate deposits in caves are also known collectively as travertine.

■ CONCRETIONS AND GEODES. Minor features associated with ground water deposition are nodular masses in sedimentary rocks known as *concretions*. They range

Figure 8-14. Stalactites and stalagmites in Floyd Collins Crystal Cave, Kentucky. (Photograph by William Austin.)

Figure 8-15. Diagram showing the two-cycle theory of cave origin. *A.* The initial solution of the limestone is produced beneath the water table. *B.* Lowering of the water table by downcutting of the stream leaves the caverns in the vadose zone. Stalactities, *a,* stalagmites, *b,* and columns, *c,* are travertine deposits of calcium carbonate formed during the vadose cycle of cave filling.

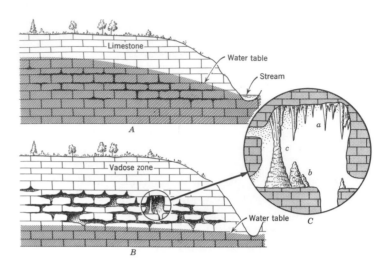

in size from a fraction of an inch to several feet and are commonly ellipsoidal or discoidal in shape. Some are highly irregular but they all represent the accumulation of calcium carbonate around a nucleus in the host rock, and literally grow in place.

Geodes are small cavities lined with

Figure 8-16. Eruption of Old Faithful Geyser in Yellowstone Park is caused by ground water heated by contact with hot underlying volcanic rock. (Photograph by George Grant, National Park Service.)

Figure 8-17.   Travertine terrace at Mammoth Hot Springs, Yellowstone Park, Wyoming, as they appeared in 1921. (Photograph by W. T. Lee, U.S. Geological Survey.)

crystals of quartz, calcite, or other compounds deposited by ground water containing mineral matter in solution.   In reality, a geode is a miniature cave in the cycle of filling by ground water deposition.

■ PETRIFACTION.   Wood or other organic material becomes petrified when its cells are replaced with mineral matter such as silica.   Shells, bones, leaves, or entire logs may be completely replaced by mineral matter carried by ground water.   The Petrified Forest National Monument in Arizona contains hundreds of petrified logs scattered over many square miles. Growth rings and other minute structural details of the woody tissue are commonly preserved during the process.

SUMMARY

Ground water originates from precipitation which infiltrates the voids in rocks.

Porosity is an expression of the per cent of the total rock volume occupied by pores.   Permeability is an index of the rate at which ground water is able to move through the rock interstices Ground water or phreatic water occurs in the zone of saturation which is separated from the vadose zone by the water table.   The water table is a subdued replica of the land surface where the water is unconfined.   Artesian water is under pressure owing to its confinement between relatively impermeable beds.

Aquifers yield water to wells and may be unconfined or confined (artesian). When a well is pumped, a cone of depression or cone of pressure relief develops. The rate of enlargement of the cone of depression and the rate of lowering of the pumping level diminishes with time.

Caves are large openings in soluble rocks such as limestone or dolomite. The two-cycle theory of cave origin requires that caves first originate below the water table, followed by a later cycle of filling with cave deposits in the vadose zone. Some enlargement may take place during the second cycle by underground streams in the vadose zone. Karst topography is characterized by many sink holes and a system of underground drainage in limestone regions. Ground water erosion by solution is the main geologic agent which produces karst terrains. Other geologic features associated with ground water are hot springs, geysers, travertine, geodes, concretions, and petrified organic remains.

REFERENCES

Bretz, J Harlen, 1956, *Caves of Missouri,* Missouri Geological Survey and Water Resources Division, Rolla, Missouri.

Hack, John T., and L. H. Durloo, Jr., 1962, *Geology of Luray Caverns, Virginia,* Virginia Division of Mineral Resources, Report of Investigations 3.

Kuenen, P. H., 1956, *Realms of Water,* John Wiley and Sons, New York.

Leopold, L. B., and W. B. Langbeing, 1960, *A primer on water,* U.S. Department of Interior, Geological Survey, U.S. Government Printing Office, Washington 25, D.C.

Meinzer, O. E., 1923, *Outline of ground water hydrology,* U.S. Geological Survey, Water Supply Paper 494.

Meinzer, O. E., 1942, *Hydrology, physics of the earth,* vol. IX, McGraw-Hill Book Co., New York.

Picton, Walter L., 1960, *Water Use in the United States 1900–1980,* U.S. Department of Commerce, U.S. Government Printing Office, Washington, 25, D.C.

Thornbury, William D., 1954, *Principles of geomorphology,* John Wiley and Sons, New York.

Todd, David K., 1959, Ground Water hydrology, John Wiley and Sons, New York.

U.S. Department of Agriculture, 1955, *Water Yearbook of agriculture,* Washington, D.C., U.S. Government Printing Office.

Vogt, Evon Z., and Hyman, Ray, 1959, *Water witching USA,* University of Chicago Press, Chicago.

IX

Rivers at Work

It is with rivers as it is with people:
the greatest are not always the most agreeable
nor the best to live with.

Henry Van Dyke

On the average, less than one-third of the precipitation striking the surface area of the United States runs directly back to the sea via surface drainage channels. This part of the hydrologic equation (p. 126) is known as the *runoff*. During its course from land to sea, the runoff flowing in stream channels does an extraordinary amount of work in transporting sediment from high to low areas. One look at the muddy waters of the Missouri River during flood stage, or a single glance at the turbid waters of the Colorado River will convince any observer that rivers can move sediment. Even more striking than these examples is the colossal volume of sediment dumped into the Gulf of Mexico by the Mississippi River. Some 2,000,000 tons of sand, silt, and mud pass by New Orleans during an average day.

The sediment in rivers is derived from the land, a fact permitting only one conclusion; the land is being worn down by running water. Some aspects of the geologic work of rivers will be considered in this chapter.

RUNOFF

The *average* annual precipitation in the United States is about 30 inches. Precipitation is the major source of runoff and ranges from a few inches a year in the arid Southwest to over 100 inches per year in the Pacific Northwest. More than ten thousand rain gaging stations in the United States provide a basis for the understanding of precipitation distribution.

The flow of water in rivers is also measurable. The records from more than six thousand gaging stations located on all principal rivers of the United States permit accurate calculations of runoff from the various drainage basins. If the runoff is expressed in inches of water per year spread over the entire drainage basin it can be compared with the annual precipitation for the same area. The percentage of the total precipitation that comprises the runoff varies from a low of 9 per cent for the Rio Grande drainage basin to a high of 55 per cent for the

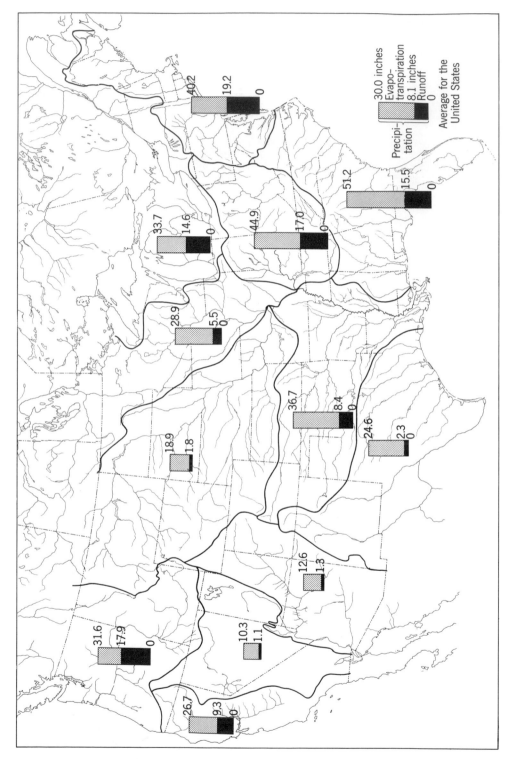

Figure 9-1. Annual precipitation, runoff, and evapotranspiration by major drainage basins in the United States. (From Report of The Interior and Insular Affairs Committee, House of Representatives, U.S. Congress, 1952, *The physical and economic foundation of natural resources,* vol. II, *The physical basis of water supply and its principal uses.*)

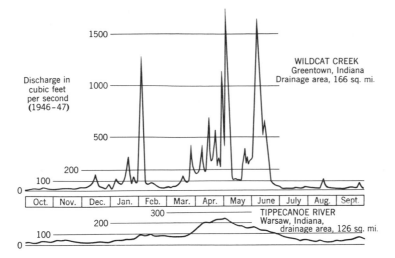

Figure 9-2.   A graph showing the discharge of a river during the water year (October 1–September 30) is called a *hydrograph*.   These two hydrographs show a great difference in two rivers draining areas of similar size in the same climatic region.   The difference in runoff characteristics of the two is ascribed to the different geologic materials of the drainage basins.   (From W. B. Langbein and J. V. B. Wells, in United States Department of Agriculture, 1955, *Water, Yearbook of Agriculture*, Washington, D.C., U.S. Government Printing Office.)

Columbia River basin (Fig. 9-1).   Also, runoff records from a particular river show great variation in discharge* of water from month to month during the water year (October 1–September 30). Two rivers draining areas of similar size with similar rainfall may show wide divergence in discharge during the same period of measurement (Fig. 9-2).

■ FACTORS CONTROLLING RUNOFF.   The preceding statements show rather clearly that the relationship of annual runoff to annual precipitation is not simple.   Studies of many drainage basins and their records of stream flow and precipitation indicate that four major factors influence runoff.   These are (1) climate, (2) geology, (3) topography, and (4) vegetational cover.

Climatic considerations chiefly involve temperature, because mean annual

temperature controls evaporation.   The higher the temperature the higher the evaporation loss.   Thus an annual precipitation of 30 inches will result in more runoff in a region where the mean annual temperature is 50°F than in one where the temperature averages 60°F.   The graph of Fig. 9-3 illustrates the controlling influence of temperature on runoff.

Another climatic factor controlling runoff is the relationship of the water table to surface streams.   In humid regions, the water table is high and slopes toward points of surface discharge.   Such streams are *effluent* (Fig. 9-4A).   In arid regions the water table is low because of high loss by evaporation and low rainfall even though the infiltration rate might be very high.   Hence, there is no discharge from the ground water reservoir to the streams during drought.   During heavy cloudbursts the water rapidly leaks through the river bottoms into the ground water reservoir.   Such streams are *influent* (Fig. 9-4B).

* *Discharge* is an expression of volume of water per unit of time such as cubic feet per second, and is not to be confused with *velocity*, a measurement of distance traveled per unit time, such as feet per second.

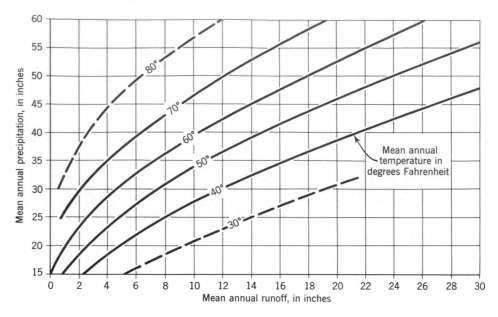

Figure 9-3. A graph showing the relationships of temperature, precipitation, and runoff. (From United States Geological Survey, 1949, Circular 52, *Annual runoff in the United States.*)

The geologic factor having the greatest impact on runoff is the kind of surficial mantle, soil, and bedrock of the drainage basin. Loose textured soils and permeable bedrock have greater infiltration capacities than heavy clay soils and relatively impermeable bedrock. The permeable geologic materials have high storage capacities and are able to absorb large volumes of water into the ground water reservoir from which the surface water courses are supplied for their *base flow.*

For example, the Wildcat Creek drainage basin shows high peaks on the time-discharge graph or *hydrograph* of Fig. 9-2,

whereas the Tippecanoe River basin nearby shows a more even hydrograph. Both basins lie in the same climate zone and do not differ greatly in size. The difference in flow characteristics is attributable to the fact that the Wildcat Creek basin is underlain by relatively impermeable clay in contrast to the permeable sand characterizing the Tippecanoe basin. Rainfall is shed rapidly from one but is partially absorbed and stored by the other. Each of the peaks on the Wildcat Creek hydrograph reflects the discharge of heavy precipitation. The absence of sharp rises on the Tippecanoe hydrograph means that the rainfall of

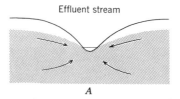

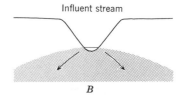

Figure 9-4. An *effluent* stream is supplied with water from the ground water reservoir in humid regions. An *influent* stream supplies water to the ground water reservoir in arid regions.

various storms was largely absorbed before it reached the river, but was later returned to the Tippecanoe and its tributaries via subsurface flow as ground water.

Topography of the drainage basin has a marked influence on the runoff rate. Steep slopes permit rapid runoff, and gentle slopes, of course, reduce the effect of gravity on free surface water. Of special note is a terrain containing numerous lakes connected by streams. The lakes act as surface reservoirs which store precipitation and pay it out later on, much as ground water storage sustains the base flow of rivers during periods of no precipitation.

The effect of vegetation on the runoff rate has been ignored by many investigators who argue that over a large drainage basin, annual runoff can be estimated dependably from a consideration of climatic and geologic factors alone. From a practical point of view, this attitude may be justified, but scientifically, this position is untenable. The impetus for paying more attention to the use of water by plants may come only when demands of water use are in excess of supply. For example, such trees as salt cedar and willow have roots that tap shallow ground water tables beneath river bottom lands and consume large quanities of water at the expense of stream flow.

DRAINAGE SYSTEMS AND
STREAM PATTERNS

■ DRAINAGE BASINS. The land drained by a large river and its tributaries is a drainage basin. The line of demarcation between adjacent drainage basins is the *divide*. Both divides and drainage basins have different orders of magnitude depending on the size of the river under consideration. For example, the Continental Divide in the Rocky Mountains separates the drainage basins discharging into the Pacific Ocean from those entering the Gulf of Mexico. But divides also exist between two tributaries of a single river, as for example, the divide between the Missouri River and the Arkansas River, both tributaries of the Mississippi. Comparative studies of two different rivers are based on their drainage basins rather than the two rivers alone.

■ STREAM PATTERNS. The map or plan view of a single drainage basin or parts of adjacent drainage basins shows the *stream pattern*. Stream patterns are indicative of the geologic materials through which the streams flow. Horizontal sediments offer uniform resistance to stream erosion and are characterized by a random or *dendritic* stream pattern, so named because of the similarity of the drainage pattern to the veins on a leaf (Figs. 9-5*A* and 9-6).

Tilted or folded strata are characterized by an *angular* drainage pattern because the upturned edges of the different strata have varying resistances to stream erosion. The major drainage lines tend to follow the weak strata whereas the tributaries flowing off the more resistant layers tend to enter the trunk streams at right angles (Fig. 9-5*B*).

A *radial* drainage pattern develops on the flanks of a dome or peak where the drainage lines radiate in all directions from the high point (Fig. 9-5*C*). All variations of these three types exist, especially where the geology is complex.

RUNNING WATER AT WORK

Running water is the most important of all geologic forces acting on the earth's surface. Even in lands with small annual precipitation, flash floods produced by sudden cloudbursts move prodigious amounts of debris. Before noting some of the gross features produced by stream action, it is necessary to examine briefly

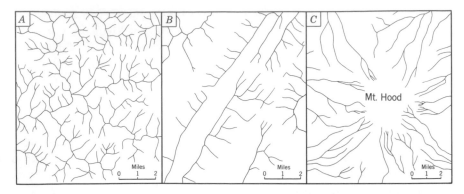

Figure 9-5. Different types of drainage patterns. *A.* Dendritic drainage, Marietta Quadrangle, Ohio–West Virginia. *B.* Angular drainage, Clearville Quadrangle, Pennsylvania. *C.* Radial drainage, Mt. Hood Quadrangle, Oregon. (United States Geological Survey.)

the factors which control the action on the stream channel.

Water flowing in an open channel possesses energy to do work. Most of the energy of running water is expended in overcoming the friction of the channel floor and sides. The remaining energy is available for movement of debris. Essentially, all streams attempt to establish a condition of equilibrium wherein the energy available to do work is balanced by the work to be done. In some rivers this condition of equilibrium is not yet attained, and in others the equilibrium status is reached only occasionally because changes in discharge require almost continuous adjustment of the stream channel. Most changes in channel cross section and water velocity can be traced to an increase or decrease in the stream discharge.

■ EROSION AND TRANSPORTATION BY RUNNING WATER. The material transported by a river is its *load*. The total load is

Figure 9-6. Dendritic drainage pattern in the southern part of Rub Al Khali, Saudi Arabia. Note the horizontal attitude of the sedimentary strata. (U.S. Air Force photograph.)

carried as solid particles and dissolved compounds. The solid portion of the load is further divided into the *bed load* and *suspended load*.

The flow of water in a river is *turbulent,* that is, the water particles do not follow parallel paths, but move in swirls and eddies in a general downstream direction. This turbulent action is what keeps small particles like clay, silt, and fine sand in suspension. Some particles are too large or too heavy to ever become part of the suspended load so they are pushed, rolled, and dragged along the river bed by the moving water. The concentration of sand, silt, and clay at various depths in the Missouri River is shown in Fig. 9-7.

With increased discharge during the rising stage of a river flowing in unconsolidated material, the water velocity increases and the channel becomes deeper and wider. This means that part of the river bed is incorporated in the suspended load during high stages of flow. When discharge decreases during the falling stage of the river, velocities decrease and the coarser fraction of the suspended load is dropped so that the channel floor builds up again.

When the entire stream bed is in motion so that the bed load is being moved across bedrock, abrasion of solid rock occurs through the wearing action of the moving sediments. Some rivers flow in narrow rock-bound channels which receive considerable wear by abrasion most of the time. The bed load itself is also abraded as particles bounce against each other. Particles become more rounded and smaller in size in a downstream direction.

■ SHEET EROSION. River channels occupy only a small fraction of the total land area, yet entire landscapes are subjected to the erosive action of running water. Much of the wearing away of the land is accomplished before the rain water ever gets to the river channel. The weathering process first reduces bed rock to mantle and mantle to soil, which can then be moved by rain water flowing over the ground as a thin film or sheet. Rains of high intensity are often referred to as "gully washers" because of their ability to carry loose soil particles along and erode deep gullies in slopes with a poor vegetational cover. Forested areas and dense grass sods are least susceptible to sheet erosion.

To reduce sheet wash and gully erosion,

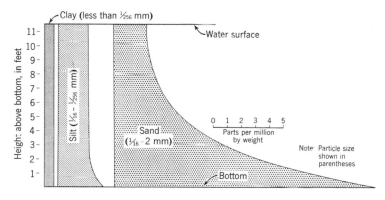

Figure 9-7. This graph shows the distribution of sand, silt, and clay at various depths in the Missouri River at Kansas City, Missouri, on January 3, 1930. Note the heavy concentration of sand near the river bottom and the even distribution of silt and clay from top to bottom. (Adapted from L. Straub in O. E. Meinzer (ed.), 1942, *Hydrology,* McGraw-Hill Book Co., New York.)

conservationists have urged better land management through reforestation of cut-over areas, establishment and maintenance of good grass cover on steep slopes, and sound agricultural practices such as contour plowing.

These methods are effective temporarily. A good example is the reduction in turbidity of the Chattahoochee River near Atlanta, Georgia, brought about by reforestation of worn-out farmland and fire protection of existing forests, stabilization of old logging roads where gullies frequently started, and the retirement of cultivated lands on steep slopes to grass or forests. The fruits of these labors reduced the sediment from sheet wash and gully erosion sufficiently in the watershed so that the average turbidity of the Chattahoochee River dropped from 800 parts per million in 1934 to less than 100 parts per million in 1952.

Man can impede the erosion process by wise land use or he can accelerate it by poor land management, but he can never *stop* it. Erosion by running water is a normal geologic process, which over periods of geologic time wears the land away and transports the sediment to the sea.

CHANGES IN RIVERS WITH TIME

Recognition of the fact that rivers cut the valleys in which they flow was the first step toward appreciation of the geologic work of rivers. We now know that entire landscapes, not just river valleys, are sculptured by running water.

■ BASE LEVEL AND STREAM PROFILE. The lowest level to which a drainage system can erode the land surface is the *base level of erosion*. The ultimate base level for rivers entering the ocean is determined by sea level, but temporary base levels along the stream course are determined by resistant rock layers, lakes, or artificial dams.

The *stream profile* shows the change in slope or gradient of the river bed from headwaters to mouth. Most profiles are concave toward the sky and decrease in gradient toward the mouth (Fig. 9-8). Over a period of years a stream profile becomes smoother and adjusts its slope and channel cross section to the discharge, so that just the velocity needed for transport of the sediment is maintained. Such a river is *graded,* or, it might be said that the graded river has a *profile of equilibrium.* Normally, the profile of equilibrium is first reached near the river mouth and progresses upstream, although in many rivers different reaches become graded regardless of their position with respect to mouth or headwaters.

■ RIVER CHANNELS AND VALLEYS. The upper reach of a river usually flows in a narrow rock-bound channel in contrast to the lower reach which flows in a broad valley. The river *channel* is the trough occupied by a nonflooding river during any one particular time of its history. The *river valley* is the incision made by the river during the entire period it has been in existence.

Valleys are generally deepened by downcutting in the upper reaches of rivers and widened by *lateral erosion* in the lower reaches. Downward erosion usually predominates where the profile is steep, and lateral erosion predominates in reaches of lesser gradient. Valley widening is also accomplished by sheet wash and landsliding along the valley walls.

■ MEANDERING RIVERS. Lateral erosion by a river widens the valley to a point where the stream channel no longer requires the entire space between the valley walls. Instead the channel develops a sinuous or arcuate course characterized by a series of S-shaped bends (Fig. 9-9). The river is said to be *meandering,*

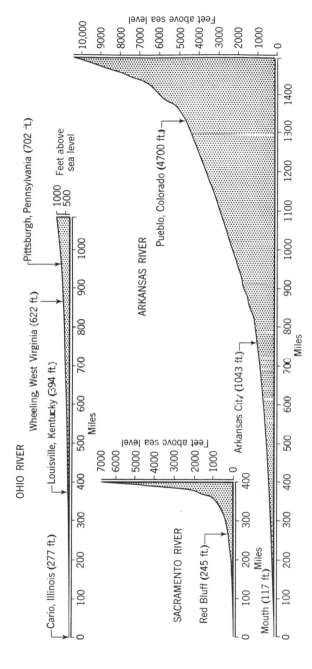

Figure 9-8. Profiles of the Ohio, Arkansas, and Sacramento rivers. Each is concave upward. Elevations are given in feet above sea level, and distances are in miles from the mouths of the rivers. Elevations of certain points on the profiles are shown in parentheses. (After Henry Gannett, 1901, *Profiles of rivers in the United States,* United States Geological Survey, Water Supply Paper 44.)

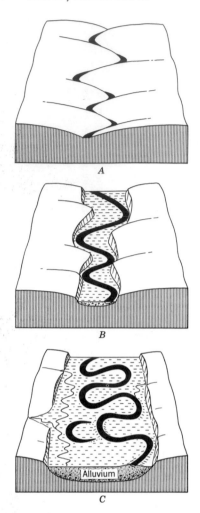

Figure 9-9. Diagrams showing the evolution of a valley. *A*. River channel before development of a flood plain. *B*. Lateral erosion by the meandering river forms a flood plain. *C*. Continued meandering causes enlargement of the flood plain and the development of oxbow lakes and natural levees. Alluvium partly fills the valley.

and the individual curves or bends are *meanders*.

RIVER DEPOSITS

Laboratory experiments with model rivers and observations on natural streams show that meanders are not sta-tionary once they are formed, but shift in a downstream direction as time passes. The maximum velocities in a meandering river occur on the outer or concave sides of the bends. Bank erosion is thus concentrated there whereas weaker velocities on the insides or convex sides of the channel promote the formation of sand bars. Experiments with colored sand in meandering laboratory channels reveal that the material eroded from one concave bank is transported to the convex bank immediately downstream and deposited there.

The shifting of meanders eventually produces a broad valley floor called the *flood plain*. The flood plain is not produced by rivers in flood, but is so named because the flood waters spread over it when the channel cannot accommodate the high discharge produced by melting snow or heavy rains. The flood plain is composed of fluvial (river) deposits collectively known as *alluvium*.

During the course of time, some of the meanders are cut off from the main channel by a break-through of the stream across the narrow neck of land separating two adjoining bends. With no current, the cutoff bend becomes a lake which gradually fills with silt and clay washed in during flood stage. These meander cutoffs are known as *oxbow* lakes and occur in great profusion along the lower Mississippi River (Fig. 9-10).

A river meandering across its flood plain overtops its banks during flood stage. As the flood waters spill out of the channel the velocity is checked and part of the suspended load is deposited near the channel banks. In this manner, *natural levees* are built up by the river after each successive flood. When normal flow is resumed, the river occupies its old channel which is now higher above the flood plain because of the natural levees.

■ OTHER RIVER DEPOSITS. When a river enters a natural or artificial lake, or finally reaches the sea, the load is depos-

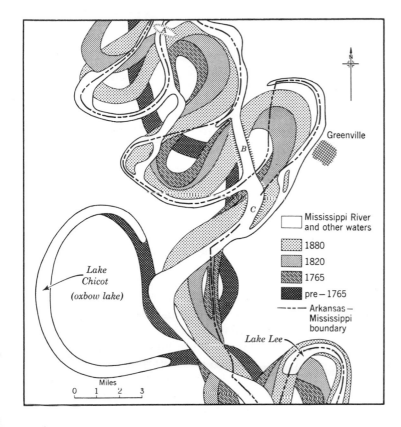

Figure 9-10. Map of a segment of the Mississippi River on the Arkansas - Mississippi boundary showing previous courses of the river, an artificial fill *A*, and cutoffs *B* and *C* made by the U.S. Corps of Engineers. The Arkansas - Mississippi boundary does not follow the modern course of the river but is fixed, in part, by the natural river channel prior to the artificial cut-offs of 1935 (*B*) and 1933 (*C*). (Based on H. N. Fisk, 1944, *Geological Investigations of the Mississippi River Alluvial Valley*, Mississippi River Commission, U.S. Corps of Engineers.)

ited as a *delta* (Fig. 9-15). As the delta expands seaward the river extends itself in length and branches into several channels called *distributaries*. Where a stream debouches from a rugged mountain range, the velocity is checked and the deposited load forms an *alluvial fan* (Fig. 9-11).

■ STREAM TERRACES. Once established, a flood plain continues its function as a catchment for floodwaters. If, however, the river should begin to incise its channel because of base level lowering, uplift of the land, or any other cause capable of drastically upsetting the stream's equilibrium, the position of the flood plain is changed with respect to the stream channel. Part or all of the flood plain may be destroyed by rejuvenated erosion of the stream, but any remnants of the old flood plain are classed as *stream terraces*. Some rivers have several terraces ar-ranged in steplike fashion in the valley (Figs. 9-12 and 9-13). Terraces afford a basis for interpreting the geologic history of a region. Some geologists have linked stream incision or terrace formation to increased rainfall, and others argue that a change to a more arid climate would be the more likely cause of a stream cutting into its flood plain. Lowering of base level is also responsible for the origin of many terraces.

THE CYCLE OF EROSION

In seeking out the details of how running water does this or that, we are likely to lose sight of the overall geologic accomplishments of stream erosion. The *cycle of erosion* is the time involved in the reduction of a land area to base level, the lowest level to which streams could reduce

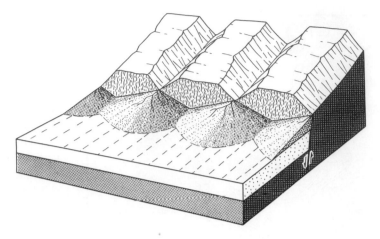

Figure 9-11.   Block diagram of alluvial fans developed along a fault scarp.

a region if all factors remained constant except time.   In essence the erosion cycle begins with a new land exposed to stream denundation for the first time.   This might be a recently emerged continental shelf or an old interior basin elevated high above sea level.   Uplift, then, sets the cycle in operation.   This concept of land-scape evolution was conceived in the late nineteenth century by the American geologist-geographer, William Morris Davis.   The principle is now called the Davisian concept.

From start to finish, the Davisian cycle of erosion passes through various stages of development, each characterized by a certain combination of land features. Theoretically, every segment of the earth's surface should fit into one of these stages, but in reality, no simple relation-

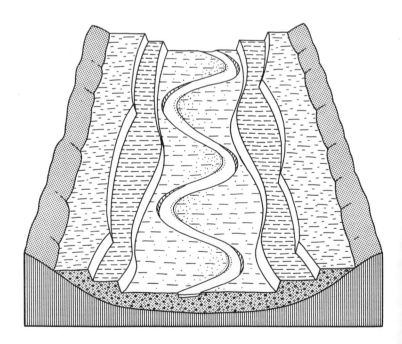

Figure 9-12.   Block diagram showing ter-races that mark former flood plains of a mean-dering river.

Figure 9-13.   River terraces, South Island, New Zealand.

ship exists.   In spite of this, the erosion cycle idea is valuable because it emphasizes the concept of geologic time and stresses the fact that landscape evolution by streams progresses toward some end point, some final product beyond which no further change is possible under the prevailing conditions.   The concept of change with time is a fundamental geologic principle that can be applied to nearly every geologic process.

■ YOUTHFUL STAGE.   The newly raised surface is immediately attacked by vigorously downcutting streams.   Stream profiles are steep and irregular with rapids and waterfalls as characteristic features. The valleys are V-shaped in cross section with no flood plains, and the inter-valley areas are flat and more or less untouched by erosion.

■ MATURE STAGE.   As time passes, erosion deepens and widens the valleys until the divides are cut back to ridges so that no flat uplands remain.   The valleys are still V-shaped, but incipient flood plains begin to appear.   The simplest way to describe

a mature topography is to say that all of the land is in slope (Fig. 9-14).

■ OLD AGE STAGE.   The rate of erosion progressively declines as stream profiles become graded and extensive flood plains develop on the valley floors.   Typically, the old age stage consists of a deeply weathered, low-lying surface called a *peneplain* ("almost a plain").   Ideally, a peneplain represents the end stage in the erosion cycle and would be characterized by sluggish, meandering streams.   The only features of positive relief would be isolated erosional remnants or *monadnocks,* rounded rock masses unconsumed by the erosional process and standing above the general level of the peneplain.

■ INTERRUPTIONS OF THE CYCLE.   The erosion cycle concept represents an ideal sequence rarely achieved because of the intervention of other controlling factors, such as climatic change, change in base level through sea level fluctuations, or uplift of the land.   Complexities of rock structure and lithology also influence the progress of the cycle, but ultimately the

Figure 9-14. Mature topography in Death Valley National Monument, California–Nevada. All of the land is in slope. (Photograph by George Grant, National Park Service.)

variable erosional resistance of different rock masses can be overcome, according to the Davisian concept.

Stream terraces show that the cycle does not progress without interruption, and deeply *incised meanders* are an indication of *stream rejuvenation* through uplift of the land or other causes that increase the downcutting ability of a stream.

■ THE CONCEPT OF DYNAMIC EQUILIBRIUM. In recognition of the fact that a growing number of geologists are convinced that the Davisian concept of landscape evolution is outmoded, it is useful here to introduce an alternative hypothesis which some geologists have suggested. The Davisian concept visualizes any landscape to be the result of three factors: process,

stage, and structure. Process refers to the way in which geologic forces attack the earth's surface and includes weathering, stream erosion, wind action, and others. Stage takes into account the length of time over which these processes have been acting more or less without any changes in the system such as increased precipitation, uplift of the land, lowering of base level, or the like. Structure refers to the type and attitude of the bedrock on which the attack of the geologic forces is directed. The main thesis of the Davisian concept is that, given sufficient time and no change in the processes involved, a land surface will be reduced to a peneplain. Vertical uplift of the crust may start the erosional cycle anew so that, eventually, the peneplain becomes thoroughly dissected save for a few accordant surfaces which are vestiges of the end stage of the previous cycle.

An American geologist, John Hack, has declared that some of the principal assumptions of the Davisian hypothesis are unrealistic, and that it is unlikely that a landscape could evolve as indicated by the cyclic concept. In its place he proposes the concept of *dynamic equilibrium* as a more reasonable basis for the interpretation of land forms in an erosionally developed landscape. According to this idea, every hill slope and every stream channel in an erosional system is adjusted to every other. The topography of a land surface reaches an equilibrium stage in which all elements of the topography are in mutual adjustment so that they are downwasting at the same rate. The resultant land forms are in a steady state of balance, according to Hack, and are not dependent on time for their shape and form. Differences in erosional land forms are attributed to difference in rock structure rather than to the passage of time. Hack recognizes no stage in the Davisian sense, but does concede that erosional energy changes in space and time, and that topographic forms will evolve in response to these energy changes.

The concept of dynamic equilibrium is not easy to grasp for a non-geologist, but the interested student is urged to examine the original work of Hack and the writings of Davis (see references at the end of the chapter).

Not all geologists are willing to accept the hypothesis of dynamic equilibrium but they are willing to evaluate it and test it in the light of geologic field evidence. An example of such an evaluation is the work of another American geologist, Bretz, who studied the Ozark Highlands in southern Missouri and northern Arkansas and concluded that the topo-

graphic forms there could be explained only by the Davisian concept of peneplanation followed by uplift and renewed erosion. He specifically argues that the concept of dynamic equilibrium fails to provide a rational basis on which to interpret the erosional history of the Ozarks.

The fact of the matter is that neither the Davisian concept nor the theory expounded by Hack can be proved from observations through time, or by laboratory experiments with models. Each hypothesis is based on certain postulates regarding the interaction of geologic forces with the earth's crust, which interaction produces certain topographic features. All we have to work with are the topographic forms themselves on which certain measurements can be made.

The basic question in the argument is, does an erosional landscape go through a gradual evolutionary sequence from youth to old age ending ultimately in a peneplain, or do land forms rapidly become adjusted to their environment and remain in dynamic equilibrium until some change in the environment causes the form to change and adjust itself to a new condition of dynamic equilibrium? Because it is impossible for humans to observe a tract of land over the enormous span of time during which it is being subjected to erosion, the difference of opinion cannot be resolved by direct observation. The disagreement should not be regarded as an *impasse;* rather the two approaches should be regarded as two working hypotheses, neither of which has been completely tested. This point of view is in keeping with the best tradition of scientific investigation.

RIVERS AND MAN

Rivers have always beckoned the explorer and inspired the poet, but they have also challenged men who would curb them and bring to submission the forces unleashed during floods. Aside from the purely aesthetic values captured by such writers as Mark Twain, rivers provide a constant test of man's ingenuity in making them work for him rather than against him. Francis Bacon wrote, "Nature, to be commanded, must be obeyed." Rivers can be trained but they cannot be muzzled. The construction of dams, the altering of river courses, and the stabilizing of meandering river channels—all of these programs can be undertaken successfully only with a thorough understanding of river processes.

■ THE MISSISSIPPI RIVER. In the early 1930's the United States Corps of Engineers shortened the course of the Mississippi River appreciably between Memphis and the mouth of the Red River by many artificial cutoffs and realignment of the channel. Concrete revetments were placed along outside bends to protect against further meandering, in hopes that the Mississippi River would "stay put." But try as they would to prevent it, the river continued to shift its channel by creating new meanders where no revetments existed. Not until the engineers set up laboratory experiments to determine the cause of meandering did they discover that the Mississippi *needed* a meandering course to maintain its condition of equilibrium. This provided a new and better basis for further rectification projects.

In the 1940's Mississippi River engineers became worried about the increased proportion of the river's discharge that was going down the Atchafalaya channel (Fig. 9-15). More and more water was entering the Gulf each year via the Atchafalaya course. Continued diversion would eventually send all of the Mississippi's discharge to the Gulf in a new channel and would reduce the cities of Baton Rouge and New Orleans to ghost ports by 1975. Geologists were engaged to study the matter. Their report showed that the Atchafalaya diversion was not a unique event because many times in the last few thousand years the Mississippi River took a new route to the sea across its own delta (Fig. 9-15). Engineers now plan to maintain the *status quo* between the Mississippi and the Atchafalaya because the latter acts as an extra outlet for flood waters of the former.

■ DAMS. Dams are built on rivers for the purposes of water power, flood control, irrigation, water supply, and recreation. Normally, a single dam cannot serve all of these interests efficiently, however, because the reservoirs used for flood control must be kept *empty* during most of the year in order to have room for flood waters. Conversely, reservoirs used for most other purposes need to be as *full* as possible all year long to provide water in time of need. To alleviate the problems caused by these conflicting interests, *multiple purpose* dams of enormous size and great cost are now being constructed. By virtue of their great size, these dams can store large quantities of water the year around and still have enough room for flood waters.

Sedimentation in a reservoir reduces its useful life. A small dam built on a turbid river may have its reservoir completely filled with sediment in less than fifty years. But Lake Mead, the reservoir behind Hoover Dam on the Colorado River, will not become filled with sediment for four centuries if the present rate of sedimentation continues (Fig. 9-16). Knowledge of a river's load is a vital requirement in estimating the longevity of newly planned reservoirs. Sedimentation can be controlled partially by reducing sheet wash and gulley erosion through the land management practices already mentioned (p. 150), but it cannot be eliminated completely.

■ RIVERS AND POLITICAL BOUNDARIES. Because state boundaries are commonly

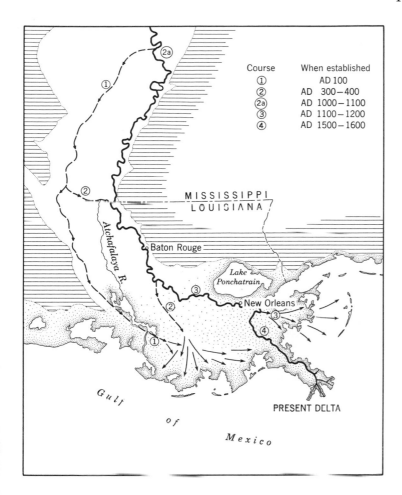

Course	When established
①	AD 100
②	AD 300—400
②a	AD 1000—1100
③	AD 1100—1200
④	AD 1500—1600

Figure 9-15. Map of the lower Mississippi River Valley showing different courses of the river during the past 1900 years and the areas of delta building. The next natural change in course will be through the Atchafalaya River unless preventative structures are built. If left alone, all the Mississippi's discharge will be diverted to the Atchafalaya channel by about 1975, according to the predictions of geologists and engineers. (After H. N. Fisk, *et al.,* 1952, *Geological investigations of the Atchafalaya Basin and the problem of Mississippi River diversion*, Mississippi River Commission, U.S. Corps of Engineers.)

defined by rivers, as for example, the states bordering the Mississippi River, some states are gaining land at the expense of others as the river meanders across its flood plain. The Federal Courts have ruled as follows:

Where running streams are boundaries between States . . . when the bed and channel are changed by the natural and gradual processes known as erosion and accretion, the boundary follows the varying course of the stream; while if the stream from any cause, natural or artificial, suddenly leaves its old bed and forms a new one, by the process known as avulsion, the resulting change of channel works no change on boundary, which remains in the middle of the old channel . . . although no water may be flowing in it.*

This rule has been applied in many interstate boundary disputes such as those between Missouri and Nebraska, Arkansas and Tennessee, and Arkansas and Mississippi (Fig. 9-10).

SUMMARY

Runoff is precipitation carried to the ocean by rivers, and is controlled by cli-

* U.S. Geological Survey, 1930, Bulletin 817, *Boundaries, Areas, Geographic Centers, and Altitudes of the United States and the Several States*, p. 3.

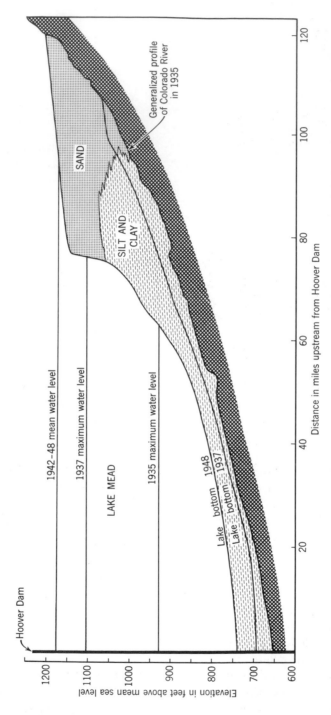

Figure 9-16. Sedimentation in Lake Mead during the 14-year period 1935–1949. At the present rate of accumulation the reservoir will not be filled with sediment until the year 2350. (From Harold E. Thomas, 1954, *The first fourteen years of Lake Mead*, United States Geological Survey, Circular 346.)

160

mate, geology, topography, and vegetation. Stream patterns may be dendritic, angular, radial, or any combination of these. Sheet wash and gulley erosion carry sediment to the stream channels where it becomes the river's load. The load is transported as dissolved minerals and suspended solids (suspended load), and as solid particles moved along the river bottom (bed load).

Rivers in rock-bound channels erode downward until lateral erosion widens the valley floor. Base level is the lowest level to which a drainage system can reduce the land surface. Stream profiles are concave upward and decline in slope in a downstream direction. Meandering rivers flow on flood plains and deposit alluvium. Natural levees form during floods and oxbow lakes are abandoned meanders severed from the main channel. Stream terraces are old flood plains. Deltas form at river mouths and alluvial fans develop on land where a river drops its load as it debouches from mountains.

The erosion cycle according to the Davisian concept starts with an uplifted surface on which a drainage system begins its work of dissection. The youthful stage is characterized by rapidly flowing streams in V-shaped valleys and by flat divides. Maturity is reached when all the land is in slope. Old age is characterized by sluggish streams flowing across a peneplain, a surface of erosion containing erosional remnants called monadnocks. Interruptions of the cycle at any stage in its development create complicating features such as stream terraces and entrenched meanders.

The concept of dynamic equilibrium is offered as an alternative to the Davisian landscape evolutionary hypothesis. According to the dynamic equilibrium hypothesis, landscapes attain a state of dynamic equilibrium in which land forms retain their form until some change, such

as climate, rate of uplift, or the like, requires the land forms to change so as to attain a new state of balance with the environment.

REFERENCES

Bretz, J Harlen, 1962, *Dynamic Equilibrium and the Ozark land forms, Am. Jour. Sci.,* **260,** 427–438.

Davis, William M., 1909, *Geographical Essays,* Chap. 13–17, Ginn and Co., Boston (reprinted by Dover Inc., New York 1954).

Friedkin, J. F., 1945, *A laboratory study of meandering and alluvial rivers,* U.S. Army Corps of Engineers, Waterways Experiment Station, Vicksburg, Mississippi.

Hahn, Charles L., 1955, *Reservoir sedimentation in Ohio,* Department of Natural Resources, Division of Water, Bulletin 24, Columbus, Ohio.

Hack, John T., 1960, *Interpretation of erosional topography in humid temperate regions, Am. Jour. Sci.,* **258-A.,** 80–97.

Interior and Insular Affairs Committee, House of Representatives, U.S. Congress, 1952, *The physical and economic foundation of natural resources,* part II, *The Physical basis of water supply and its principal uses.*

Judson, Sheldon, 1958, *Geomorphology and geology,* Transaction of the New York Academy of Sciences, Ser. II, Vol. 20, No. 4, p. 305–315.

Judson, Sheldon, 1960, William Morris Davis—An Appraisal, *Zeitsch. Geomorphol.,* Band 4, Heft 3/4, p. 193–201. (in English)

Langbein, Walter B., 1949, *Annual runoff in the United States,* U.S. Geological Survey, Circular 52.

Leopold, Luna B., and Thomas Maddock, 1953, *The hydraulic geometry of stream channels and some physiographic implications.* U.S. Geological Survey, Professional Paper 252.

Leopold, L. B., and W. B. Langbein, 1960, *A primer on water,* U.S. Dept. of Interior, Geological Survey, U.S. Govt. Printing Office Washington, D.C.

Senour, Charles, 1946, New project for stabilizing and deepening lower Mississippi River, *Proc. Amer. Soc. Civ. Engrs.* **72,** 145–158.

Thornbury, W. D., 1954, *Principles of geomorphology,* John Wiley and Sons, New York.

Trask, Parker D., 1950, *Applied sedimentation,* John Wiley and Sons, New York.

U.S. Department of Agriculture, 1955, *Water, yearbook of agriculture,* Washington, D.C., U.S. Government Printing Office.

Land Sculpture by Glaciers

*Some vast store of ice beyond seemed to take advantage
of the break in the mountain chain, and to pour down
in one great river of ice to the sea*

Robert Falcon Scott

A glacier is a flowing mass of land ice. About 10 per cent of the earth's land area is covered by glaciers, and they contain about 3 per cent of the earth's water. During the last million years, however, glaciers covered nearly a third of the land and contained an estimated 8 per cent of the earth's water. In one sense glaciers are vast storehouses of solid moisture removed temporarily from the hydrologic cycle. A worldwide growth of glaciers would cause a lowering of sea level, and conversely, a general shrinking of the glaciers of the world would cause a rise in sea level. In another sense glaciers are geologic agents capable of modifying the parts of the land which they occupy.

Glaciated landscapes are among the most spectacular in the world as any visitor to the Alps, Himalayas, or Greenland will testify. We are concerned in this chapter not so much with the inspiring natural beauty and grandeur of glaciers as we are with the geologic activity of existing glaciers and the way in which

modern and ancient ones have changed the shape of the land beneath them.

GROWTH AND MOVEMENT OF GLACIERS

To most people who live in the populated regions of the world, a glacier is usually associated with the cold polar climates. Although it is true that the largest masses of glacier ice are concentrated poleward from the Arctic and Antarctic circles, some glaciers occur in the equatorial regions of Africa and South America. But wherever they occur, the chief requirement for glacier growth is a climate conducive to the *accumulation* of snow, the source of nourishment for all glaciers. Glaciers can originate only where more snow accumulates annually than wastes away by melting. Each year a layer of residual snow is added to the accumulation of past years until a sizable thickness is reached. When buried be-

163

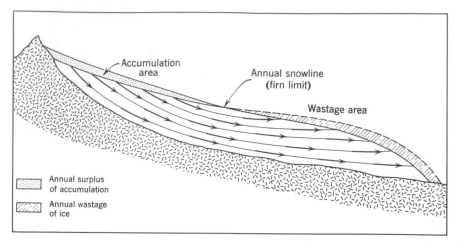

Figure 10-1.   Longitudinal profile through an idealized valley glacier showing the area of net annual accumulation and net annual wastage.   The arrows show lines of flow in the glacier.   (After R. P. Sharp, 1960, *Glaciers,* Condon Lectures, Oregon State System of Higher Education, Eugene, Oregon.)

neath successive snowfalls, the older snow layers are transformed first into *firn,* a granular material of lower density than pure ice.   Eventually, because of more compaction and further *recrystallization,* firn gradually becomes solid crystalline glacier ice.

■ GLACIAL GROWTH.   Most glaciers can be divided into two zones, a zone of net accumulation and a zone of net wastage (Fig. 10-1).   Each winter a layer of fresh snow covers the entire glacier surface. During the summer months melting in the zone of wastage removes all of the snowfall of the previous winter plus some of the glacier ice formed from older snows in the accumulation zone.   The summer melting in the accumulation area is insufficient to remove all the snow which fell during the previous winter.   The boundary between the zones of net accumulation and net wastage is referred to as the *firn limit* or *annual snowline.*

Flowage of ice from the accumulation area to the zone of wastage continues in both the summer and the winter.   Over a period of several years a rough balance may exist between accumulation, wastage,

and flowage as long as more or less uniform conditions prevail.   The glacier continues to flow because of the annual buildup of glacial ice in the zone of accumulation.

Early glacier studies in the Alps were concerned mainly with the recording of the positions of a glacier's down-valley edge called the *toe* or *snout.*   Advances and retreats of many Alpine glaciers have been noted over a period of two centuries. Most glaciers also showed a marked thinning during the process of retreat, as for example the Hintereisferner in the Austrian Alps (Fig. 10-2).

Modern glaciological research is concerned with the actual measurement of net wastage and net accumulation for a given *budget year.*   Net accumulation is determined by measuring the residual snow layer of a single year above the firn limit.   This requires snow thickness measurements at several points on the upper reaches of the glacier surface at the end of the wastage season, and also, density determinations of the snow blanket so that the net accumulation can be reduced to an equivalent volume of water.   The net loss or wastage is measured by setting stakes or poles into holes drilled into the glacier surface at well-spaced locations below the annual snow line. Repeated measurements of the intersection of a number of these stakes with the glacier surface at different times of the year provide the basis for calculating wastage. Comparison of the values of wastage and accumulation over a period of years can then be made to determine whether the glacier is losing or gaining mass, or is in a state of balance. The relationship of wastage and accumulation during a budget year is shown graphically in Fig. 10-3.

■ GLACIER FLOW. We are used to thinking of flowage as a phenomenon associated with liquids. The ability of glaciers to flow while in the solid state is a peculiar behavior which has puzzled and fascinated scientists for a long time. The proof that glaciers do flow was provided in the eighteenth century when straight lines of stakes set in glacier ice at right angles to the long axis of the glacier were observed to move down the valley over a period of time. The velocity of glaciers is so slow that the perception of movement by short periods of visual inspection is normally precluded. Surface movements in different glaciers reveal velocities rang-

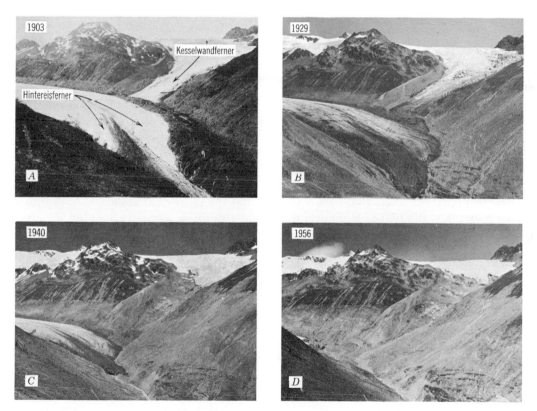

Figure 10-2. Sequence of photographs of two Austrian glaciers near the Italian border in Tirol. The Hintereisferner occupies the main valley to which the Kesselwandferner is a tributary. The retreat of both glaciers during the period 1903 to 1956 is well demonstrated in the sequence. Most of the Alpine glaciers have had a similar history. (*A*, by F. Peter; *B* by Alpiner Kunstverlages Much Heiss; *C* and *D* by H. Hoinkes, August 4, 1940, and August 31, 1956, respectively. All photographs courtesy of H. Hoinkes, University of Innsbruck, Austria.)

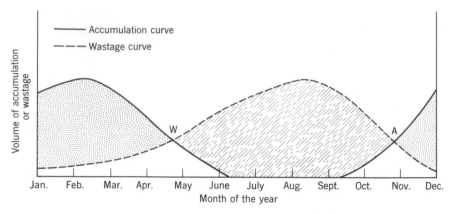

Figure 10-3. Diagram illustrating the relationship of the volume of total wastage to total accumulation for a single calendar year on a glacier in the Northern Hemisphere. The budget year begins in late autumn (point A), and the wastage season begins in late spring (point W). If the stippled area (net accumulation) equals the shaded area (net wastage), the glacier is in a state of balance for that particular budget year. (After R. P. Sharp, 1960, *Glaciers,* Condon Lectures, Oregon State System of Higher Education, Eugene, Oregon.)

ing from less than a foot per day to more than 125 feet per day.

Stake measurements reveal only the surface velocity of a glacier. The determination of the ice velocity between the glacier surface and the floor over which it flows is a more difficult procedure. Vertical holes drilled in various glaciers deform with time according to the diagram of Fig. 10-4. Note that part of the movement is by slip of the glacier over the rock floor, but most of the movement is by internal flow.

The mechanics of internal flow are not clearly understood. Several different hypotheses have been proposed during the last century to explain the phenomenon of flowage in the solid state in general and ice deformation in particular. Because ice is a crystalline solid, it is difficult to envision any common mechanism whereby it could change shape without breaking. An ice cube dropped on a hard surface will shatter. The question is, why does this same substance deep within a glacier flow without disrupting?

Glaciologists have learned that glacier ice consists of individual ice crystals with very irregular shapes. Laboratory experiments on these crystals reveal that they can be deformed without destroying their solidity or coherence under certain conditions of stress. The crystals actually deform by an internal gliding or slipping along a crystallographic plane. In other words, the atomic structure of ice is such that the individual atoms will shift into a new position without changing the crystallinity of the ice. Internal gliding, if continued indefinitely, would result in distortion of the crystals into extremely long shapes unlike anything ever seen in a glacier; so, along with the internal gliding process, there must be some sort of continual recrystallization of each deformed ice crystal in order that the general equidimensional shape of the crystals is not appreciably altered.

■ CREVASSES. The upper 100 or 150 feet of a glacier may be described as brittle because the surficial ice is not under a heavy overburden of ice and snow, the weight of which makes the deeper ice plastic so that it can flow. Hence differential flow in the surficial parts of a glacier cause cracks to form. These cracks, called *crevasses* (Fig. 10-5), open as flow deeper in the glacier continues. Crevasses are abundant in areas where the slope of the glacier bed steepens markedly or near the lateral margins of a valley glacier. They are characteristic of *icefalls,* places along the course of a glacier where flow is greatly accelerated by an abnormally steep floor of the valley.

The study of crevasse patterns reveals some useful information on the general flow pattern of the ice. When first formed they are perpendicular to the direction of flow at that point, but as they are carried down glacier by the underlying ice, their orientation changes. A crevasse may even close again after it has moved into a different part of the glacier system.

Crevasses rarely exceed 100 feet in depth and are usually only 5 or 10 feet

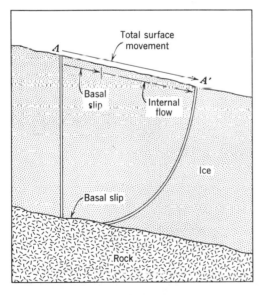

Figure 10-4.   Sketch of part of a longitudinal profile of a valley glacier. A bore hole drilled vertically at "*A*" deforms into a curved line *A'* after a few years. This experiment proves that a glacier moves partly by slippage on its bed and partly by internal flow. (After R. P. Sharp, 1960, *Glaciers,* Condon Lectures, Oregon System of Higher Education, Eugene, Oregon.)

Figure 10-5.   A crevasse in the Ross Ice Shelf, Antarctica. The view is diagonally upward toward an opening in a snow bridge. The crevasse is about 80 feet deep. (Photograph by William Austin.)

wide where they intersect the glacier surface. In the Antarctic, however, some crevasses 150 feet deep and 50 to 100 wide have been observed. Crevasses large enough to permit the descent of a man on a rope afford an unusual opportunity for the study of the annual layers of firn and other details of glacier ice that could otherwise only be observed by laborious core drilling methods.

Crevasses make travel over the surface of a glacier very dangerous, especially when they are obscured by the presence of a *snow bridge,* a snow drift that extends from one side of the crevasse to the other.

KINDS OF GLACIERS

Glaciers can be separated into three general groups, (1) *valley glaciers,* (2) *piedmont glaciers,* and (3) *ice caps.* Valley glaciers are literally rivers of ice because they flow between valley walls in mountainous regions. Piedmont glaciers develop wherever one or several valley glaciers spread out at the foot of a mountain range. Ice caps cover broad areas and flow outward in all directions from a zone of accumulation.

■ VALLEY GLACIERS. In mountainous re-

gions where conditions are favorable for snow accumulation, a network of valley glaciers may occupy a conspicuous part of the landscape. These ice streams may radiate from a central volcanic peak such as Mt. Rainier in Washington or they may form a tributary system feeding into a main valley glacier such as those in southeastern Alaska and Yukon territory (Fig. 10-6).

The glacier surface usually contains rock debris worn from the valley walls. The debris forms dark bands parallel to the flow direction of the glacier and are known as *moraines.* When viewed from the air or when seen on aerial photographs, the moraines are plainly visible and their relationship to the glacier system is readily apparent. Three kinds of moraines are usually present. Those that occur along the sides of the glacier are *lateral moraines.* At the confluence of two valley glaciers, the lateral moraines of each join to form a *medial moraine* as seen in Fig. 10-6. At the glacier snout or terminus the debris contained in the lateral and medial moraines as well as stones and other clastics carried in the glacier are released from the melting ice and heaped into an *end moraine.*

■ PIEDMONT GLACIERS. If the snout of

Figure 10-6. Logan Glacier system in southeastern Alaska. (Courtesy of Robert P. Sharp.)

Figure 10-7. Small piedmont glacier, Ellesmere Island, Canada. (Courtesy of Royal Canadian Air Force.)

a valley glacier spreads out in a bulbous form, or if the snouts of several valley glaciers coalesce into a single broad mass, the result is a piedmont glacier. These types are relatively rare. The best known and largest piedmont glacier is the Malaspina Glacier in Alaska. A small piedmont glacier is shown in Fig. 10-7.

■ ICE SHEETS. Only two major ice sheets are in existence today, Greenland and Antarctica, but many smaller ones occur in Iceland, Baffin Island, and the Canadian Archipelago. Together, Greenland and Antarctica contain about 99 per cent of all the glacier ice in the world.

THE GREENLAND ICE SHEET. Greenland is a large elongate land-mass between North America and Europe. Its maximum length in a north-south direction is 1500 miles, and its greatest width in an east-west direction is 700 miles (Fig. 10-8). The total area of the Greenland ice sheet is 666,400 square miles which represents about 83 per cent of the area of Greenland itself. The mean elevation of the surface of the ice sheet is 7000 feet above sea level, and almost one-third of the base of the ice sheet lies below sea level.

The ice flows from the two domed-shaped high points toward the margin where it spills through valleys in the coastal mountains as outlet glaciers (Fig. 10-9). In other places it debouches directly to the sea where massive portions break off and become *icebergs*.

The mean thickness of the ice sheet is almost 5000 feet, but the maximum thickness is nearly 10,000 feet. The total volume of glacier ice on Greenland is 620,000 cubic miles, which, if melted and distributed over the world's oceans, would raise sea level by 21 feet.

Measurements of accumulation and wastage indicate that Greenland is gaining in mass, that is, the ice sheet is expanding. Wastage takes place by direct melting and the breaking off of large

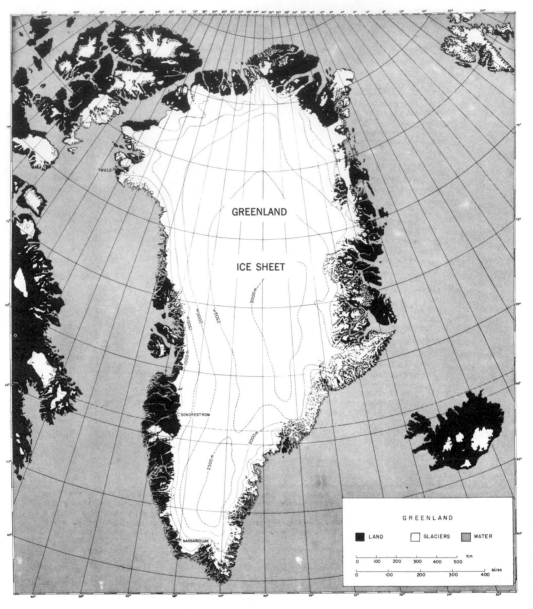

Figure 10-8. Map of the Greenland ice sheet and smaller ice sheets on Iceland and the Canadian Arctic. (After a map by P. E. Victor in Henri Bader, 1961, *The Greenland Ice Sheet*, U.S. Army Cold Regions Research and Engineering Laboratory, Publication 1-B2.)

masses of glacier ice directly into the ocean, a process called *calving*. The total annual loss by calving is estimated to be about 57 cubic miles of water equivalent. Losses by direct melting are figured to be between 29 and 64 cubic miles annually, whereas net accumulation is considered to be about 150 cubic miles per year. So, even if we use the maximum value for wastage of 121 cubic miles (64 cu. mi. plus 57 cu. mi.) and subtract this from the net accumulation of 150 cubic miles, a net gain of some 29 cubic miles of water equivalent remains at the end of each year.

ANTARCTIC ICE SHEET. Before the International Geophysical Year (IGY) of 1957–58, very little was known about the largest of all ice sheets. The map shown in Fig. 10-10 is largely the result of IGY and later studies. Studies begun during the IGY and still in progress permit a more exact picture of the glaciological conditions in the Antarctic, but definite answers to major questions are still unanswered. The reason for this, even after the expenditure of millions of dollars by several nations, lies in the enormous size of the ice sheet.

The surface area of the Antarctic is 5.2 million square miles. Thickness measurements by seismic methods* during the IGY reveal an average of about 5800 feet. The greatest ice thickness reported anywhere on earth occurs about 100 miles east of Byrd Station (USA). There,

* A small charge of dynamite is exploded at the surface of the ice. The time required for the sound waves thus generated to travel to the base of the ice and back is measured, which, along with the knowledge of the speed of sound through glacier ice permits the determination of the ice thickness.

where the ice surface is 5840 feet above sea level, the ice is 14,000 feet thick! This means that more than 8000 feet of the ice lies *below* sea level. As a matter of fact, a large part of the Antarctic continent lies below sea level because the crust of the earth is depressed about 1000 feet for each 3000 feet of ice piled on the land.*

The total volume of glacier ice in the Antarctic is probably in excess of 5.7 million cubic miles, which amounts to enough water to raise the level of the oceans about 195 feet.

There is no firm agreement about the relationship between wastage and accumulation in the Antarctic, primarily because of the lack of data on the various wastage factors such as calving. Also, the value assigned to net accumulation is based on widely spaced measurements which could result in considerable error. Yet, even if the *minimum* known accumulation value is compared with the *maximum* wastage value, it appears that the Antarctic ice sheet, like Greenland, is

* This ratio of 1 to 3 derives from the ratio of the density of ice, 0.9, to the density of the earth's crust, 2.7. The ratio of 1 to 3 is further based on the assumption that perfect isostatic adjustment exists.

Figure 10-9. Outlet glaciers descending to Søndre Strømfjord near the west coast of Greenland are forms of valley glaciers.   (United States Air Force.)

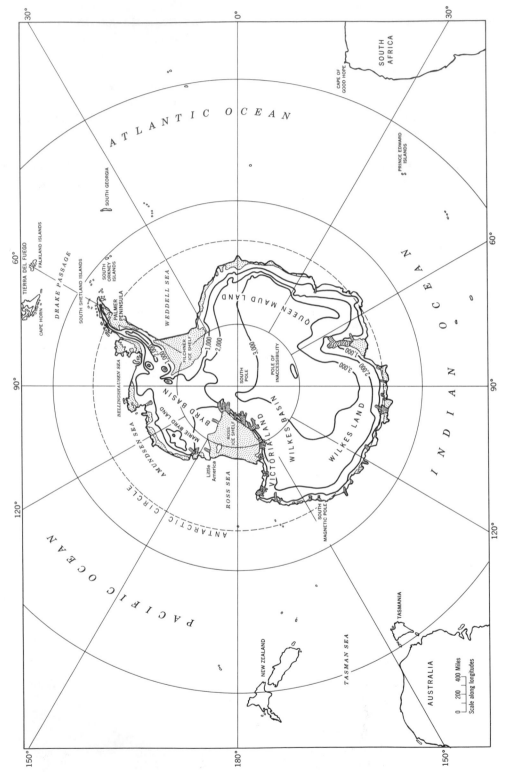

Figure 10-10. Map of the Antarctic ice sheet. Elevations of contour lines are in meters. (Based on a map in *Scientific American*, September, 1962. Original based on a map of the American Geographical Society by William A. Briesemeister.)

Figure 10-11. Air photograph of the Nimrod Glacier, a massive outlet glacier which feeds the Ross Ice Shelf in the Antarctic. The broad surface of the main Antarctic ice sheet forms the horizon which is faintly visible beyond the distant mountain range. (Official U.S. Navy photograph, November, 1960.)

increasing in mass. More refined measurements of both wastage and accumulation are needed before a more reliable statement on the state of balance of this enormous ice sheet can be made.

Fringing the Antarctic continent are floating masses of glacier ice called *ice shelves*. They are attached to the main ice sheet and maintain themselves mainly by snowfall on their surfaces, and also by outlet glaciers from the inland ice (Fig. 10-11). The two largest ice shelves in the world are the Ross Ice Shelf (200,000 sq. mi.) and the Filchner Ice Shelf (160,000 sq. mi.). The Ross Ice Shelf is about the size of Spain and ranges in thickness from 800 feet near the seaward margin to 2300 feet in the interior. It is floating on water 1000 feet deep beneath its base. Icebergs which calve from ice shelves are flat-topped; some of these tabular masses of ice are tens of miles long and hundreds of feet thick.

GLACIER REGIMEN AND
FORMER GLACIERS

The position of a glacier's snout or toe is determined by (1) the rate of accumulation, (2) the rate of flow, and (3) the rate of wastage. When these three factors are in equilibrium, the glacier toe remains in a fixed position and an end moraine is built. If wastage increases due to a warming of the climate, or if accumulation decreases, the glacier snout *retreats*. Conversely, the glacier is said to advance when the opposite is true. Many small glaciers in the world today are retreating, a fact which is not in accord with the evidence from Greenland and Antarctica.

The positions of end moraines beyond the snouts of existing glaciers attests to their former expanded condition. Similarly, end moraines distributed throughout the northern United States and Canada as well as in northern Europe and Russia testify to the presence of former ice caps of continental dimensions. These great ice caps or *continental glaciers* reached maximum positions within the last million years during the *Ice Age* or *Pleistocene,* as that period of geologic time is technically known. The activity of these former glaciers is well documented by geological evidence, much of which is covered in Chapter seventeen. However, many land forms produced by the glaciers of the past are discussed in this chapter.

Figure 10-12.   These deep grooves on Kelley's Island in western Lake Erie were produced by the abrasive action of debris-laden glacial ice moving over limestone.   The slope in the background is composed of drift.   (Photograph by Raoul Choate.)

GEOLOGIC WORK OF GLACIERS

■ GLACIAL EROSION.   Glaciers carry a load of rock debris frozen in the basal ice layers.   The result of the abrasive action of ice is visible as scratches (*striations*) and grooves on glaciated rock surfaces, as shown in Fig. 10-12.   When plotted on a map, striations show the overall pattern of movement of former ice caps.

Glacial abrasion is far less effective in eroding bedrock than glacial *quarrying* or *plucking*.   This process involves the lifting and removal of blocks of bedrock by the moving ice.   Glacial quarrying operates most effectively in rocks with closely spaced joints that define the incipient

blocks to be removed by plucking action.

A combination of quarrying and abrasion of a projecting rock surface produces an asymmetrical rock hill with the steep side facing in the direction of ice movement (Fig. 10-13).   The terrane produced by ice-cap erosion consists of rounded and smoothed bedrock surfaces with less relief than the preglacial topography.

■ GLACIALLY ERODED VALLEYS.   A valley glacier is a more effective agent of erosion than the stream which originally formed the valley.   Instead of the V-shaped cross section produced by stream erosion, a glaciated valley appears as a deep U-shaped trough (Fig. 10-14).   Tributary valleys occupied by smaller glaciers are

Figure 10-13.   Cross section of a bedrock knob shaped by glacial erosion.

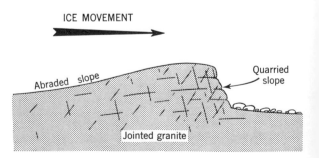

less deeply eroded than the main valley and hence are left "hanging" above the trunk valley. With the disappearance of the glaciers, the *hanging valleys* are reoccupied by streams which discharge into the main valley via waterfalls over precipitous cliffs, such as the Bridalveil Fall in Yosemite National Park (Fig. 10-15). In the headward reaches of a glaciated valley, *bedrock basins* formed by glacial erosion contain lakes, such as Iceberg Lake in Glacier National Park (Fig. 13-7). Other glacially-formed lakes are the result of end moraines which act as dams.

In general, the terrane sculptured by valley glaciers undergoes a pronounced increase in ruggedness of relief. Direct action by valley glaciers plus the effects of intense frost action on the adjacent unglaciated peaks produces sharp divides, steep slopes, and pyramidal peaks (Fig. 10-14).

■ GLACIAL DEPOSITS. The landscape left by a retreating glacier contains various deposits formed beneath the ice and in front of the ice margin. These deposits are visible long after the ice has disappeared. The general term *drift*, used to designate all deposits associated with glaciers, is a holdover from the days when the loose, unconsolidated deposits found in Europe and North America were attributed to the results of the Noachian deluge described in the Scriptures. The huge boulders and heterogeneous assort-

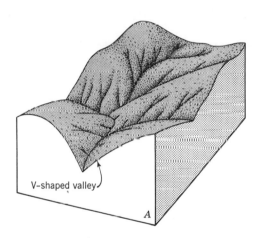

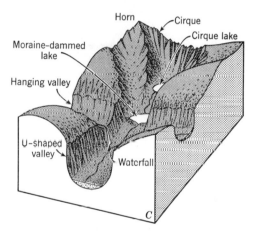

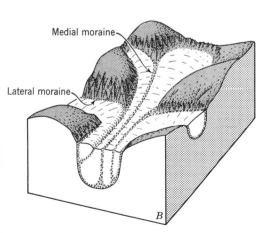

Figure 10-14. Block diagrams showing changes brought about by valley glaciation. *A.* Unglaciated mature topography. *B.* A system of valley glaciers occupies the former stream valleys and causes deep erosion. Frost action causes weathering of the unglaciated slopes and provides a source of debris for lateral moraines. *C.* Climatic change causes disappearance of glaciers, leaving behind a tell-tale topography which includes hanging valleys, U-shaped valleys, lakes, end moraines, and rugged peaks.

Figure 10-15.   Yosemite Valley in Yosemite National Park, California, is a beautiful example of a glaciated valley.   Its U-shape and tributary hanging valleys attest to the presence of a valley glacier at one time in the geologic past.   Bridalveil Fall at the right plunges over the lip of a hanging valley.   (Photograph by F. E. Matthes, U.S. Geological Survey.)

ment of stones were thought to have originated from floating icebergs that "drifted" through the Noachian seas and dropped their load of debris when melting destroyed them.   Such a view is no longer tenable since the origin and distribution of drift is definitely related to the action of former ice caps which covered one-third of the land surface during the Pleistocene.

There are two general types of glacial drift, *nonstratified* and *stratified.*   Nonstratified drift is distinguished chiefly by its unsorted texture and lack of bedding.   It represents an accumulation of material deposited directly by the ice without the intervening action of water.   Stratified drift, on the other hand, is deposited by

melt water from the glacier and accumulates in streams issuing from the ice, in temporary lakes along the ice border, or in the sea marginal to the glaciated regions.

NONSTRATIFIED DEPOSITS.   All these deposits are generally referred to as *till.*   Texturally, till ranges from a hard dense clay with intermixed sand, stones, and boulders, to a collection of boulders with very little intermixed fines (Fig. 10-16).   Till occurs in two topographic forms, *ground moraine* and *end moraine.*

Ground moraine is characteristically a gently rolling to nearly flat terrane.   Streamlined ridges called *drumlins* occur on many ground moraine surfaces (Fig. 10-17).   They are ice-molded hills devel-

Figure 10-16.   Glacial till exposed in a road cut in southern Michigan.   Note the heterogeneous size of the particles and the lack of bedding or stratification.   Hammer handle near the center of the photograph is 12 inches long.

Figure 10-17.   Aerial photograph showing drumlins in Charlevoix County, Michigan.   Ice movement was from the northwest to southeast. (U.S. Department of Agriculture photograph.)

oped beneath the glacier as the till is plastered onto the ground. The long axis of a drumlin is parallel to the direction of ice movement. End moraines are belts of hills which mark the former position of the ice front. End moraines deposited by the continental glaciers during the Pleistocene are traceable for many miles in the Great Lakes region (Fig. 17-1).

STRATIFIED DEPOSITS. Sand and gravel deposited by glacial meltwater streams is commonly referred to as *outwash*. Many topographic features are made of outwash. Streams emerging from the ice front carry a great deal of bed load and suspended load. The bed load dropped by several coalescing streams forms a broad *outwash plain*, but outwash confined

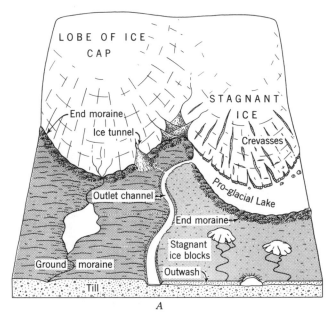

A

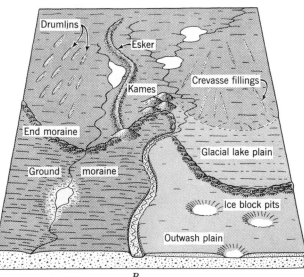

B

Figure 10-18. Block diagram showing the conditions that prevail during the retreat of an ice sheet (*A*), and the glaciated landscape after the ice has disappeared (*B*).

Figure 10-19. Air photograph of a glaciated area in east-central Alberta, Canada showing an intersecting system of ridges which are believed to be crevasse fillings. The ridges are 10 to 25 feet high and 50 to 150 feet wide. (Photograph reproduced by Courtesy of the Technical Division of the Department of Lands and Forests, Edmonton, Alberta, Interpretation by C. P. Gravenor, 1956, *Air Photographs of the Plains Region of Alberta,* Research Council of Alberta, Edmonton, Alberta.)

to a single valley beyond the snout of a valley glacier or ice cap constructs a *valley train.* Residual blocks of glacier ice buried in the outwash become ice-block pits when they melt. Some ice-block pits contain lakes (Fig. 10-18).

Much sand and gravel outwash collects close to the ice front and adjacent blocks of dead ice, which is ice thinned by melting so that movement ceases. Such outwash features are known as *ice-contact* deposits. Although stratification is visible where roads have been cut through such features or where gravel pits have been opened in them, the bedding shows signs of slumping and distortion produced when the supporting walls of ice melted away. *Kames* are irregularly shaped knolls or hummocks commonly associated with end moraines. *Kame terraces* form between dead ice in a valley and the adjoining valley walls. *Eskers* are

gravelly ridges deposited by subglacial streams in ice tunnels. *Crevasse fillings* are similar to eskers but form in an ice valley rather than an ice tunnel (Figs. 10-18 and 10-19).

Most of the glacial outwash deposits are suitable sources of sand and gravel for concrete (Fig. 10-20). If large quantities of shale, soft sandstone pebbles, or even small amounts of chert particles are present, however, the outwash makes a poor concrete aggregate. Shale and soft sandstone pebbles are not durable, and the chert reacts chemically with the cement, resulting in a poor quality concrete. Some large gravel operators find it profitable to remove the deleterious stones by mechanical means, thereby producing a high quality aggregate which can be marketed at a premium.

LAKE DEPOSITS. Glacial meltwater impounded around the retreating ice front provides collecting basins for sediment. Lakes fringing the ice border are called *proglacial* lakes, and their deposits are widespread around the Great Lakes in Canada and the United States. Predecessors of the modern Great Lakes covered much of the land fringing the present water bodies, as is indicated by the flat topography of the old lake bottoms in the Great Lakes states (Fig. 17-2).

Lake sediments are known as *lacustrine* deposits and they consist of deep water clays and silts, and shallow water sands and beach gravels. Much of the deep water sediment consists of *rock flour,* a finely ground material produced by abrasion of debris-laden ice moving over bedrock surfaces. Glacial meltwater streams carry this sediment in suspension to the proglacial lakes where it eventually settles to the bottom in the deeper, quiet waters. Some of these deposits are finely laminated or banded, indicating a cyclic type of deposition. Each cycle is represented by a relatively coarse layer of very fine sand a fraction of an inch thick, on top of which is a thinner layer made up of fine silt and clay. A pair of such bands make a *varve* which represents the sediments of one year. The coarse layer was deposited during the spring and summer months at the height of the melting season, and the fine layer was laid down during the fall and winter months after the lake had frozen. Varves have been used by some geologists to construct time scales of glacier recession during the Pleistocene.

The shores of proglacial lakes are well marked by *beach ridges* of sand and gravel produced by wave action (Fig. 10-21). The tracing of such beaches over many miles permits the glacial geologist to reconstruct the former positions of different proglacial lakes during the final recession of the Pleistocene ice caps (see Chapter seventeen).

SUMMARY

Glaciers are moving bodies of land ice and are classified as (1) valley glaciers, (2) piedmont glaciers, and (3) ice caps.

Figure 10-20. A gravel pit in glacial outwash near Ann Arbor, Michigan. (Photograph by William Kneller.)

LAKE
HURON

0   ½
Mile

Figure 10-21. Air photograph of beach ridges in Huron County, Michigan. These ridges were produced by waves of older and higher lake stages in the Huron basin during the late Pleistocene. (U.S. Department of Agriculture photograph.)

They are composed of snow that compacts and recrystallizes first into firn and eventually into glacier ice. Glaciers advance when snow accumulation exceeds wastage, and they retreat when the reverse is true. Today, some glaciers are retreating in response to a general climatic warming. Glacial erosion by ice caps produces a terrane of rounded and smoothed bedrock knolls, whereas the erosive action of valley glaciers produces a terrane of sharp, rugged relief. Glacial deposits include nonstratified till laid down by the ice in the form of ground and end moraines, stratified deposits consisting of outwash sands and gravels, and lacustrine sediments such as varves and beach ridges associated with proglacial lakes.

REFERENCES

Ahlman, H. W., 1953, *Glacial variations and climatic fluctuations*, American Geographical Society, Bowman Memorial Lectures, Series 3.

Bader, Henri, 1961, *The Greenland ice sheet*. U.S. Army Cold Regions Research and Engineering Laboratory (CRREL), Publication 1-B2, Corps of Engineers, Hanover, N.H.

Committee on Polar Research, 1961, *Science in Antarctica;* Part II, The physical sciences in Antarctica, Pub. 878, National Academy of Sciences, National Research Council, Washington, D.C.

Crary, A. P., 1960, *Status of United States scientific programs in the Antarctic*, IGY Bulletin 39, National Academy of Sciences, Washington, D.C.

Flint, R. F., 1957, *Glacial and Pleistocene geology*, John Wiley and Sons, New York.

Meier, M. F., 1960, *Mode of flow of Saskatchewan glacier, Alberta, Canada*, U.S. Geological Survey, Professional Paper 351, 70 p.

Mellor, Malcolm, 1961, *The Antarctic ice sheet*, U.S. Army Cold Regions Research and Engineering

Laboratory (CRREL), Publication 1-B1, Corps of Engineers, Hanover, N.H.

Sharp, R. P., 1960, *Glaciers,* Condon Lectures, Oregon State System of Higher Education, Eugene, Oregon.

Shumsky, P. A., 1959, *Is Antarctica a continent or an archipelago, Jour. Glaciology,* **3,** No. 27.

Thiel, E. C., 1962, *The amount of ice on planet Earth, Antarctic Research,* Monograph No. 7, American Geophysical Union, pp. 172–175.

Wave Action and Shorelines

I have seen the hungry ocean gain
Advantage on the kingdom of the shore . . .

Shakespeare

The ocean is the storehouse of water that feeds the hydrologic cycle. The mysteries of its deeps are still practically unknown even though new methods of probing beneath the sea are rapidly being developed. But where land and sea meet along the thousands of miles of coastline, the attack of wind-driven waves on the shore provides a variety of geologic phenomena within the reach of man's observation. Unlike many other geologic processes, wave action can produce geologic changes in a relatively short time so that the cause and effect relationships are apparent after a period of a few tens of years. Some changes are so rapid that they are almost catastrophic and others develop over hundreds or thousands of years. This chapter deals in particular with the way in which shorelines along the oceans and lakes are modified by the action of water waves. Most water waves are wind generated, but some of the most disastrous are produced by sudden displacements of the sea floor. Both types are considered in the paragraphs that follow.

MECHANICS OF WAVE ACTION

■ ORIGIN AND DESCRIPTION OF WAVES. Waves result from the friction of wind passing over a water surface. Wave size depends on (1) wind velocity, (2) the length of time the wind continues to blow from a single direction, and (3) the length of the open water over which the wind blows. The highest point on the wave is its *crest* and the adjacent low point is the *trough*. The distance from crest to crest or trough to trough is the wavelength L, and the difference in elevation between the crest and the trough is the wave height H (Fig. 11-1). A standard method of describing a single wave is by means of the ratio of length to height L/H. The height of waves generated by storm winds in the open sea are often exaggerated. The average height is about 30 to

183

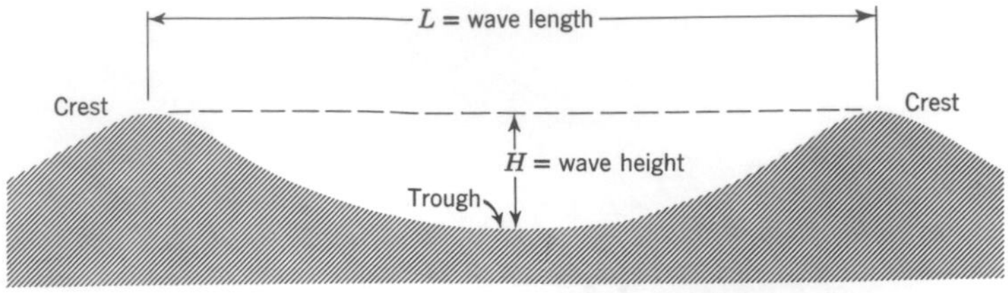

Figure 11-1. Cross section of a deep water wave.

Crest

Trough

L = wave length

H = wave height

Crest

40 feet, but individual waves of 75 feet have been recorded, and one wave over 110 feet high was observed in the North Pacific during a prolonged storm.

■ WAVE MOTION. The motion of waves in the open sea is somewhat analogous to the surface of a field of grain being disturbed by the wind. Only the wave *shape* is transmitted during the process of wave motion. The paths taken by various surface water particles are shown in Fig. 11-2. The time necessary for a wave crest to travel one wavelength is the wave period *T,* and the velocity *V* of the wave is equal to the wavelength divided by the wave period, or, expressed as a simple equation:

$$V = \frac{L}{T}$$

Wave motion dies out with depth since the orbital paths of the water particles become smaller and smaller. The dividing line occurs at a depth equal to one-half the wave length, $\frac{1}{2}L$, known as the *wave base* (Fig. 11-2); below this level winds can cause no water motion. A submarine can easily ride out a storm when submerged, while a surface vessel of the same size is wildly tossed about.

Waves produced by high winds in the open ocean may travel hundreds or even thousands of miles away from the storm center. During this period of travel a

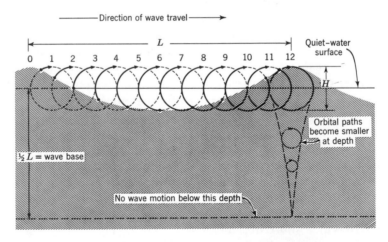

Figure 11-2. Cross-sectional diagram of a water wave showing motion of water particles at 12 different points on the surface of the wave. Solid arrow shows the direction and distance traveled by each point as the crest reaches that particular position. When the water particle at position 12 has made one complete circuit in its orbital path, the wave crest will have traveled one wavelength. The orbital paths decrease in diameter down to a depth of water equal to about $\frac{1}{2}L$ (wave base). (After P. H. Kuenen, 1950, *Marine Geology,* John Wiley and Sons, New York.)

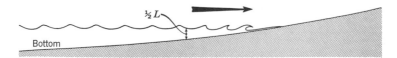

Figure 11-3. Cross section of waves breaking on shore. Wave becomes distorted upon reaching water with a depth of $\frac{1}{2}L$. Wave height increases and wavelength decreases. The period remains about the same.

single wave undergoes a certain amount of modification. For example, by the time a 15-foot wave with a length of 300 feet travels 2000 miles across the open sea, its height decreases to $2\frac{1}{2}$ feet and its length increases to 1300 feet. It will be noted that the L/H of the original wave is 20 whereas the L/H of the same wave after 2000 miles is 520. Waves with L/H ratios between 10 and 35 are considered storm waves by the Beach Erosion Board of the United States Army Corps of Engineers. Those with an L/H ratio between 35 and 70 are intermediate waves, and those whose L/H ratio is greater than 70 are the well-developed *swells* that strike many shores in fair weather.

■ WAVES IN SHALLOW WATER. In the near-shore areas where the water is shallow the incoming swells undergo a marked change in shape due to the effect of the sea bottom. The wave height increases and the length becomes shorter, but the period remains more or less constant. Eventually the wave becomes so high that the crest topples over and the wave is said to *break* (Figs. 11-3 and 11-4). It is the energy of breaking waves crashing on shore that is able to bring about the geologic changes on almost all shorelines.

■ DISTRIBUTION OF WAVE ENERGY. A wave approaching an irregular shore does not reach wave base everywhere along its crest at the same time. The part of the wave which "feels bottom" first is slowed down, thereby causing a flexure in the crest line (Fig. 11-5). If a single deep-water wave is divided into equal units along the crest line, each unit contains

Figure 11-4. Breaking waves on the coast of Maine. (Photograph by M. R. La Motte, Maine Department of Economic Development.)

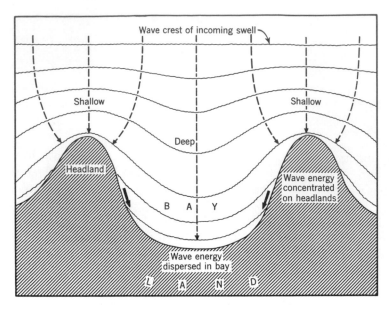

Figure 11-5. Diagrammatic map view of waves striking an irregular shore. Wave crests are refracted or bent when one part of the wave strikes shallow water before the rest of the wave. Dashed arrows are lines of equal energy. They are equally spaced along the crest of the incoming swell in deep water but converge toward the headlands as the water shoals off the headlands. Wave energy is thus concentrated along the headlands and dispersed in the bays. Short solid arrows show direction of beach drifting. See Fig. 11-6.

the same amount of energy. As the wave is bent or *refracted* when wave base is reached along part of its crest, the lines of equal energy are concentrated on the headlands, whereas the waves reaching the shore of the bay are less potent and

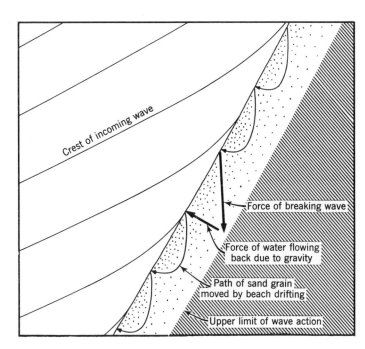

Figure 11-6. Map diagram showing the paths taken by sand particles moved by beach drifting.

act more in the role of transporting agent rather than as an erosive force.

The material eroded from the headlands is carried toward the bay by a process of *beach drifting.* As the waves strike the shore obliquely, sand is thrown diagonally up the beach, but on its return trip, the water flows directly down the slope and carries sand and pebbles with it. The result is a net movement of beach sand parallel to the shore through a series of curved paths, as shown in Fig. 11-6.

GEOLOGIC WORK OF WAVES

■ WAVE EROSION. The susceptibility of promontories and headlands to wave attack is obvious to anyone who has ever seen the waves lash out against an unprotected shore. Waves striking a shore are capable of doing great damage to manmade structures, but they are also able to produce permanent changes in the configuration of the shore itself.

One of the chief results of wave erosion on a headland is the landward retreat of the shore. The wave attack is concentrated in the zone between low tide and the highest point reached by storm waves. Material is removed by abrasion, solution, or simply by the hydraulic action of the waves as they smash into poorly cemented sediments or loosely jointed rock. A surface sloping gently seaward is undermined by wave action near its base and is eventually transformed into a precipitous *wave-cut cliff* (Fig. 11-7). The rock is planed off just below water level and becomes a *wave-cut* platform. Residual rock columns, isolated by wave erosion from the retreating sea cliff, are called *stacks,* because of their vague resemblance to smoke stacks. *Sea caves* are undermined notches at the base of a sea cliff.

Secondary results of wave erosion are landslides. A landslide occurs when the base of a wave-cut cliff is removed by wave attack so the cliff becomes oversteepened and part of it slides into the water. Wave erosion may actually initiate a landslide, although in some cases waves produce only the initial steep slope, and sliding does not occur until some later date when heavy rains, earthquakes, or vibrations from trucks trigger a landslide. Buildings and other installations perched near the edge of a wave-cut cliff face possible destruction from landslides (Fig. 11-8). Other causes of landslides exist, but wave action is a prominent one.

Protection against extensive shore erosion is expensive. *Sea walls* built parallel to the shore are especially difficult to construct properly (Fig. 11-9), but less expensive and equally effective are *groins,* impervious "fences" of heavy timber or concrete installed at right angles to the shore. The groins trap the sediment transported by beach drifting and thereby establish a protective beach at the base of the cliff (Fig. 11-10). Groins are also

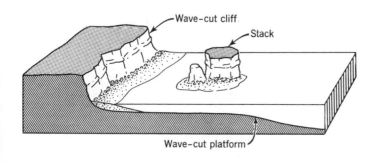

Figure 11-7. Block diagram of a wave-cut cliff and stack. The base of the cliff is eroded by storm waves but is not reached by smaller waves in calm weather.

Figure 11-8. *A.* Wave-cut cliff near St. Joseph on the eastern shore of Lake Michigan, November 1, 1952. Landsliding was initiated by wave attack at the base of the cliff during high lake levels of the early 1950's. Unconsolidated glacial deposits are exposed in the cliff face. *B.* Same area as *A,* October 18, 1954. Continued landsliding caused retreat of the cliff and endangered houses, many of which were evacuated and wrecked or moved. (Hann Photo Service, Hartford, Michigan.)

Figure 11-9. Sea walls near South Haven on the eastern shore of Lake Michigan. Note the ineffectiveness of the offshore "fence" as a protective measure against wave erosion. December 7, 1952. (Hann Photo Service, Hartford, Michigan.)

an effective measure against extensive loss of beach sand where no wave-cut cliffs exist.

■ WAVE DEPOSITION. The transportation of sand along the shore by beach drifting accounts for many of the beaches, bars, and spits common to coastal areas. Although a complex terminology has been adopted by coastal engineers and geologists, a simplified system of nomenclature is used in this book. A *bar* is a submerged ridge of sand or gravel lying offshore more or less parallel to the mainland. A *beach* is a zone of unconsolidated shore material lying between the waterline and the upper limit of normal storm waves. *Beach ridges* above the upper limit of fair weather swells are products of

storm waves. Several parallel storm beaches are produced by waves of different storms varying in intensity. A *spit* is a sandy ridge projecting into a body of water from the shore. The landward side of a spit is simply an extension of a beach but its tip is submerged. Spits are generally curved landward (Fig. 11-11).

All variations of these three basic features exist, for example, the *offshore* or *barrier bars* extending almost continuously along the Atlantic Coast from Atlantic City to Miami. The crests of these ridges are *above* water, a condition not easily accounted for by normal wave action. A better explanation suggests that they originate as a result of extension of spits by beach drifting.

Figure 11-10. Groins placed to protect the highway along the top of the wave-cut cliff near St. Joseph, Michigan. December 7, 1954. (Hann Photo Service, Hartford, Michigan.)

SHORELINES AND SEA LEVEL

Sea level has not maintained its relative position with respect to the land throughout geologic time. The land itself may be uplifted or depressed because of earth movements. In one case sea level falls, in the other it rises. The volume of sea water is also variable through geologic time as continental ice caps wax and wane. During extensive land cover by glaciers sea level is lowered, and during the nonglacial periods sea level rises. But whatever the cause or causes, the *relative* movement of land with respect to sea level is the important point. Thus it is sufficient to know whether the land is *emergent,* or *submergent,* in a relative sense.

Some shore features bear a definite genetic relationship to emergent or submergent conditions, that is, by their very presence, they reveal the last relative movement of land and sea. But the situation is not always crystal clear because the relative movement of sea level may have been both up and down so that both submergent and emergent conditions prevailed in rapid succession, geologically speaking. Probably the best approach toward interpreting the geologic history of any shoreline is to first postulate what conditions should arise when either submergence or emergence (relatively speaking) of the land has taken place.

■ SUBMERGENT FEATURES. If sea level rises or the coast is depressed, the marine waters inundate the lowest parts of the land such as the mouths of rivers. The chief results of submergence, therefore, are drowned river valleys and the increase in irregularity of the shoreline (Fig. 11-12*A*). As time progresses, however, the headlands are cut back by wave erosion and the bay mouths are blocked with bars and spits, resulting eventually in a straighter shoreline (Fig. 11-12*C*). The coast of Maine contains excellent examples of submergent features in various stages of development. Submergent conditions also prevail along the south shores of Lake Erie and Lake Superior.

■ EMERGENT FEATURES. A lowering of sea level or rise of the land exposes portions of the sea floor. Wave-cut platforms and formerly submerged bars are now subject to weathering and erosion by subaerial geologic agents. Uneroded beach ridges marking recessional stages in the retreat of the shoreline are also good indicators of recent emergence (Fig. 10-15). Offshore bars were formerly regarded as indicative of relative sea level lowering, but this association is no longer regarded as absolute proof of shore emergence. Until the real origin of offshore bars is established, their relationship to the relative sea level changes will remain unknown.

■ SHORELINE EVOLUTION. The reader must be cognizant of the dynamic aspects of shorelines. They are undergoing profound changes of both the short- and long-term varieties. Shorelines, therefore, must be evaluated in terms of their development with the passage of time. This point needs repeated emphasis because it is the very heart of geologic reasoning and distinguishes the science of physical *geology* from physical *geography*. The latter is more often concerned with the description of earth features as they now appear, whereas the geologist places

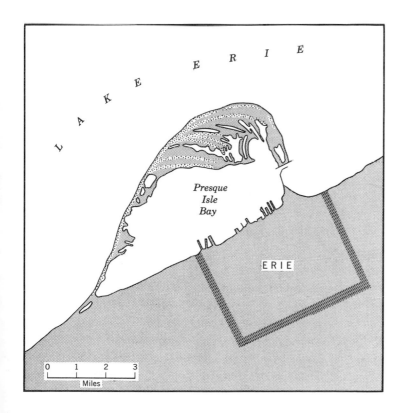

Figure 11-11. A compound spit is responsible for Presque Isle Bay in Lake Erie near Erie, Pennsylvania. It was formed by currents from the southwest. Coarse stippling shows progressive growth of the spit. (From U.S. Geological Survey, Erie Quadrangle, edition of 1900.)

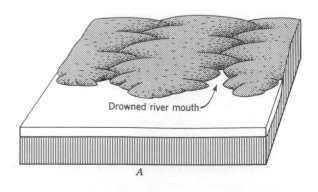

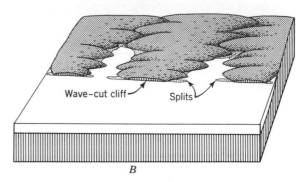

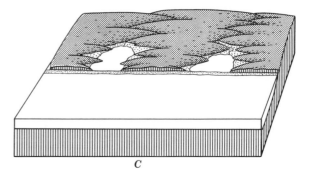

Figure 11-12. Block diagram showing the evolution of a shoreline of submergence. The shoreline is irregular to begin with but becomes straighter as wave action cuts back the headlands and builds spits across the mouths of the drowned rivers.

the emphasis on the *origin* of land forms, not merely their size, shape, and distribution. This cannot be accomplished without consideration of the factor of time.

Applying this fundamental concept to the geologic interpretation of a particular shoreline, be it on the sea coast or the Great Lakes, it seems self-evident that the shoreline evolved to its present condition through a series of gradual changes. What we observe today may be only a stage in its developmental history, not necessarily the end result.

TSUNAMIS

The most destructive of all water waves are not produced by wind but by large submarine landslides, subocean earthquakes, or volcanic eruptions beneath the sea. Any of these events results in a rapid displacement or dislocation of the ocean bottom which, in turn, generates a series of water waves, or *wave trains,* capable of traveling for thousands of miles across the open ocean until they strike distant shorelines with tremendous destructive force.

In popular descriptions these waves are called tidal waves, but they have nothing to do with the tide. The technical term is *tsunami* (tsoo-nah-mee), a Japanese word now employed more or less universally for these large types of waves. A more precise and better descriptive term is *seismic sea wave.*

In 1883 the eruption of Krakatoa, a volcano in the East Indies, produced a train of about a dozen seismic sea waves which traveled at a velocity of three to four hundred miles per hour. They reached such distant points as South Africa (4690 miles way), Cape Horn on the southern tip of South America (7280 miles distant), and Panama (11,470 miles). The understanding of the cause and nature of seismic sea waves has been a rather recent development in the field of geophysics, but much remains to be done in this intriguing area.

The Hawaiian Islands are especially susceptible to tsunamis generated around the margin of the Pacific Ocean basin. Since 1837 six tsunamis have struck the Hawaiian Islands with severe violence. In April 1946, a submarine landslide in the Aleutian submarine trench produced a tsunami which killed several hundred people on Hawaii. More recently, the Chilean earthquake of May 23, 1960 threw the sea into violent motion and sent a wave chain speeding across the Pacific toward the Hawaiian Islands. At Hilo, on the Island of Hawaii, one of the larger waves rose to a height of 35 feet above sea level and smashed into the city, demolishing part of the business district, killing 61 people, and injuring 282 others.

The scientific studies of the Hilo disaster are available in documented reports which clearly show that the residents of all the Hawaiian Islands were warned of the impending disaster about 12 hours before it struck. The warning was made possible by the fact that seismograph stations recorded the earthquake waves produced by the Chilean quake, thereby fixing its location and exact time of occurrence. Based on this information and the knowledge of the distance and depth of water between Chile and Hawaii, a prediction of the time of arrival of the tsunami could be calculated. Actually, the main wave traveled the 6600 miles from its source along the Chilean coast to Hilo in 14 hours and 56 minutes at an average speed of 442 miles per hour.

With such information at hand, the alert sounded by the United States Coast and Geodetic Survey Observatory in Honolulu was based on more than a mere hunch. Yet, it appears that nearly two-thirds of the residents of the stricken area failed to take it seriously enough to move to higher ground, an act which they had ample time to accomplish before disaster struck. Clearly, better public education in the urgency of such warnings and their response to them is needed if further loss of life from tsunamis is to be avoided, not only in the Hawaiian Islands, but elsewhere in the coastal regions of the world.

SUMMARY

Storm waves, generated in the open sea, undergo a decrease in height and increase in length as they travel in deep water. The change from a storm wave to a swell involves an increase in the L/H ratio. Upon entering water equal in depth to about half the wavelength, the wave height increases and the length decreases. Headlands are eroded where wave energy is concentrated, and the debris derived from this erosion is carried toward the bay by beach drifting.

Wave-cut cliffs, stacks, and sea caves are features produced by wave erosion. Some landslides are secondary results of erosion by waves. Depositional features include bars, beaches, offshore bars, and spits. The origin of offshore bars is not clearly understood, but one possibility is that they are extended spits.

Shoreline development is an evolutionary process strongly influenced by relative changes in the level of land and sea. Submergent shorelines are irregular and are characterized by deeply indented bays between prominent headlands during the early stages of development. As time progresses, the headlands are cut back and shore irregularities are decreased. Emergent shorelines are characterized by freshly appearing wave-cut benches and elevated beach ridges. Many shorelines bear evidence of repeated oscillations of the sea and hence cannot be considered either emergent or submergent in the strict sense of the word.

Tsunamis or seismic sea waves are wave trains generated when the ocean floor is suddenly displaced through the action of submarine earthquakes, landslides or volcanic eruptions. Seismograph records permit the time of occurrence and location of the sea floor disturbance so that a very accurate record of the time of arrival of tsunamis anywhere in the path of the wave train is possible. The high-level precision of such tsunami forecasting is of little value unless the response of the people for whom it is intended can be made more positive.

REFERENCES

Bascom, Willard, 1959, Ocean Waves, *Scientific American,* August, p. 75–84.

Caldwell, J. M., 1948, An elementary discussion of tides, currents, and wave action in beach erosion. U.S. Army Corps of Engineers, *Bull., Beach Erosion Board,* **2,** 8–12.

Eaton, J. P., D. H. Richter, and W. V. Ault, 1961, The tsunami of May 23, 1960, on the Island of Hawaii I. *Bulletin of the Seismological Society of America,* vol. 51, p. 135–137.

Kuenen, P. H., 1950, *Marine geology,* John Wiley and Sons, New York.

Kuenen, P. H., 1956, *Realms of water,* John Wiley and Sons, New York.

Thornbury, W. D., 1954, *Principles of geomorphology,* John Wiley and Sons, New York.

Wiegel, Robert L., 1956, *Waves, tides, currents, and beaches, glossary of terms and list of standard symbols.* The Engineering Foundation, Council on Wave Research.

PART 2

The Geological Story

The Key to the Past

There rolls the deep where grew the tree.
Oh Earth, what changes hast thou seen!

Tennyson

In the preceding chapters attention has been devoted largely to the dynamic aspects of contemporary geologic processes. We have seen how the present face of the earth is undergoing constant change due to the many geologic forces that are continually in operation, both from within and without. Now we are going to shift the perspective from the present to the past and delve into the geologic history of the earth. The chief objective will be to reconstruct past events of earth history into a coherent and logical chronology which has been deduced from observations made over the course of many years by geologists who have strived to interpret the record of the rocks.

It is from the rocks alone that the facts about our ancient earth have come to light during the course of man's never-ending search for the truth. During his attempt to unravel earth history man has erred, has made false starts, and has followed evidence leading into blind alleys. But slowly and surely the secrets of Mother Earth's diary have been un-

locked, so that we now have a fascinating account of the major changes she has undergone during her life span. To be sure, some pages of this autobiography still remain undeciphered because they are written in a language yet unknown, and other pages, even whole chapters, have been lost forever.

But the search goes on. Geologists are probing the far reaches of the earth with a vigor equaling that of the earliest investigators in quest of additional facts concerning the earth's past history. Perhaps through the reading of the chapters to follow, the student can participate vicariously in this intriguing study, and will enjoy the thrill of discovering something new about the planet he calls Earth.

UNIFORMITARIANISM

During the early nineteenth century Baron Georges Cuvier (1769–1832), a prominent French scientist and statesman, promoted the idea that the history

199

of the earth was punctuated by sudden and violent catastrophic events. Followers of Cuvier formed what may be called the "catastrophic school" of geologists. Opposed to this line of thinking was Sir Charles Lyell (1797–1875), a contemporary of Cuvier, who held that earth changes were gradual, taking place at the same uniform slowness that they are today. Lyell is thus credited with the propagation of the premise that more or less has guided geologic thought ever since, namely, that the *present is the key to the past*. In essence, Lyell's *doctrine of uniformitarian-* *ism* stated that past geologic processes operated in the same manner and at the same rate they do today.

The basic principle is vital to the full appreciation of geologic history, even though many geologic events constitute catastrophes in the strictest meaning of the word. Tidal waves, volcanic eruptions, earthquakes, landslides, and floods are catastrophic from man's point of view, but within the framework of earth history they are but normal happenings of no greater or lesser magnitude today than they were a million years ago.

Figure 12-1. Aerial photograph of Duncan Lake and vicinity, Northwest Territories, Canada, showing rocks of three different ages. Black areas are lakes. The lightest gray areas are outcrops of a granite mass intrusive into the older metamorphic rocks. The linear belts (emphasized by narrow bays of the various lakes) are outcrops of dikes intrusive into the granite and metasediments. (Royal Canadian Air Force.)

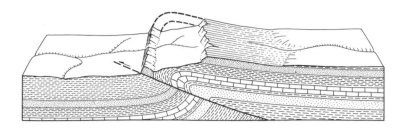

Figure 12-2. Block diagram showing how older beds may be thrust over younger beds along a thrust fault. Thrust faults are associated with orogenic movements of past geologic time.

From a purely scientific point of view, it is unwise to accept uniformitarianism as unalterable dogma. As pointed out in Chapter one, man's experience with geologic processes is restricted to only a minute fraction of the total span of earth history. He should never close his mind to the possibility that conditions in past geological time were different than today, and that the doctrine of uniformitarianism may not apply in every case where the reconstruction of some segment of earth history is involved.

FUNDAMENTALS OF HISTORICAL GEOLOGY

■ RELATIVE AGE OF SEDIMENTS. Armed with a firm belief in the principles of uniformitarianism, we can now proceed to certain fundamental relationships between rock units on which geologic chronology is based. The first of these relationships is embodied in the *law of superposition* which is so simple in essence that it hardly needs elaboration. This law states that, in any series of sedimentary rock layers lying in their original horizontal position, the rocks at the bottom of the sequence are older than the rocks at the top. Furthermore, in a single rock layer, such as a sandstone, the minerals at the bottom of the layer had to be deposited before those near the top. Hence, even though the strata are highly folded or even overturned, it is necessary only to determine the top or bottom of a single bed in order to know whether it is older or younger than the beds above or beneath.

■ RELATIVE AGE OF IGNEOUS ROCKS. A second basic relationship between rock masses involves intrusive igneous rocks. Briefly, *igneous rocks are younger than the rocks they intrude.* This applies not only to small dikes and sills, but also to large stocks and batholiths. Figure 12-1 shows rocks of three different ages. The light gray tone represents a granite intruded into metamorphosed sediments shown in darker gray. Both the metasediments and granite have been intruded by dikes.

■ AGE OF FAULTS. Where rock units are displaced by a fault, it is simple logic that *the fault is younger than the youngest bed cut by the fault.* One type of fault is responsible for a condition in which older rocks lie on top of younger rocks as shown in Fig. 12-2. Strong compressive forces have thrust the rock layers on one side of the gently inclined fault plane to a position on top of the beds on the other side of the fault. Thrust faults are not uncommon in mountainous regions where the earth's crust has been subjected to intense lateral stresses.

So far, in the examples cited, there has been no evidence that would permit the absolute ages of the rocks to be established. The relationships reveal only the *relative* ages. To determine the age in years requires other information and methods that are described later in this chapter.

■ GEOLOGIC MAPS. The physical relationships of the rock units of a certain area may not be clearly revealed in a single exposure or outcrop. Therefore, the geologist may be obliged to observe the rock outcroppings in many isolated localities within the area he is studying, and he may not be able to determine the relative ages until he has completed field observation involving considerable time.

To assist him in drawing general conclusions about the rocks with which he is concerned, the geologist constructs a geologic map. The importance of geological structures is emphasized in Chapter three, but here, the subject is reintroduced because of the significance of geologic maps in the field of historical geology. The making of a geologic map is the first step in the unraveling of the geologic history of any given area, and is an art unique to the field geologist. Basically, a geologic map shows the boundaries of the various rock units drawn on a map of suitable scale. The individual rock units are called *formations,* and the boundaries between different formations are called *contacts.*

A formation is a rock layer or unit of sufficient size and with sufficiently distinct boundaries that a geologist can plot its distribution on a map. It may be a single sandstone layer 300 feet thick, a 100-foot thick conglomerate, or it may consist of alternating beds of shale and limestone with an aggregate thickness of 1000 feet. Formations are named after geographical localities where they were first described, and a good geologic map will contain a description of the formations shown on it as well as an indication of their relative ages.

Once the geologic map is completed, geologic cross sections can be constructed from it and the geologic history can be reconstructed. The more detailed the map, the more precise the reconstruction of geologic history, although samples of the formations may have to be studied in the laboratory before their exact origin can be determined.

THE MEANING OF SEDIMENTARY ROCKS

The field geologist encounters many kinds of rocks during the course of his geologic mapping. The variety of rock types and number of formations he finds depends on the nature of the geologic history of the area in question. But whatever rock types are involved, the geologist ultimately will be required to gain from them an understanding of their origin and subsequent geologic history. His task is more difficult and his conclusions are less certain if he is dealing with a complexity of highly metamorphosed rocks rather than a series of relatively undeformed sedimentary rocks.

It is, therefore, from the sedimentary rocks that the geologist receives the most accurate information, because the processes which produce sedimentary rocks are not beyond the reach of direct observation. Indeed, sandstones of future geologic ages are now being deposited in shallow waters of the coastal areas, and the muds collecting in the Gulf of Mexico will someday become hardened shales. Let us, therefore, consider what meaning can be read into some of the many different kinds of sedimentary rocks in terms of their origin. This is the branch of geology called *stratigraphy.*

FACTORS THAT CONTROL
SEDIMENTARY ROCK PROPERTIES

If sedimentary rocks are to be used as a means of deciphering earth history, it is important that the factors which control sedimentary rock properties be understood. These factors are:

1. Kind of rock in the source area (provenance).
2. Environment of the source area.
3. Earth movements in the source area and in the depositional area (tectonism).
4. Environment of the depositional area.
5. Postdepositional changes of the sediment (lithification).

■ KIND OF ROCK IN THE SOURCE AREA (PROVENANCE). Most of the sediments which come to rest in an area of deposition were originally derived from some other kind of rock on the earth's surface. For instance, the sediments now accumulating in the Gulf of Mexico were derived by the weathering and erosion of rocks in the drainage basin of the Mississippi River and other small rivers. Thus, the mineralogical composition of the sediments must bear some relationship to the mineralogical composition of the rocks in the source region. It might be possible, therefore, to determine in a general way, by the study of certain mineral assemblages in the resulting sediment, the type of rock or rocks from which they were derived. In a large drainage basin like the Mississippi River system, it is unlikely that an analysis of the Gulf of Mexico sediments would yield much diagnostic information about the rocks exposed in the source area for the simple reason that the source area encompasses rock types of great diversity. But where the source area is more restricted in its geographic extent, the rocks formed in adjoining depositional environments are likely to provide some information about the nature of the parent rock. This is especially true of sandstones which contain *accessory minerals* of higher specific gravity than the more abundant quartz and feldspar grains. These *heavy minerals* can be studied under the microscope in the laboratory after they have been separated from the lighter minerals. The mineralogical composition of the sediments thus yields information on the source area or *provenance*.

Certain heavy mineral suites are characteristic of definite source rock types, and it is possible for a geologist to specify the provenance from which certain sediments were derived. Usually he can state the provenance only in a general way, for example, acid igneous rocks, basic igneous rocks, metamorphic rocks, or reworked sediments. Heavy mineral analysis of a sediment does not always yield a detailed picture of the provenance, but it can be a valuable tool for the stratigrapher.

■ ENVIRONMENT OF THE SOURCE AREA. Although the term environment in the usual sense refers to the sum total of external conditions affecting the existence of some form of life, it can be used in a more general sense in reference to all conditions which prevail in an area, including the plants and animals themselves. Moreover, environment as used in this sense refers to the interplay of all external forces brought to bear on an area. So defined, it would include climate, topography, vegetational cover, animal population, and all the geologic processes at work during a specific span of time.

Climate involves rainfall, evaporation, and temperatures, all of which in turn determine the kind and rate of weathering that will prevail. This is important because the way in which rocks weather influences the kind and amount of sediment that will be available for transportation by geologic agents.

Topography has a bearing on the competence and capacity of streams to carry the sediment to the depositional area. Vegetation influences the rate of runoff and the amount of organic matter added to the streams. The role of animal populations is extremely important in the formation of sedimentary rock. Some invertebrate animals such as reef-building corals concentrate vast quantities of calcium carbonate in the form of the shell material they secrete, and other microscopic animals with hard shells are added to marine sediments as the animal dies and his shell falls to the sea bottom. Whole layers of organic limestone were produced in this fashion.

Foremost among environmental factors that prevail in the source area are the geologic processes themselves. The first part of this book is devoted to an understanding of these processes so there is little need for further elaboration here, except to emphasize the fact that the geologic processes active in the source area have a profound influence not only on the kind of sediment produced, but also on the manner in which the sediment is carried to the place of deposition, and on its distribution and special structures.

■ EARTH MOVEMENTS IN THE SOURCE AREA AND IN THE DEPOSITIONAL AREA (TECTONISM). This term refers to the movement of any segment of the earth's crust during or between the periods of sedimentation. Tectonism includes not only the rapid rise of a continental block constituting a source area from which sediments are derived, but also the subsidence of the sedimentary environment in which the sediments accumulate.

During the middle of the last century, American geologists recognized the fact that great thicknesses of sediment—50,000 feet in some cases—were deposited in relatively shallow sea water, probably on the order of magnitude of 200–300 feet. This led to the conclusion that the basin or region in which the sediments were accumulating must have been constantly sinking during long periods of geologic time. Although no firm agreement exists among geologists as to the cause of this subsidence, they all agree that it did take place. Geologists still disagree as to whether the subsidence was caused by the weight of the accumulating sediments, or whether the initial subsidence took place independently of the sedimentary load.

Even though the answer to this question is not resolved, it does not deter us from considering the impact it has had on our ideas concerning the effect of uplift and subsidence on the sedimentary process. First, let us consider tectonism of the depositional (negative) area, and secondly, the tectonism of the source (positive) area.

After geologists had agreed that most of the sedimentary rocks now lying on the continents were produced in relatively shallow sea water, it became necessary to classify sedimentary areas according to the degree of tectonic movement during major cycles of sedimentation. This led to the recognition of several different kinds of tectonic environments, three of which are of prime importance even to the casual student of geologic history. The first of these is the *geosyncline,* a linear belt of subsidence on a continent in which great thicknesses of sediments have accumulated (Fig. 12-3). The geosyncline may sink rapidly and continuously, or sporadically and at variable rates. The result, however, is a prodigious accumulation of sediments during long spans of geologic time.

The second negative tectonic element is the *shelf,* a relatively stable, or perhaps mildly oscillating submerged continental platform receiving sediments. Such shelves are not unlike the present continental shelf bordering eastern North America where water depths range from a few feet at the present coastline to about 600 feet at the outer edge. In past geologic time, shelf areas were more widespread than they are now, because greater areas of the continent were flooded by shallow inland seas.

The third major negative tectonic element is the *intrashelf basin,* a more or less

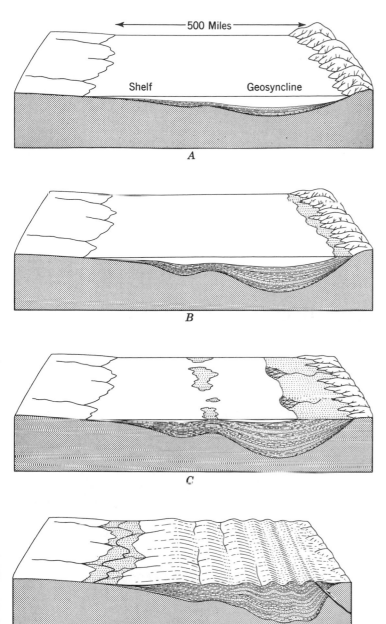

Shelf   Geosyncline

A

B

C

D

Figure 12-3. Series of block diagrams showing various stages in the development of a folded mountain range from geosynclinal sediments.

isolated feature, moderately subsiding and surrounded by a more stable shelf area.

Turning now to positive tectonism, or the uplift that characterizes the source area, two kinds of movement are recognized. Vertical uplift or warping of the land is an *epeirogenic* movement, whereas *orogenic* movements are more intense and produce considerable uplift of the land as well as deformation of the rocks in the source area.

■ ENVIRONMENT OF THE DEPOSITIONAL AREA. Tectonism provides the major framework of the depositional pattern, but on this larger picture are superimposed the various types of *sedimentary environments.* The classification of these environments is based on several factors, chief among which is the site of deposition with respect to sea level. The three major sedimentary environments are (1) *continental,* (2) *marine,* and (3) *transitional.*

The continental environments include the terrestrial deserts and glaciated regions as well as the aqueous environments of rivers (alluvial), lakes (lacustrine), and swamps. The marine environment is subdivided on the basis of depth of water and includes three zones: the *neritic* zone, extending from low tide to the edge of the continental shelf; the *bathyal* zone, from the edge of the shelf to 6000 feet in depth; and the *abyssal* zone

which includes all oceanic depths greater than 6000 feet.

Transitional environments are mixtures of continental and marine zones and are classed as deltaic, lagoonal, or littoral (the zone between high and low tide).

Generally speaking, each of the sedimentary environments imparts certain characteristics to the sediments which accumulate in it, and depending on how carefully sedimentary rocks are examined, some understanding of the environment of deposition usually can be gained.

■ POSTDEPOSITIONAL CHANGE OF THE SEDIMENT (LITHIFICATION). As sediment accumulates on the sea floor it begins to undergo transformation of varying degrees. One significant change is *compaction,* owing to the weight of new sediment

Table 12-a.   Possible Inferences Made from Various Sedimentary Rocks

ROCK TYPE	SOURCE AREA			DEPOSITIONAL AREA		
	CLIMATE	TOPOGRAPHY	TECTONISM	CLIMATE	TECTONISM	ENVIRONMENTAL ZONE
Quartz ss.	Temperate	Moderately rugged	Stable	Variable	Mildly sinking	Shallow water
Graywacke	Temperate	Mountainous	Rapid uplift	Variable	Rapidly sinking (geosynclinal)	Shallow water
Evaporites (salt, gypsum)	Humid temperate	Moderate relief	Stable	Arid	Moderately sinking	Closed basins or restricted arms of the sea
Pure limestone	Humid temperate	Low to moderately high or distant	Stable	Warm	Stable	Clear shallow water
Gray shales	Temperate	Low or distant	Moderate uplift	Variable	Stable	Open sea
Black shales	Warm humid	Low or distant	Stable	Warm humid to tropical	Sinking	Restricted zones on the shelf or geosyncline
Coal	Warm humid	Low	Relatively stable	Humid tropical	Gently emergent to submergent	Swamp conditions
Red clastics	Humid	Moderate to rugged	Moderate to strong uplift	Humid to arid	Stable	Delta, flood plain, open sea
Conglomerate	Variable	Rugged, swift streams	Rapid uplift	Variable	Sinking	Near shore along unprotected coast
Arkose	Arid temperate	Rugged granite	Rapid uplift	Variable	Sinking	Shallow water near shore

that is continuously being added. Compaction increases the density of the sediment by reducing the pore space between particles. This is a far more important process in fine clastics like mud and silt than it is in sand. For instance, a mud at the bottom of the sea may contain over 50 per cent of voids or pore space. By the time it is buried beneath 500 feet of additional mud the porosity will be reduced to 40 per cent, and when that same mud layer is covered with 2000 feet of younger sediment only about 20 per cent of its total volume will be pore space. Rocks composed of sand grains are not affected very much by the weight of overlying sediments, although a slight increase in density does take place during compaction.

Another change imposed on clastic sediments is *cementation,* the process whereby minerals form in the spaces between individual grains. This involves precipitation of such chemicals as silica, calcium carbonate, or iron oxide, which bind the grains together like the cement in concrete and further reduces their porosity. Sands thus become sandstones and gravels become conglomerates.

Under certain conditions, newly deposited sediment will undergo some change in crystalline texture, a process called *recrystallization.* This is especially common in the chemical sediments such as limestone and dolomite. During recrystallization, some grains are dissolved while others grow larger because of redeposition of the dissolved material. Recrystallization usually increases the density of the sediment and when complete, tends to obscure the original sedimentary properties.

Many other changes take place in a sediment between the time it is first deposited on the sea floor and the time it is exposed as rock somewhere on the earth's surface. These changes may obscure or mask entirely the properties of the original sediments, thereby making

the task of reconstructing past environments more difficult, but not impossible. Table 12-*a* summarizes possible inferences that can be made from some sedimentary rocks.

PALEOGEOGRAPHY

After the geologist thoroughly understands the origin of sedimentary rocks of a particular age, he is ready to reconstruct the broad physical relationship between the source area and the depositional environments. Paleogeography involves determining the distribution of ancient seaways and adjoining land masses through an interpretation of the sedimentary rocks of a certain age. This is one of the ultimate goals in historical geology, and although it often involves considerable interpretation on the part of the geologist, a paleogeographic map is based on factual data derived from geological observations.

Furthermore, because the sediments yield clues not only to the environment but also to the nature of the source area, the geologist may be able to deduce whether the land mass was a rugged mountain range, a chain of volcanic islands, or a low-lying plain. At best, paleogeography can give only the broad picture of the earth during past episodes of its history, and it approaches the truth only when the sediments themselves are thoroughly understood.

FOSSILS

Any evidence of past life on earth is a *fossil.* This definition is qualified to the extent that the fossil gives evidence of past life not recorded in written history. A fossil may be anything from the complete skeleton of an ancient fish entombed in shale to the tracks of a dinosaur preserved in sandstone. It may be the imprint of a leaf in a siltstone or the carcass of a mammoth locked in the frozen ground of Alaska or Siberia. *Paleontology* deals with the study of fossils and is a science in itself. However, because fossils are integral parts of sedimentary rocks in which they are found, they provide corroborating facts about environments of deposition. But most of all, fossils add another facet to earth history because they provide the means whereby we can study the parade of life through the ages (Fig. 12-4).

But fossils were not always regarded as the remains of living things. The ancients considered them "sports of nature," or the works of the devil placed in the ground to mislead mankind. Some

Figure 12-4. Fossil trilobite from a shale in Yoho Park, British Columbia. These creatures are now extinct, but they flourished in great numbers during the Paleozoic Era. (Courtesy of Geological Survey of Canada. Norford, B.S., 1962, *Illustrations of Canadian fossils Cambrium, Ordovician, and Silurian of the western Cordillera,* Department of Mines and Technical Surveys, Paper 62-14.)

writers held that fossils were generated *in situ* within the earth in the same way that minerals formed. In fact, the word fossil was first applied to all objects dug from the earth's crust, and included metals and minerals as well as organic remains.

Gradually, however, the evidence grew to overwhelming proportions in favor of the view that fossils were once living organisms that were naturally entombed after death and became incorporated in the rocks themselves. By the sixteenth and seventeenth centuries such men as Leonardo da Vinci (1452–1519) upheld this view, but it remained for Baron Cuvier (1769–1832), the learned French nobleman, to put the science of paleontology on a firmer footing. He recognized that the fossil bones in the sedimentary rocks of France belonged to species of animals that had since become extinct. Cuvier was opposed to the idea of evolution, however, and believed that living things of the past were the result of an initial creative act of God. Cataclysmic upheaval of the earth's crust later destroyed parts of the organic world resulting in a redistribution of the remaining organisms.

Probably no one individual deserves more credit for relating paleontology to geology than William Smith (1769–1839), an astute English surveyor who lacked any formal training in geology. Smith was the first to recognize the fact that fossils could be used as a means of identifying the strata in which they occurred. This was because he was a careful observer, and noticed that the *same groups of fossils always occurred in the same rock layers,* and that whenever he could not trace a single stratum from one place to the next, he need only examine the isolated rock outcrops for their fossil content in order to know exactly which formation he was working with. And so the science of stratigraphy was born and fossils were finally recognized as a valuable tool in the science of geology.

The important discovery of William Smith led eventually to the establishment of the *law of faunal succession,* the concept that explains the distinct faunal assemblages associated with each of the sedimentary rock layers as the result of organic evolution. Evolution shows that the more complex forms of plants and animals have evolved from their less complicated ancestors during the course of geologic time. The exact *mechanism* by which the transformation from simple to complex forms took place is not yet known, nor does the answer lie solely in the fossils. But the fossils do reveal the fact that the lower forms of life existed long before the higher organisms appeared. This fact has been unquestionably established by the simple law of superposition applied to fossil-bearing strata.

■ RESTORATION. The hard skeleton of an animal is much more susceptible to natural preservation than the softer parts such as skin, tissue, and delicate membranes. Because of this, the paleontologist hardly ever finds the complete remains of a creature of the past, and is therefore obliged to restore the appearance of the animal by the addition of flesh and other soft parts. This act of *restoration* is guided by his knowledge of certain anatomical relationships in all animals, especially in living forms related to the fossils. Restorations of the same organism by different workers may be different, however, especially in the vertebrate group of animals, because the skeletal parts do not reveal the exact muscular conformation or coloration of the animal, although some exceptional fossil discoveries have revealed the imprints of very delicate features of the animal's skin. Figure 12-5 shows a fossil skeleton and restorations by two different paleontologists.

THE GEOLOGIC TIME SCALE

The law of faunal succession has been verified countless times from strata in widely separated parts of the earth so that geologists are confident that rocks containing similar fossil assemblages are of similar geologic age. This momentous discovery paved the way for the formulation of a geologic time scale.

Time scales are of two types, relative and absolute. The relative age of an event fixes its age in relationship to other events and does not imply an age in years. For instance, a certain rock layer is younger than all the layers beneath it, and older than all the layers above it. Relative age only can be determined from the geologic relationships of the rocks, but no accurate indication of age in actual years can be inferred from the field relationships alone.

A comparatively recent development in the science of geology, however, now permits the assigning of ages in years to certain rock units. Consequently, an absolute time scale has arisen, which not only verifies the validity of the relative ages of the various strata, but also gives a more complete picture of the immense length of time that has elapsed since the oldest rocks were formed. Before investigating this method, however, let us examine the geologic time scale as it was originally conceived and as it has since evolved to its present form. We will then be in a better position to judge the impact of the absolute methods of dating.

■ THE GEOLOGIC COLUMN. The first attempt to subdivide the history of the earth was based on the observations of Abraham Gottlob Werner (1749–1815), a German mineralogist of the late eighteenth century. Werner believed that all rocks were the result of precipitation from sea water and envisioned them as belonging to four chief subdivisions. Werner's ideas on the origin of rocks were soon

Figure 12-5. Two restorations of an extinct dinosaur, both based on the same skeleton. The animal is known as *Stegosaurus*. (The restoration below the tail of the skeleton is by Edwin Colbert and the lower right restoration is by Charles Knight.)

disproved, but the seeds of his idea of subdividing geologic time into major units did not die.

The nineteenth century saw the gradual development and piecing together of a standard geologic column and time scale that now has universal acceptance. The subdivision of geologic time was based on strata exposed in Europe, especially Britain, France, and Germany, and as a result the names given to the different geologic periods are chiefly of European origin.

The geologic time scale embodies four major units, each of which is separated into smaller units. The major units do not all encompass the same amount of time, nor do their smaller subdivisions represent similar lengths of time. Except for the Precambrian, each has certain characteristic fossils associated with rocks

formed during a particular time. Figure 12-6 shows the time scale now used in the United States.

■ BASIS FOR SUBDIVIDING GEOLOGIC TIME. The passage of geologic time was accompanied by certain events that are recorded in the rocks. To subdivide geologic time, it became necessary to pick out certain events of such importance and magnitude that they provided natural "punctuation marks" in earth history. The time at which mountains were formed and the shallow epicontinental seas were drained from the continental platforms provided the local "natural" breaks for the initial studies of earth history. *Orogeny*, or mountain building, was thus considered the time keeper of the geologic clock. The growth of mountains was thought to represent an event of worldwide importance. That is to say, the major geologic time

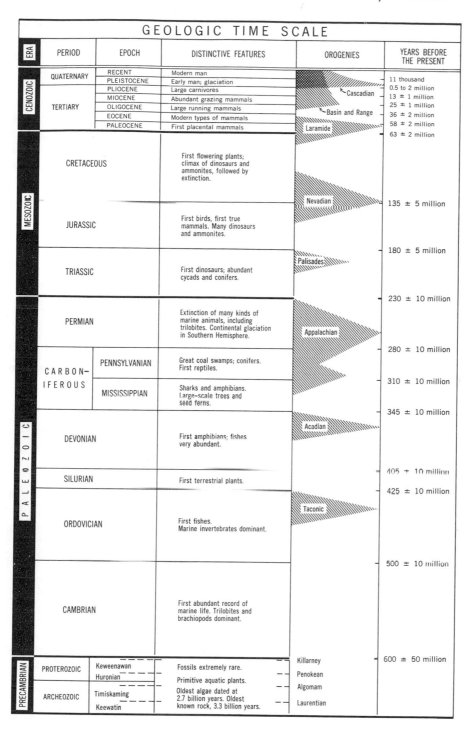

			GEOLOGIC TIME SCALE		
ERA	PERIOD	EPOCH	DISTINCTIVE FEATURES	OROGENIES	YEARS BEFORE THE PRESENT
CENOZOIC	QUATERNARY	RECENT	Modern man		11 thousand
		PLEISTOCENE	Early man; glaciation		0.5 to 2 million
	TERTIARY	PLIOCENE	Large carnivores	Cascadian	13 ± 1 million
		MIOCENE	Abundant grazing mammals		25 ± 1 million
		OLIGOCENE	Large running mammals	Basin and Range	36 ± 2 million
		EOCENE	Modern types of mammals		58 ± 2 million
		PALEOCENE	First placental mammals	Laramide	63 ± 2 million
MESOZOIC	CRETACEOUS		First flowering plants; climax of dinosaurs and ammonites, followed by extinction.	Nevadian	135 ± 5 million
	JURASSIC		First birds, first true mammals. Many dinosaurs and ammonites.		180 ± 5 million
	TRIASSIC		First dinosaurs; abundant cycads and conifers.	Palisades	230 ± 10 million
PALEOZOIC	PERMIAN		Extinction of many kinds of marine animals, including trilobites. Continental glaciation in Southern Hemisphere.	Appalachian	280 ± 10 million
	CARBONIFEROUS	PENNSYLVANIAN	Great coal swamps; conifers. First reptiles.		310 ± 10 million
		MISSISSIPPIAN	Sharks and amphibians. Large-scale trees and seed ferns.		345 ± 10 million
	DEVONIAN		First amphibians; fishes very abundant.	Acadian	405 + 10 million
	SILURIAN		First terrestrial plants.		425 ± 10 million
	ORDOVICIAN		First fishes. Marine invertebrates dominant.	Taconic	500 ± 10 million
	CAMBRIAN		First abundant record of marine life. Trilobites and brachiopods dominant.		600 ± 50 million
PRECAMBRIAN	PROTEROZOIC	Keweenawan	Fossils extremely rare.	Killarney	
		Huronian	Primitive aquatic plants.	Penokean	
	ARCHEOZOIC	Timiskaming	Oldest algae dated at 2.7 billion years. Oldest known rock, 3.3 billion years.	Algomam	
		Keewatin		Laurentian	

Figure 12-6.   Geologic time scale used in North America.   Absolute time scale is given in the column at the right, which is based on radioactive decay of minerals found in strata of known relative age.   (After Kulp, J. Laurence, 1961, Geologic time scale, *Science,* **133,** 1105–1114, and Newell, Norman D., 1962, *Geology's time clock,* Natural History, **71,** 32–37.

intervals were supposedly represented by continuous deposition of sediments in epicontinental seas, and each episode of deposition was brought to a close by alleged worldwide orogeny causing retreat of the seas and subsequent erosion of the sediments deposited in them. The sequence was started anew after the mountains were worn down by erosion and the seas once again invaded the land. Hence, the sediments of the later advance of the sea were laid down on the older rocks that had been subjected to deformation and erosion during the "break" in the depositional history. Such breaks constituted lost records because no sediments were being deposited. The break or gap in the record of the rocks was present in the form of a surface of erosion or nondeposition, an *unconformity* in geologic terminology. Figure 12-7 shows, diagrammatically, two unconformities in a theoretical sequence of layered rocks. It is self-evident that the oldest group was deformed, faulted, and eroded before the middle sequence of sediments was deposited, and that erosion of the middle group took place before the last sequence was laid down.

The general belief in worldwide orogeny has dwindled until now geologists have come to realize that mountain building is not necessarily a worldwide event but may be restricted to a single continent or even part of one continent during any one interval of geologic time. Definite unconformities in one area may not appear at all in another area but are represented, instead, by a complete sequence of sedimentary rocks. As a matter of fact, it is quite possible that every century of geologic time is represented somewhere by a sequence of sedimentary rocks.

Orogeny has been almost entirely abandoned as the basis for partitioning geologic time because it is only of local significance. However, the use of the fossil plant and animal assemblages from the different rock layers, largely those of the European sequence of formations, are employed as the basis for comparison with fossils in strata from other parts of the world. The standard rock column as we know it today is still based on the strata of Western Europe and is universally used as the basis for the geologic time scale.

AN ABSOLUTE TIME SCALE

When the European geologists began the long and arduous task of piecing together the strata on which our modern time scale is based, they had no firm basis for dating an individual rock layer or unit in terms of actual years. The chronology built by the fathers of modern geology was based solely on the law of superposition, and for this reason was only a relative chronology.

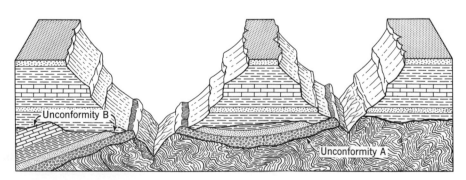

Figure 12-7. Block diagram showing two unconformities. Both represent periods of erosion and hence are gaps in the geologic record.

For many years geologists had dreamed of a method whereby the various rocks could be dated in terms of actual years. They tried all sorts of things. One idea involved the rate of sedimentation in the sea. The early geologists thought that the thickness of a layer of rock was directly proportional to the time it took to accumulate. Thus, by multiplying the thickness of all rock layers in feet by the time in years necessary to form one foot, some idea of age was arrived at. But their assumption might almost be classed as naive and would certainly not stand the rigorous scrutiny of modern science. The basic assumption that all rock layers were laid down at the same average rates can be disproved simply by observing the widely different rates at which different types of sediments are forming today. A single flood in the lower Mississippi River might deposit 5 feet of mud in one day, whereas many thousands of years would be required for 1 foot of mud to accumulate in the bottom of one of the Great Lakes.

■ RADIOACTIVITY AND GEOLOGIC TIME. The dream of the geologists started to come true when the phenomenon of radioactivity was discovered around the turn of the century. Essentially, radioactivity is the spontaneous disintegration of some elements from an unstable condition to a more stable condition. No outside energy is needed to keep the process of radioactivity going. Indeed, the disintegration of a radioactive element proceeds at a rate independent of exterior forces such as heat, pressure, or chemical environment. So far as is known, a radioactive element decays at a constant rate measurable in the laboratory.

The principle of age determination is thus quite simple. Element A is radioactive; it decays at a known rate into element B. Therefore, to determine the age of rock containing elements A and B, the total amount of each must be determined. Assuming that all of B was derived from A, the ratio of B to A is an index of time since the rock was formed.

For example, uranium (U_{238}) is a radioactive element that decays to lead (Pb_{206}) through a series of radioactive changes. The time it takes for half the original amount of material to change to the end product is defined as the *half life,* and for U_{238} this constant is 4507 million years. Thus, a gram of U_{238} would be reduced to one-half gram of U_{238} in 4507 million years, while in another 4507 million years only one-fourth gram of the original U_{238} would be left. Therefore, in order to determine the age of rock containing U_{238}, it is necessary to know the exact amount of U_{238} and Pb_{206}. These analyses require great skill and precision because the lead formed by decay of uranium is not the same as ordinary lead. Furthermore, the total amount of radioactive materials may be extremely small and easily masked by outside contamination. But in spite of these inherent difficulties, certain dates based on uranium-lead ratios have been determined.

Other radioactive elements that are now used for age determinations include thorium decaying to Pb_{208}, and rubidium (Rb) changing to strontium (Sr). Another method involves the potassium-argon (K-Ar) ratio which has become the most widely used value in age determinations because of its application over a broad range of geologic time. But since argon is a gas, it can escape from the rock in which it is formed by radioactive decay, thereby rendering the "age" determination unreliable. Slight heating through metamorphism increases the probability of argon loss. In igneous rock such as granite the most common mineral used for K-Ar age determinations is biotite, and in sedimentary rocks, the mineral glauconite (iron-potassium-silicate) from marine sandstones is commonly employed.

All these methods require very careful

quantitative chemical analyses to determine minute amounts of radioactive products and the exact knowledge of decay rates of each original element. Each method is based on the primary assumption that none of the radioactive decay products has been leached from the rock, and that none has been introduced from outside sources.

Although some discrepancies are present between the "absolute ages" and the geologic relationships, especially in Precambrian rocks, a fairly consistent absolute chronology has evolved for the geologic periods later than Precambrian. The most reliable dates are those based on two or more independent determinations such as the K-Ar and U_{238}-Pb_{206} ratios. Figure 12-6 is a composite time scale based on ages derived mainly from the K-Ar method.

■ OLDEST ROCKS AND THE AGE OF THE EARTH. Radioactive age determinations have demonstrated that the oldest rocks of the earth's crust are about 3.3 billion years old and that the earth itself may be on the order of magnitude of $4\frac{1}{2}$ to 5 billion years old. The astounding thing about this revelation is that the earth seems to be about as old as the meteorites and the universe itself, as deduced by astronomers using its expansion rate as a basis for calculation. This suggests that all elements of our universe, including the earth, originated at the same time, a theory which had little support among scientists less than a few decades ago.

SUMMARY

Sedimentary rocks and the fossils they contain provide the basis for the relative geologic time scale. Studies of the relationships of rock layers result in a geologic chronology for any given locality. Comparison of fossil assemblages with the fossils of the type localities aids in the correlation of geologic strata from all parts of the earth.

Detailed study of sedimentary rocks provides the clues to their origin, and by applying the doctrine of uniformitarianism, geologists can reconstruct the general relationships between source areas and areas of deposition during past geologic ages. Paleogeography is the science which deals with the distribution of major geographical features such as mountain ranges and geosynclines during any given geologic time interval.

Periods of mountain building (orogeny) were not worldwide events and thus do not provide a basis for worldwide correlations. Orogenies are recorded as unconformities in deformed strata.

Radioactive dating of rocks provides an absolute time scale which confirms the correctness of the relative time scale established by the law of superposition, especially for the latter part of the geologic record (from Cambrian time to Recent). The oldest rocks found so far are 3.3 billion years old. Radioactive determinations now place the earth's age at about $4\frac{1}{2}$ billion years, the same as that of meteorites and the same order of magnitude as the entire universe.

REFERENCES

Adams, Frank D., 1954, *The birth and development of the geological sciences,* Dover Publications, New York.

Bell, W. C., *et al.,* 1961, Note 25—Geochronologic and chronostratigraphic units, *Am. Assoc. Petroleum Geologists Bull.,* **45,** 666–670.

Dunbar, Carl O., and John Rodgers, 1957, *Principles of stratigraphy,* John Wiley and Sons, New York.

Knopf, Adolf, 1949, *Time in earth history,* National Research Council, Report of Committee on Measurement of Geologic Time.

Krumbein, W. C. and L. L. Sloss, 1951, *Stratigraphy and sedimentation,* W. H. Freeman and Co., San Francisco.

Kulp, J. Laurence, 1961, Geologic Time scale, *Science,* **133,** 1105–1114.

Ladd, Harry S., 1959, Ecology, paleontology, and stratigraphy, *Science,* **129,** 69–78.

Levorsen, A. I., 1960, *Paleogeologic maps,* W. H. Freeman and Co., California.

Rusnak, G. A., Tj. H. Van Andel, J. E. Nafe, B. C. Heezon, and D. B. Erickson, 1960, *Marine sedi-ments,* McGraw-Hill Encyclopedia of Science and Technology, p. 132–147.

Zeuner, Frederick E., 1950, *Dating the past,* Methuen and Co., London.

XIII

The Precambrian

. . . and some rin up hill and down dale,
knapping the chucky stanes to pieces wi' hammers,
like sae mony road-makers run daft—
they say it is to see how the world was made!

Sir Walter Scott

Five hundred million years ago a large portion of the eastern and western United States was invaded by a shallow sea teeming with invertbrate marine organisms. The deposits of sand and sediment that accumulated in this advancing sea are called Cambrian because they are similar to rocks first studied in Wales ("Cambria"). The rocks underlying the Cambrian sediments and the rocks from which those sediments were derived are the subjects of this chapter (Fig. 13-1).

Precambrian time is thus the whole of geologic time from the very beginning of earth history until the earliest fossiliferous Cambrian beds were deposited. If the earth is $4\frac{1}{2}$ to 5 billion years old, the Precambrian represents 80 to 85 per cent of all earth history. And yet this vast period of geologic time is among the least known segments of the geologic record, primarily because of the way in which the rocks of the Precambrian have been inexorably metamorphosed since they first came into being (Fig. 13-2). Not once but many times have some Precambrian rocks gone through an episode of metamorphic change, and each time the nature of the original rock was further obscured. This, of course, hampers the interpretative efforts of the geologist trying to reconstruct Precambrian history. He must remove this metamorphic mask before the real meaning of the rock in terms of its original character can be determined.

PRECAMBRIAN CORRELATION

The geologic record is not complete everywhere. Parts of it are scattered all over the surface of the earth. In order to tie these fragmentary records together, some basis for recognizing rocks of the same age in widely separated localities is necessary. The identification of rocks of the same age in two different localities is called *correlation*.

Fossils are the best means of correlating the beds of post-Precambrian age, but where the rock units are barren of fossils, the correlation problem becomes more

Figure 13-1. Angular unconformity between Cambrian sandstone and Precambrian rocks north of Kingston, Ontario. (Photograph by A. S. MacLaren, Geological Survey of Canada.)

difficult.   Precambrian   *metasediments* (metamorphosed sediments) are practically void of fossils, with perhaps a half dozen exceptions, and this has led to a completely different basis for correlation of Precambrian rocks.   Similarity of lithology, degree of deformation, intensity of metamorphism, and similarity of sequence have all been invoked by Precambrian geologists in correlating rocks of different localities.

With the lack of any better methods, such bases for correlation are not wholly unreasonable, but theoretically there is no compelling reason why two granites of the same general appearance and composition in two widely separated areas must necessarily represent the same episode of magmatic activity.   Nor is there any absolute reason why quartzites, schists, gneisses, or slates occurring in separate localities must be of similar age just because they look alike.   Similarity of *rock sequence* and similarity in geologic history as inferred from field studies form the most reliable basis for correlation of the Precambrian.

The difficulties in correlation of Pre-

cambrian rocks have been further emphasized by recent advances in radioactive methods of dating rocks.   The comparison of some of the ages determined by conventional geologic methods are in serious discordance.   These discrepancies have led to a reappraisal of Precambrian correlations based on older methods.   But it is not to be assumed that the radioactive methods are without error in view of the fact that age determinations on the *same* sample have yielded different dates when different methods were used.

It is still to early to predict the outcome of these conflicting determinations of age relationships, but the end result should be a more accurate record of Precambrian geologic history.

DISTRIBUTION OF
PRECAMBRIAN ROCKS

Precambrian rocks occur on all continents including Antarctica.   They are exposed in three general regions: (1) the large areas of relatively low relief called *shield areas,* (2) the cores of folded mountain ranges, and (3) the bottoms of deeply carved canyons.

■ SHIELD AREAS. The shield areas are so named because of their vague similarity to the gentle convex shape of the shields used by ancient warriors. Every continent contains an extensive Precambrian shield, Eurasia has the Angara shield in north-central U.S.S.R., and the Baltic shield of Scandinavia. Nearly half of Africa is occupied by the Ethiopian shield, and South America contains the great Amazonian shield which covers much of Brazil. Australia and Antarctica both have extensive areas of Precambrian shields, and North America is the site of one of the largest of all shield areas, the Canadian Shield (Fig. 13-3). Within the shields the complex relationships of sedimentation, volcanic eruptions, intensive deformation (folding and faulting), intrusive activity, and widespread metamorphism are abundantly displayed. These areas were very active, tectonically, during the Precambrian, but since the beginning of Cambrian time the shields have been relatively stable with respect to earth movements.

The Canadian Shield covers 2,800,000 square miles in all (including part of Greenland), of which nearly two-thirds lies in Canada. The Shield has been under investigation for more than a hundred years because of the occurrence of a variety of valuable ore deposits. In spite of this interest, however, only a little more than 10 per cent of the Canadian Shield is covered by detailed geologic maps. Most of these are concentrated in mineralized areas so the geologic origin of the various ore deposits can be better understood. This, in turn, is a helpful guide to further exploration for ores of similar geologic occurrence elsewhere in the Shield area.

Hence, one might say that the detailed knowledge of the Shield area that we possess today has grown through the accumulation of geologic data from widely separated localities rather than by a systematic investigation of the area as a whole. This type of approach is the normal one, for without the lure of ore deposits of economic value to justify the geologic mapping programs carried on by

Figure 13-2. Strongly metamorphosed rocks of the Canadian Shield in Hastings County, Ontario. (Photograph by M. E. Wilson, Geological Survey of Canada.)

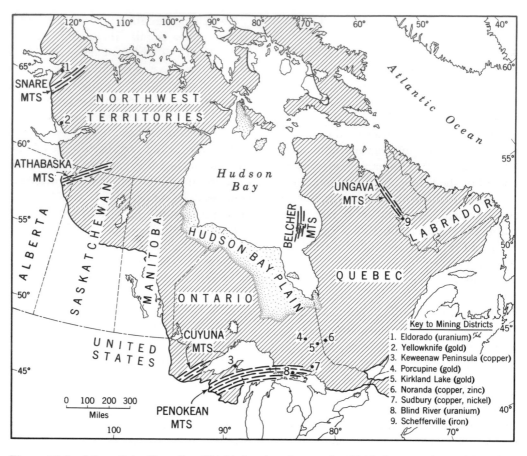

Figure 13-3.   Map of the Canadian Shield showing the trends of folded mountains and locations of some important mining districts.   (After Geological Survey of Canada, 1947, *Geology and economic minerals of Canada,* Ottawa, Canada, Department of Mines and Resources; and J. E. Gill, 1952, *Mountain building in the Canadian Pre-Cambrian Shield,* Report of the Eighteenth Session of the International Geological Congress, Great Britain, 1948, Part XIII.)

private enterprise as well as by government surveys, it is clear that very little detailed geologic mapping would be accomplished.   And, of course, without geologic maps of considerable detail, the geologic history of an area would never be deciphered.

SUBDIVISIONS OF THE PRECAMBRIAN

Ultimately, the geologist expects his investigations to reveal a sequence of geologic events that will allow him to

understand the geologic history of a certain area.   Generally speaking such sequences are divided and subdivided into time units of various magnitudes, depending to a large degree on the details of earth history which can be read from the record in the rocks.

Because of correlation problems, the Precambrian rocks of the Canadian shield do not permit the establishment of very small subdivisions of time.   Agreement has not even been reached as to how many major divisions of time lie within the Precambrian period.   Most Precambrian geologists subscribe to a two-fold subdivision, but another group insists on a three-fold classification system, and still another favors even more major time units. A great deal of this controversy is somewhat academic, but it helps to illustrate the amount of disagreement among Precambrian geologists which, incidentally, is usually a healthy sign of progress.

Without proclaiming that a two-fold classification is necessarily the correct one, it is the most widely used and will be followed in this book. Table 13-*a* is a summary tabulation of the different units of Precambrian time according to a scheme followed by some Canadian geologists. It does not necessarily apply to the whole Shield but is probably satisfactory for a restricted part of the Shield around the Great Lakes area.

THE ARCHEOZOIC

The oldest rocks of known geologic history belong to the Archeozoic. They consist of highly metamorphosed volcanics and sediments which have been intruded by granite batholiths.

Two different assemblages of rocks are defined, and although the terms used to designate them are in widespread use, they have more the connotation of lithology than time spans. The two units are Keewatin and Timiskaming.

■ KEEWATIN ROCKS. This term is generally applied to a folded assemblage of metamorphosed volcanics possibly with some interlayered conglomerate, impure coarse clastics, slate, and iron formation. The term Keewatin is normally used to designate the oldest Precambrian rocks within the Shield. This name was first applied to rocks near Lake of the Woods in southwestern Ontario.

Many of the rocks of Keewatin age are locally known as "greenstone" because of their dark greenish color. They are metamorphosed lava flows, some of which have a "pillow structure." The "pillows" are globules of lava deposited in water. As the lava entered the water it separated into globules, each of which

*Table 13-a. Classification of Precambrian Rocks of the Canadian Shield**

——————————— EROSIONAL UNCONFORMITY ———————————

Killarney granite intruded.
Keweenawan: Essentially lava flows, basic intrusions, and clastics.

Proterozoic ——————————— EROSIONAL UNCONFORMITY ———————————

Huronian: Quartzites, slates, dolomite, and iron formation.

——————————— GREAT UNCONFORMITY ———————————

Algoman granite intruded.
Timiskaming: Graywacke, slate, arkose, conglomerate, and minor volcanics.

Archeozoic ——————————— EROSIONAL UNCONFORMITY ———————————

Laurentian granite intruded.
Keewatin: Metamorphosed basic volcanics and minor sediments.

* This is the "standard" classification of the Canadian shield. The trend is toward using the names as lithologic types rather than as time terms over the entire area of the shield.

Figure 13-4.   Pillow structures in lavas southeast of Gordon Lake, Northwest Territories.   The bottom of the flow is toward the lower right.   Note how the pillows are "draped" over each other. (Photograph by J. F. Henderson, Geological Survey of Canada.)

quickly formed a tough glassy skin around its outside thus resembling a balloon filed with molasses.   These settled to the bottom where they became "draped" over each other, after which the whole mass solidified and clastic material filled the spaces between the individual pillows (Fig. 13-4).

■ TIMISKAMING ROCKS.   These rocks are folded and metamorphosed sediments interlayered with iron formations and some volcanics.   In some areas the Timiskaming series rests unconformably on the Keewatin, and separation of the two is well defined.   Elsewhere on the Shield the unconformity is not pronounced, so that differentiation between the two is impossible.   Some of the Timiskaming and Keewatin rocks are so strongly deformed and metamorphosed that it is very difficult, if not impossible, to determine the composition of the original rock.

■ ARCHEOZOIC GRANITES.   Both the Keewatin and Timiskaming rocks were invaded by granite batholiths.   In the Lake Superior region, especially Min-

nesota, granites of two different ages are recognized, one pre-Timiskaming named *Laurentian,* and one post-Timiskaming called *Algoman.*   A long period of erosion followed each, during which time the batholiths were exposed at the surface and the unconformities shown in Table 13-*a* were formed.

THE PROTEROZOIC

Most authorities agree that there is a vast difference between rocks of Archeozoic and Proterozoic age.   Whereas the early Precambrian rocks contain some units that are of sedimentary origin, the scarcity of quartzites (originally quartz sandstones) and marbles (originally limestones and dolomites) in the older Precambrian assemblages is noteworthy. The Proterozoic is marked by several layers of quartzite and dolomite as well as slate and other clastics, including a considerable thickness of iron formation of great economic importance.   The Proterozoic formations are generally less metamorphosed than the older rocks on which they rest unconformably.

Two subdivisions of the Proterozoic are usually recognized, the Huronian (older) and the Keweenawan (younger). Where the two occur together, the Huronian rocks are clearly older than the Keweenawan rocks, but this consistant sequence does not prove that the Huronian of one area is the same age as the Huronian of another area. Rocks of two widely separated areas may be similar in all respects (i.e., "Huronian-type rocks"); it does not necessarily follow that they are the same age. This is a difficult idea to get across and extremely confusing to a person dealing with the Precambrian terminology for the first time. The lack of a detailed rock record for the Precambrian necessitates the use of longer time subdivisions in comparison with those determined for later geologic eras.

■ HURONIAN ROCKS. This name was originally applied to an assemblage of metamorphosed sediments north of Lake Huron and is now in general use in Michigan and Ontario. Lithologically, Huronian rocks are flat-lying to closely folded sediments, mainly limestone, quartzite, slate, conglomerate, and iron formation, the latter being somewhat diagnostic of the entire series. One Huronian formation in southern Ontario is a tillite and is therefore evidence of glaciation during the Proterozoic.

The iron formations are rocks containing appreciable amounts of iron oxide, usually more than 25 per cent and rarely more than 40 per cent (Fig. 13-5).

■ KEWEENAWAN ROCKS. The last well-defined episode of Precambrian time is represented by a great thickness of lava flows, conglomerates, sandstones, and shales. Great sheets of basic magmas were intruded, some of which contain important ore bodies. Keweenawan rock layers are steeply tilted in northern Michigan, but elsewhere are nearly horizontal. Most of them are not the least bit metamorphosed, and, as in other Precambrian rocks, fossils are totally absent.

■ LATE PRECAMBRIAN GRANITE. A final period of intrusive activity involved the emplacement of a granite designated Killarney. The intrusion of the Killarney granite batholiths was accompanied

Figure 13-5. A close view of a Huronian iron formation near Negaunee, Michigan. The dark bands are red jasper and the lighter bands contain mostly iron minerals. The ruler is 6 inches long.

by orogenic movements which brought the recorded Precambrian period to a close. A long period of erosion then set the stage for the invasion of the Cambrian seas.

MOUNTAIN BUILDING DURING THE PRECAMBRIAN AND PROBLEMS OF CORRELATION

The older ideas concerning mountain building in the Shield area were based on the concept that orogenies were world-wide. Three orogenies, each accompanied by intrusion of granite, and followed by a long period of erosion, was the generally accepted view of the Precambrian. Each of the three granites, Laurentian, Algoman, and Killarney was used as the basis for this argument.

Recently, however, this idea has been shown to be very much over-simplified. Even without complete coverage of the Canadian Shield with detailed geologic maps, it is very clear that many orogenies occurred in different places at different times within the Shield area. There has been enough detailed geologic mapping of various parts of the Shield to reveal numerous folded belts, each with a distinctive structural trend. This fact alone rules out the possibility of simultaneous Shield-wide deformation. Instead, it strongly points to a succession of deformations which took place in different parts of the Shield at different times.

Within certain restricted areas such as northeastern Minnesota or southeastern Ontario, a sequence of Precambrian events can be established fairly well on the basis of the field relationships of the various rock units. But when the relative chronologies of two distant areas are placed side by side, the correlation of individual rock units between the two is far less certain than Precambrian

geologists would like it to be. Is there a solution to this formidable problem facing Precambrian workers?

ABSOLUTE AGES OF PRECAMBRIAN ROCKS

Problems of Precambrian correlation stand at the threshold of solution now that the dating of rocks by radioactive methods has entered the picture. No longer will the Precambrian geologists have to throw up their hands in despair and lament the lack of fossils in Precambrian strata. Slowly but surely an absolute time scale is being established for the Precambrian. Although vague in some places and generally incomplete, the outlook for future improvements in the time scale is encouraging. Some of these radioactive dates have established the fact that certain correlations based on the older concepts were way off their mark. In other cases the radioactive age determinations were in error because certain factors had not been taken into account. Nevertheless, the old is giving way to the new, and within the foreseeable future, radioactive age determinations should greatly expand the present skeleton of the Precambrian absolute chronology.

■ LENGTH OF PRECAMBRIAN TIME. The generally accepted classification of the Precambrian of North America was proposed in 1905. At that time the age of the earth was thought to be about 20 million years old, and the notion was held that all of Precambrain time was relatively short. But even though new evidence came to light and pushed the dawn of earth history further and further back, the original Precambrian classification of Archeozoic and Proterozoic remained.

The oldest rocks dated by radioactive methods are about 3.3 billion years old.

The Cambrian began about 600 million years ago which makes a known total of about 2.7 billion years for the Precambrian. The oldest dates come from pegmatites, very coarse-grained granitic dikes, intruded into still older metamorphosed sediments and volcanics, which are, of course, older than the pegmatites. Hence, the 2.7 billion years for the duration of the Precambrian is a *minimum!*

■ THE PRECAMBRIAN AND CONTINENTAL GROWTH. One of the oldest dogmas of geology is that the continents were products of an original cooling of the earth's crust. These granitic masses were supposed to have been in existence in the earliest part of earth history. Many older students of Precambrian geology believed that somewhere in the great shield areas of the world some vestige of the original granitic crust ought to be found. Among the vast areas of the Shield where granite crops out at the surface, not one granitic mass can be cited as evidence of an original granite crust. All of them are intrusive into older metamorphics.

EARLIEST LIVING ORGANISMS

The Cambrian seas were inhabited by many of the advanced forms of invertebrate life. Since these are supposed to be products of an evolutionary sequence, we naturally assume that the ancestors of Cambrian marine creatures evolved in Precambrian time. But actually the dearth of fossils in rocks of Precambrian age presents somewhat of a problem. Although it is quite true that a good many of the Precambrian strata are so strongly metamorphosed that any fossils would have been destroyed in the process, there are many areas in which the Proterozoic beds are still largely unmetamorphosed and are not even folded.

That these beds should be so devoid of the remains of Precambrian life is a mystery not easily explained.

Some fossils do exist in Precambrian strata, however, although they are too rare to be used as a means of correlation. One of the more recent discoveries is the occurrence of fossilized forms of plant life in southern Ontario in a bed of chert considered to be Huronian. Rough age determinations on magnetite from a stratigraphically younger bed yields a value of 1.3 billion years.

In Southern Rhodesia in the Precambrian Shield of South Africa, rocks of a confirmed age of 2.7 billion years contain some concretionary structures believed to be of algal origin. The exact idenification of these "fossils" has by no means been proven; indeed, there is considerable speculation as to whether any of the "algal structures" from Rhodesia or from the Canadian Shield are truly of organic origin.

One of the better known Precambrian "algal structures" is *Eozoön canadense,* an alleged primitive algal colonial form. These peculiar features occur in rock and are composed of concentric bands of various minerals. The prevailing opinion is that the Eozoön forms are inorganic in origin because some of the minerals in the bands cannot possibly have had an organic origin.

Probably a good case can be made for abundant Precambrian life of some sort because a considerable quantity of graphite interbedded with metamorphosed limestone is found in the so-called Grenville rocks of unknown Precambrian age.* The theory is that the graphite, which is a crystalline form of carbon, had an organic origin, but obviously, all vestiges of original structures of these

* The Grenville rocks of eastern Canada and the Adirondacks of the United States are considered Archeozoic in age by some geologists and Proterozoic by others.

alleged creatures have been destroyed. Probably they were marine forms in view of their association with limestone.

In 1947 a discovery of fossiliferous Precambrian sandstones in the Ediacara Hills in South Australia revealed some startling life forms including specimens of jelly fish and segmented worms. Of the more than 600 specimens studied by Australian geologists, all were apparently soft-bodied forms and some are unlike any known type of animal, living or fossil. The Precambrian age of the Ediacara Hills is undoubted because the strata form a very simple structure in which fossiliferous Cambrian beds form the upper part of the sequence.

Paleontologists have suggested that the lack of Precambrian fossils is due to the absence of hard parts such as shells or internal rigid members in the animals themselves. Obviously, the soft membranes and tissues of jelly fish-type creatures could not have been very prone to preservation after death except under very unusual circumstances. Such rare conditions call for mud bottoms in which the soft-bodied forms settled after death and were rather quickly covered with another layer of sand or mud so that the shapes of the soft animals were preserved as molds in the sediment.

Why Precambrian animals had no hard parts is not known, but it may be that the capability of building shells or internal hard skeletons was an evolutionary development of later geological history. This idea seems preferable to the concept that the development of shells in the Cambrian was the result of a sudden change in the physical environment of the oceans or the habits of the animals themselves.

SOME PRECAMBRIAN ROCKS ELSEWHERE IN NORTH AMERICA

■ THE GRAND CANYON. The mile-deep gorge of the Colorado River slices through some 3000 feet of Paleozoic sedimentary rocks and provides a spectacular lesson in geology to the thousands of tourists who visit this scenic wonder (Figs. 13-6 and 16-7). Near the bottom of the canyon a complex of deformed and metamorphosed rocks lie unconformably below a horizontal sandstone layer which is of Cambrian age.

The Precambrian rocks consists of an older assemblage of schist (the Vishnu schist) containing intrusive granite and pegmatite dikes. Both schist and dikes are classified as Archeozoic, but here again the assumption that these rocks are the same age as the Keewatin-type or Timiskaming-type rocks of the Canadian

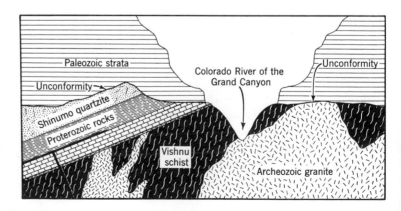

Figure 13-6. Cross-sectional sketch of the lower portion of the Grand Canyon of the Colorado River showing the relationships of the various rock units. (From a diagram by L. F. Noble.)

Figure 13-7. The rocks exposed in this steep wall are in Glacier National Park, Montana. They are Proterozoic in age and are known as the Belt series. Iceberg Lake in the foreground. (Photograph by M. R. Campbell, United States Geological Survey.)

Shield is unwarranted. They do, however, constitute the oldest rocks in the Grand Canyon section, and this is why they were correlated with the Archeozoic of the Shield.

Lying unconformably on the Vishnu schist are the strata of the Grand Canyon series of Proterozoic age. Besides beds of conglomerate, limestone, and shale, the Grand Canyon series includes a layer of massive quartzite and sandstone 1500 feet thick known as the Shinumo quartzite.

Both the Archeozoic (Vishnu schist) and Proterozoic (Shinumo and other sediments) were extensively eroded during the intervals of Precambrian time as indicated by the two pronounced unconformities shown in Fig. 13-6. The pre-Proterozoic erosion surface is remarkably flat with a maximum relief of about 50 feet. The post-Proterozoic erosion surface is marked by some monadnocks which rise as much as 800 feet above the general level of the unconformity.

A study of the rocks immediately be-

neath each erosion surface reveals that feldspars were altered to kaolinite, and biotite was changed to iron oxide. Such changes are normally induced by chemical weathering under relatively humid conditions. It is therefore concluded that a humid climate prevailed during both periods of prolonged erosion during Precambrian times.

■ NORTHEASTERN MONTANA. An exceptionally fine sequence of relatively unmetamorphosed sedimentary rocks of Precambrian age known as the Belt series is exposed along the rock walls of Glacier National Park in Montana (Fig. 13-7). More than 25,000 feet of nearly flat-lying rock layers including shale, limestone, and sandstone were deposited in a geosyncline that may have been a northern extension of the one in which the Grand Canyon series was deposited. These rocks are visible in many cliff faces throughout the park. One of the striking features of them is their content of primitive plants or algae, which in rock exposures resemble a group of cabbage heads split open.

Some of the most magnificent scenery in the northwestern United States is found in Glacier National Park where the rocks of the Belt series have been carved by valley glaciers into steep-walled valleys between serrated ridges. These rocks can be observed at close range from the foot trails which ascend the valley walls to the high country above the timber line. The rugged peaks forming the Continental Divide or Garden Wall of Glacier Park expose nearly 2000 feet of Beltian rocks.

MINERAL WEALTH FROM THE CANADIAN SHIELD

It would be difficult to overestimate the importance of the Canadian Shield to the mineral industries of the United States and Canada. The Precambrian rocks are locally mineralized with important ores containing iron, nickel, copper, cobalt, uranium, gold, silver, and others. Some of the mines from which these metals have been produced have been in operation for more than a hundred years, and others were discovered only a few years ago. Before describing some of the more important mining districts of the Shield, a few remarks about mining in general may be appropriate.

THE MINING INDUSTRY

A mine is an excavation from which minerals of economic value are or have been produced. An *ore mineral* is a metalliferous mineral sought for its economic value. It occurs in association with *gangue,* a mineral or mineral aggregate of no economic value. Together, the ore minerals plus the gangue make up the *ore.* One distinction that ought to be stressed in connection with the definition

of ore is that it must yield metals *at a profit* to the miner. This restriction seems to be the only feasible one to employ in clearly defining ore. Obviously, many rocks contain small quantities of some metalliferous mineral, but unless the content of that mineral can be freed from the associated minerals, *economically,* the rock is not ore in the real sense of the word. Ores may be *high grade* or *low grade* depending on the concentration of the ore mineral.

■ HOW ORE BODIES ARE DISCOVERED. The individual prospector has been responsible for the discovery of some major ore deposits, but most prospectors working alone and with little or no geologic background except what they have picked up, prospect all their lives without "striking it rich." But as long as the chance exists, no matter how slim, the lure of quick riches will still entice those with the adventurous spirit. That such people still exist was amply demonstrated in the uranium rush of the late 1940's and early 1950's.

Today the discovery of new ore bodies is usually the result of a concentrated effort by geologists and geophysicists. It is true that many concentrations of ore have been discovered purely by accident, but by and large, geologic exploration is now being employed not only to locate new deposits, but also to determine the extent of known deposits.

■ MINE OPERATIONS. Ore may be removed from surface workings called *open pits.* Open pit operations are feasible only where the ore lies close enough to the surface that it can be mined economically. Two factors that determine to a large extent the feasibility of open pit operations are the grade of the ore and thickness of the *overburden,* either rock or unconsolidated material, that must be removed before the ore body becomes accessible.

Underground mines are developed where

the ore body lies at a depth too great for open pit operations. It is usually a more costly method of mining because of special techniques and special machinery required.

ORE DEPOSITS OF THE CANADIAN SHIELD

Billions of dollars worth of metalliferous ores have been produced from mines in the Canadian Shield. The details of the origin and occurrence of the many different kinds of deposits are far beyond the scope of this introductory textbook. But even in the relatively small space that can be devoted to this intriguing subject it is possible for the beginner to gain a brief insight into the romance of discovery and development of an ore deposit.

■ IRON. Probably no other metal is as important in our modern mechanized age as iron. In the form of steel, iron is literally the life-blood of industry. Without it wars could not be won and the wheels of industrial progress would most surely grind to a halt. Iron is one of the most abundant metals in the earth's crust. It usually occurs in chemical combination with oxygen as the minerals hematite, magnetite, and limonite (see Table 3-a).

Iron was discovered in the Northern Peninsula of Michigan near the south shore of Lake Superior in 1844 by a land surveying party whose magnetic compasses were thrown into wild paroxysms by the iron ore bodies near the surface. By 1865 the discoveries of new ore bodies were extended to Minnesota, a state that is still the greatest producer of iron ore in the United States. Minnesota supplies about 65 per cent of all iron produced in the United States.

The iron ranges in the Lake Superior region are all of Precambrian age (Fig. 13-8). The six ranges in Minnesota, Michigan, and Wisconsin provide about 80 per cent of the total production in the United States. The iron is mined by both open pit and underground methods. The largest iron mine in the world is the Hull-Rust-Mahoning pit on the Mesabi Range

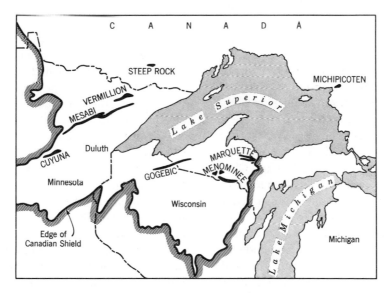

Figure 13-8. Map showing the distribution of iron ranges in the Lake Superior district. All are Proterozoic in age except the Vermillion Range in Minnesota which is Archeozoic.

Figure 13-9.   A view of the Hull-Rust-Mahoning open pit iron ore mine near Hibbing, Minnesota.   This is the largest open pit mine in the world.   Between 1895 and 1957, 545 million tons of ore have been shipped from this pit and 450 million tons of waste and overburden have been removed.   (Courtesy of Oliver Iron Mining Division, United States Steel Corporation.)

(Fig. 13-9).   One-fourth of all the iron ore mined in Minnesota has come out of this huge man-made cavity, which covers 1535 acres.   It is $3\frac{1}{4}$ miles long, $\frac{1}{2}$ to 1 mile wide, and has a maximum depth of 490 feet.   From the pit the ore is transported to the surface and then goes by rail to the loading docks at Duluth and other ports on Lake Superior.   From there the ore is carried by lake vessels to ports on the lower lakes which serve steel centers such as Chicago, Detroit, Buffalo, Cleveland, and Pittsburgh.   The importance of iron ore transportation is illustrated by the fact that the Duluth-Superior port is the third largest in the United States in terms of total annual tonnage handled.

Iron ore produced from the Lake Superior district averages about 50 per cent iron.   The tremendous production of World War II pointed up the fact that the high-grade ores of the Lake Superior district would not last forever.   This realization turned attention to the large unused deposits of low-grade magnetite-bearing rocks of the region.   This low-grade ore averages about 20 to 40 per cent iron and is known as *taconite*.   As it occurs in nature, taconite does not contain enough iron for profitable exploitation, so a way was devised to increase the iron content by a concentration process whereby the magnetite was separated from such gangue minerals as quartz and other silicate minerals.   The taconite industry is rapidly gaining in importance as the high-grade reserves are depleted.

The origin of the iron ore in the Huronian rocks of Minnesota and Michigan has long been the subject of heated debate by Precambrian geologists.   The facts are that the iron ore represents the results of a leaching process in which the initial iron-bearing rocks lost silica, thereby increasing the percentage of residual iron. The two main questions still unanswered are: (1) What kind of environment favors the deposition of iron minerals and silica (chert, SiO_2) in such large volumes? and (2) was the silica leached by (a) cold surface waters, (b) surface waters that became heated by deep circulation, or (c) water in the form of steam rising upward from underlying magmas? The reader may gain the impression that such questions are purely academic, but the discovery of new deposits is vitally dependent on the knowledge of the origin of the known occurrences of ore.

Newly discovered iron ores in Labrador are very similar to those of the Lake Superior district and pose the same problem of origin.

■ COPPER. The Canadian Shield produces about 10 per cent of the world's copper. Most of the copper deposits are associated with igneous activity of one kind or another. Some of the copper occurs in association with other metals such as nickel, zinc, silver, and gold.

On the southern fringe of the Precambrian shield in the Upper Peninsula of Michigan, *native* copper occurs in tilted lava flows and conglomerates of Keweenawan age. The copper occurs in its elemental form, hence the term native. Most of the high-grade deposits of native copper are now depleted, but some ore with as little as 2 per cent copper is still mined. Primitive tribes of Indians used this copper for ornamental and utilitarian purposes.

The origin of the Keweenawan copper deposits is attributed by some geologists to ascending hot solutions which deposited the copper in the porous lavas and in the spaces between pebbles of the conglomerates.

■ NICKEL. World nickel production is dominated by the famous deposits of Sudbury, Ontario. There, nickel occurs in chemical combination with iron and sulfur and in association with other metallic minerals which yield copper, platinum, gold, silver, and cobalt. The larger deposits occur near the base of a saucer-shaped basic intrusive about 35 miles long. The origin of the ore deposits is in debate, but most geologists concur that a genetic relationship exists between the basic intrusive and the ore minerals; that is, both may have been derived from the same magmatic source.

■ URANIUM. The atomic age ushered in an intensive search for uranium minerals, and the Canadian Shield received much attention in this respect, especially the Blind River district of Southern Ontario just north of Lake Huron. The chief ore mineral is pitchblende associated with other uranium minerals which occur in a Precambrian conglomerate of Huronian age. In spite of the fact that the ore is extremely low grade, the volume of mineralized rock is so enormous that the Blind River district could become one of the largest uranium-producing areas of the world.

Another deposit of Precambrian pitchblende occurs in the veins around Great Bear Lake in the Northwest Territories. There the uranium minerals occur with quartz as well as other compounds containing native silver, copper, and iron sulfides. The mineralization is probably related to granitic intrusives of uncertain Precambrian age.

■ GOLD. Canada produces most of its gold from the Shield, where the gold occurs in quartz veins. The Porcupine district of Ontario produces about one million ounces of gold annually. The gold-quartz veins are related to the Algoman granites which invaded the Keewatin volcanics and Timiskaming sediments.

The Kirkland Lake District is another gold-producing region of Canada in which

Precambrian rocks were invaded by igneous rocks. Hot solutions given off by the magma were responsible for the implacement of the gold-quartz veins. At Kirkland Lake gold is now being mined from some of the deepest mines in North America, some of which extend to depths of nearly 8000 feet.

SUMMARY

The Precambrian rocks are concentrated in the great shield areas of the world, but where younger sediments occur the Precambrian rocks ("basement complex") may be thousands of feet below the surface. Precambrian time began when the earth was cooled to the point where geologic processes could start operating, and it ended with the advance of the Cambrian Seas.

The absence of fossils in Precambrian rocks makes the correlation of rocks from one locality to the next very difficult. Radioactive dating of certain minerals in Precambrian rocks may be the only solution to the establishment of a valid Precambrian chronology. The oldest known rocks of Precambrian age are fully confirmed at 3.3 billion years. Life may have existed in Precambrian time although the evidence for prolific life is very indirect.

The use of terms like Keewatin, Timiskaming, Laurentian, and other well-established names for Precambrian rocks of the Canadian Shield probably should be restricted to the areas where they were originally applied. They are more meaningful in terms of lithology and structure than as time terms.

The mineral wealth of the Canadian Shield has been the greatest impetus to continuing studies of the geology and mineralogy of the area as a whole. Production of copper, iron, nickel, gold, and uranium as well as several other metallic ores has been the backbone of industrial development in the Great Lakes region of the United States, as well as in a large part of Canada. Future discoveries in the Shield area will undoubtedly add greatly to the mineral wealth of these two countries.

REFERENCES

Canadian Institute of Mining and Metallurgy, 1948, *Structural geology of Canadian ore deposits,* (a symposium), Montreal, Mercury Press, Montreal.

Geological Survey of Canada, 1947, *Geology and economic minerals of Canada,* Ottawa, Canada, Department of Mines and Resources.

Gill, J. E., 1952, *Mountain building in the Canadian Pre-Cambrian Shield,* Report of the Eighteenth Session of the International Geological Congress, Great Britain, 1948, part XIII, 97–104.

Gill, J. E., 1955, Pre-Cambrian history of the Canadian Shield with notes on correlation and nomenclature, *Proc. Geol. Assoc. Can.* part II, 117–124.

Glaessner, Martin F., 1961, Pre-Cambrian animals, *Scientific American,* p. 72–78, March.

Ross, Clyde P., and Richard Rezak, 1959, *The rocks and fossils of Glacier National Park: The Study of their origin and history,* U.S. Geological Survey, Professional Paper 294-K.

Sharp, R. P., 1940, Ep-Archean and Ep-Algonkian erosion surfaces, Grand Canyon, Arizona, *Bull. Geol. Soc. Amer.* **50,** 1235–1270.

Wilson, J. Tuzo, 1949, The origin of continents and Precambrian history, *Trans. Roy. Soc. Can.* **43,** 157–182.

Wilson, Morley E., 1956, Precambrian classification and correlation in the Canadian Shield, *Bull. Geol. Soc. Amer.,* **67,** 1743–1744.

XIV

The Paleozoic Era

The interest in a science such as geology
must consist in the ability
of making dead deposits represent living scenes.

Hugh Miller

The clarity of the geologic record from the beginning of the Paleozoic to the present is a great contrast to the vagueness of Precambrian chronology. The reason for this lies mainly in the presence of abundant fossils in the Cambrian and later sediments. Without fossils the details of geologic history never could have been pieced together; for it is by means of fossils found in strata of widely separated localities that the various segments of the geologic record can be connected into a logical sequence of events.

Recognition of this fact requires the addition of another dimension to the geologic story, the element of organic life. From the Cambrian on, the history of the earth carries the threads of two stories. One is the physical history of deposition, erosion, and orogeny; the other is the pageant of life through the ages revealed by the fossils.

Although the full appreciation of the fossil story is obtained only when the reader has at his command the fundamentals of the classification of plants and animals, he can, nevertheless, appreciate the significance of the fossil record with only a rudimentary concept of botany and zoology.

The basic concepts of classification of the animal and plant kingdoms will be supplied where necessary in the pages that follow, but because of obvious limitations of space, many details must be left unmentioned. It is hoped that the reader who is especially intrigued with the paleontological aspects of historical geology will seek further knowledge outside the pages of this book by reading from the selected reference list at the end of this and subsequent chapters.

GENERAL SETTING IN NORTH AMERICA DURING THE PALEOZOIC ERA

The North American continent at the beginning of Paleozoic time was vastly different in its physical geography than it is today. Probably the most striking difference was the absence of the Appalachian Mountains of the eastern United States, and the Rocky Mountains and

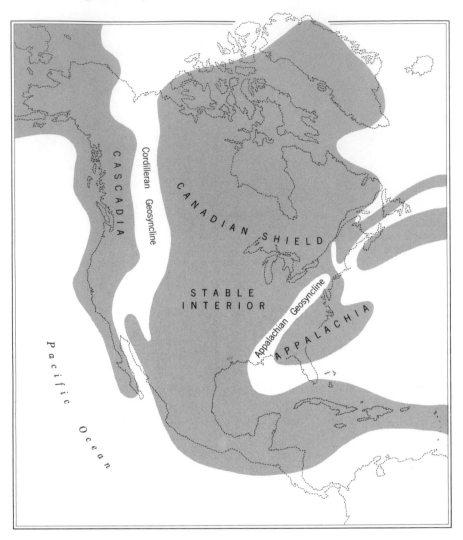

Figure 14-1. Paleogeographic map showing the distribution of land and sea during the middle part of the Cambrian Period. (After Charles Schuchert, 1955, *Atlas of Paleogeographic Maps of North America,* John Wiley and Sons, New York.)

coastal ranges of the western United States. In place of these conspicuous topographic features, there existed geosynclines in which marine sediments accumulated throughout most of Paleozoic time (Fig. 14-1).

The eastern geosyncline is known as the Appalachian geosyncline and the western trough is referred to as the Cordilleran geosyncline. Between these two slowly sinking areas lay a vast stable interior region which at times during the

Paleozoic was partially submerged beneath epicontinental seas.

The pioneer geologists of the United States visualized two lofty land masses, *Appalachia* and *Cascadia,* lying marginal to the two geosynclines. Appalachia lay east of the Appalachian geosyncline, while its counterpart on the western edge of the continent, Cascadia, bordered the western side of the Cordilleran geosyncline. Both were thought to have consisted of crystalline Precambrian rocks from which the Paleozoic geosynclinal sediments were derived.

This paleogeographic picture has been modified somewhat by more recent work in both the eastern and western United States. In contrast to borderlands of granites and metamorphic rocks contributing to their marginal subsiding geosynclines, it is now postulated that an arcuate archipelago of volcanic islands existed in place of the sporadically uplifted Appalachia and Cascadia. Evidence for this belief comes from the abundance of geosynclinal sediments that were derived from volcanic sources. But whatever the nature of the source rocks was, the evidence clearly shows that the bulk of sediments deposited in the Appalachian geosyncline came from the east, and the thousands of feet of sedimentary rocks laid down in the Cordilleran geosyncline came from a source to the west. So far, no evidence exists that would require a substantial volume of sediment to be shed from the central stable region. Presumably, it was never a highland region during Paleozoic time in the sense that it was subjected to vigorous stream erosion. In fact, the occurrence of Paleozoic sediments on parts of the stable interior shows that it, too, was from time to time invaded by epicontinental seas.

The complete details of the stratigraphic and tectonic history of the Paleozoic would occupy several volumes. In the paragraphs that follow, we can do little more than hit the "high spots" of Paleozoic history, trusting that even though only a few salient features of each period are mentioned, the thread of the story may not be lost.

SUBDIVISIONS OF THE PALEOZOIC ERA

The framework of Paleozoic history was established first in Europe, especially in the British Isles. American geologists have used many of the same names for the major subdivisions of Paleozoic time because the fossils in the North American strata permit correlation across the Atlantic Ocean. The major time units of the Paleozoic Era are called periods and are as follows (the youngest is at the top of the column):

> Permian
> Pennsylvanian ⎱
> Mississippian ⎰ Carboniferous
> Devonian
> Silurian
> Ordovician
> Cambrian

Cambrian time began about 600 million years ago and the Permian ended about 230 million years ago. The reader must not infer that each of the seven periods was of the same duration. Radioactive dating shows that the Cambrian was about twice as long as the Permian and that the Silurian was shorter than any of the others. The periods are based on *natural* geologic episodes, and although some geologists have tried to read a rhythmic concept into the pattern of events, there is no real evidence that such was the case. Above all, the reader should not lose sight of the fact that at best the geologic periods represent man's attempt to classify geologic time as he reads the record from the rocks. Let us now see what the record reveals.

THE CAMBRIAN PERIOD

The Cambrian seas began their slow but persistent encroachment on parts of the North American continent by invading two geosynclinal troughs. Before the period drew to a close, the seas had spread not only the full length of the Appalachian and Cordilleran geosynclines, but they also had advanced over what is now the upper Mississippi Valley region as well as across parts of Texas, Oklahoma, New Mexico, and Arizona.

The earlier Cambrian rocks are well displayed in California, and the rocks formed in mid-Cambrian time are beautifully exposed in the Canadian Rockies in the province of Alberta. The youngest Cambrian strata are widely distributed and occur in about half of the fifty states.

■ LIFE OF THE CAMBRIAN. As the curtain of time is drawn back, the Cambrian stage is revealed as a world in which many different forms of invertebrate animals lived. The fossiliferous Cambrian strata contain a faunal assemblage the likes of which no older sedimentary strata have yielded. The remains of vertebrates (animals with backbones) are significantly absent and no land plants are known from Cambrian rocks.

Outstanding among the creatures which lived in the Cambrian seas were the *trilobites* and *brachiopods* (Fig. 14-2*M* and *N; O* and *P*). The trilobite is extinct today, but during the Cambrian many species existed. The trilobite is an ancient cousin of the modern crabs and crayfish, collectively classed as *arthropods*. Zoologically, the arthropods are structurally among the most complex forms of invertebrates. They have segmented bodies and jointed legs and are able to move about with considerable agility. Trilobites were probably the scavengers of the Cambrian seas although this is a supposition. Most trilobites are small, a few inches or so in length, but some species attained lengths of more than one foot.

The brachiopods differ decidedly from the trilobites. They are shelled animals attached to the sea bottom by a flexible stalk or *pedicle*. These animals have declined in numbers and species since the Paleozoic but during the Cambrian they were very prolific. A brachiopod is equipped with an external shell consisting of two halves hinged together. When opened the animal extends two coiled appendages, or *brachia,* to entrap food particles.

Cambrian animals of lesser note include some sponges, worms, and jellyfish. The remarkable preservation of the imprints of more than 100 species of soft bodied animals from a formation in Alberta known as the Burgess shale, reveals that Cambrian life was much more varied than one might gather from the dominance of fossil trilobites and brachiopods in Cambrian rocks.

THE ORDOVICIAN PERIOD

The contact between the Cambrian and Ordovician strata in the eastern United States gives no indication of widespread land emergence at the end of Cambrian time. Actually, the evidence is quite to the contrary, for the Ordovician strata rest conformably on the Cambrian rocks, indicating that deposition may have been continuous. In northern Wales, however, the Ordovician rocks lie unconformably on the gently folded and eroded Cambrian sediments, indicating a break between the two systems (Fig. 14-3). Where Cambrian and Ordovician rocks occur together in the eastern United States they can be distinguished by the different fossils contained in each.

The spread of the Ordovician seas, first into the Appalachian and Cordilleran geosynclines, and later over much of the stable interior, culminated in what was the greatest flooding of the North American continent during all of Paleozoic time. At least half the continent was submerged beneath the warm Ordovician seas before the period came to an end, as proved by the widespread distribution of the younger Ordovician rocks. Even part of the Canadian Shield was covered by the slowly spreading Ordovician marine waters. The Cordilleran geosyncline was occupied from what is now the Arctic coast of Alaska to the Gulf of California

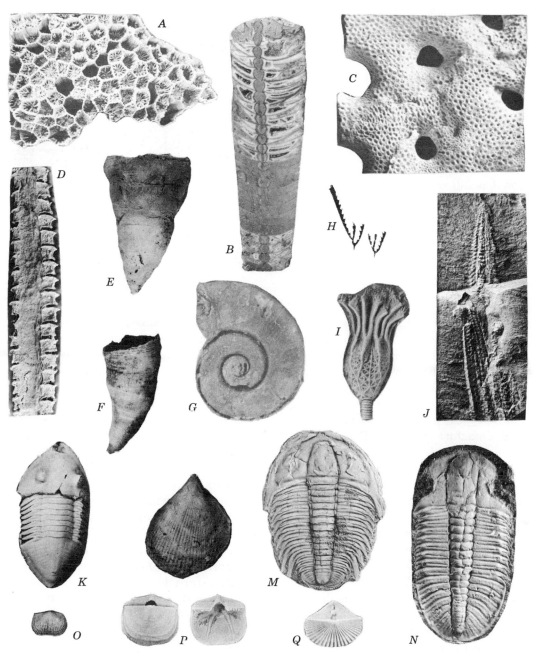

Figure 14-2. Cambrian and Ordovician fossils. (*A*) Ordovician coral, × ¾. (*B*) Ordovician cephalopod, × ¾. (*C*) Ordovician bryozoa, × ¾ (Minnesota). (*D*) Ordovician graptolite, × 5 (Minnesota). (*E* and *F*) Ordovician horn corals, × ¾ (Ohio). (*G*) Ordovician cephalopod, × ½ (Michigan). (*H*) Ordovician graptolite, × 1½ (Australia). (*I*) Ordovician crinoid, × ½. (*J*) Ordovician graptolite, × 1½ (Norway). (*K*) Ordovician trilobite, × ½ (Michigan). (*L*) Ordovician pelecypod, × ¾ (Ohio). (*M* and *N*) Cambrian trilobites, × ¾. (*O*) Cambrian brachiopod, × ¾ (Montana). (*P*) Cambrian brachiopod, complete specimen (left), interior of one shell (right), × 1 (Texas). (*Q*) Ordovician brachiopod, × 1 (Minnesota). (*A, B, C, D, J, M, P,* and *Q,* courtesy of W. Charles Bell, University of Texas. *E, F, G, H, K, L, N,* and *O,* from University of Michigan Museum of Paleontology. *I* from University of Minnesota Paleontological Collection.)

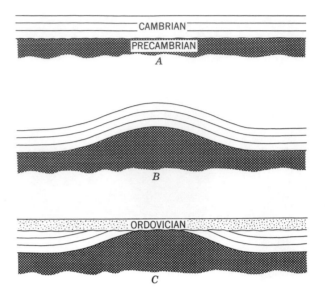

Figure 14-3. Diagrams showing the development of the unconformable relationship between the Cambrian and Ordovician strata in North Wales, England. (After A. K. Wells, and J. F. Kirkaldy, 1951, *Outline of Historical Geology,* Thomas Murby and Company, London.)

while the Appalachian geosyncline contained a continuous stretch of sea from Newfoundland to the Gulf of Mexico. So great was the transgression of land by sea that the marine waters of the eastern and western geosynclines merged through an east-west trending seaway known as the Ouachita Trough. This depressed area extended from Arkansas, across Oklahoma, Texas, New Mexico, and Arizona, and finally merged with the Cordilleran geosyncline in southern California.

Although the bulk of Ordovician sediments eventually became limestone, a vast muddy delta was built in the part of the Appalachian geosyncline that lay in what is now New York State and southern Ontario. The Queenston shales, as these deltaic deposits are now known, are red in color, a characteristic attributed to the lateritic sediments from which they were derived. The Queenston shale lies beneath a younger limestone bed in the gorge of the Niagara River. Niagara Falls (Fig. 14-7) itself has retreated through the years by the undermining action exerted against the Queenston shale by the erosive force of the falling water.

Conditions changed from deposition to erosion in the northern part of the Appalachian geosyncline, however, when the Ordovician and underlying Cambrian rocks were compressed into folds and thrust westward during a period of mountain building known as the *Taconic orogeny* during the latter part of the Ordovician period. The upended edges of Cambrian and Ordovician strata overlain by younger Paleozoic sediments of Silurian and Devonian age testify to the orogenic activity during the second half of Ordovician time (Fig. 14-4). Younger Paleozoic sediments deposited on top of the bevelled Cambrian and Ordovician strata in the northeastern United States record the next period of marine invasion during the Paleozoic.

■ LIFE OF THE ORDOVICIAN. The panorama of living things revealed by the fossil remains found in Ordovician rocks unfolds in great splender. More varied life forms existed in the Ordovician seas than during any previous period of geologic time. The organic world had reached a new level of diversification through the ever active process of organic evolution. Probably the most important fossil discovery in Ordovician rocks was made in sedimentary strata in Colorado. There, the fragments of the bony covering of a primitive fish are considered the earliest known vertebrate fossils. The fragmental character of the fossils provides little evidence as to what these early fishes looked like. As a matter of fact, the only reason that the paleontologist is at all justified in attributing the fossils to a fish is that they closely resemble the more complete fossil remains of fish from the rocks of the younger Silurian and Devonian geologic periods. From a study of the sandstone in which the Ordovician fish remains were found, geologists have concluded that it represents a *fresh water* deposit. Hence, the logical deduction is that primitive fish were inhabitants of a fresh water environment.

INVERTEBRATES. Although the appearance of the first vertebrate animal is a significant event in the history of life on earth, it does not overshadow the great diversity of invertebrate marine life of the Ordovician. Along with the trilobites (Fig. 14-2K) and brachiopods, (Fig. 14-2Q) which continued to dominate the life scene, several new kinds of creatures became important during Ordovician times. Among these are the *corals* belonging to a group of animals known as the *coelenterates,* which possess the elements of digestive, nervous, and muscular systems. Modern examples of the coelenterate group are jellyfish and corals.

The *graptolites,* once considered members of the coelenterate clan, are now thought to be chordates, hence more closely related to vertebrates (Fig. 14-2D, H, and J). Graptolites are now extinct but that they were widely dispersed in Ordovician seas as free-floating forms is indicated by there widespread occurrence in Ordovician shales and limestones of marine origin.

The coral is well suited to fossilization because it secreted a hard exterior cup (exoskeleton) of calcium carbonate (Fig. 14-2E, and F). All corals are attached to the bottom of the sea. Some of those inhabiting the Ordovician seas lived as solitary forms and were conical in shape, but others lived in colonies (Fig. 14-2A). The cup corals are now extinct, but colonial forms are prolific in warm shallow seas of the modern world.

Another large group of invertebrate animals represented by many fossilized forms is known as the *echinoderms.* This group includes starfish (asteroids), sea lilies (crinoids), sea-buds (blastoids), and sea urchins (echinoids) (Fig. 14-5). The echinoderms are generally characterized by a five-fold radial arrangement of appendages such as the five "points" of the starfish.

The sea lilies possess long branched arms attached to a bulbous body which in turn is fastened to the sea floor by a flexible stem or stalk. Upon death, the segments of the arms and stem (Fig. 14-5), came

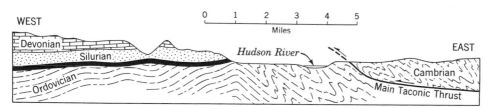

Figure 14-4. Geologic cross section in New York showing the results of the Taconic orogeny. The Ordovician beds were folded as the Cambrian sediments were thrust westward. The Silurian and Devonian beds lie unconformably on the Ordovician. (After P. B. King, 1951, *The tectonics of middle North America,* Princeton University Press, Princeton, N.J.)

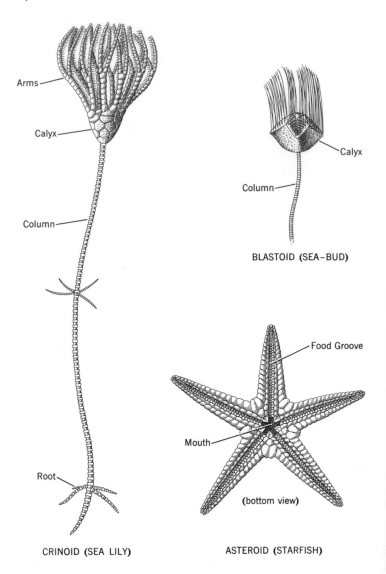

Arms

Calyx

Column

Root

CRINOID (SEA LILY)

Calyx

Column

BLASTOID (SEA–BUD)

Food Groove

Mouth

(bottom view)

ASTEROID (STARFISH)

Figure 14-5. Sketches of three different echinoderms.

apart and were strewn over the sea bottom by currents and scavengers. In rare cases, the nearly complete animal was buried so rapidly by sediment that the arms and stalk were not completely dismembered, as shown in Fig. 14-2*I*.

The crinoids became diversified in the Ordovician, although well-preserved specimens of nearly complete crinoids are extremely rare. Fossil starfish and blastoids are also very rare.

A final group of animals that became highly diversified in the Ordovician includes such well-known types as clams and snails. Collectively they are known as *mollusks*. Three categories of mollusks are (1) pelecypods (clams and oysters), (2) gastropods (snails), and (3) cephalopods (squid, octopus, and nautilus) (Fig. 14-6).

As a group the mollusks are more advanced physiologically than the coelenterates.   Besides well-developed digestive, muscular, nervous, and circulatory systems, the mollusks possess good sensory organs and means of locomotion.   Some mollusks have eyes and most are adapted for free movement, either on the sea floor or through the water.

Some cephalopods possess an external shell only, either in the shape of a straight cone or a coiled tube.   Although superficially resembling a coiled snail shell, the shell of a cephalopod contains chambers connected by a tube.   The soft part of the animal occupies only the outermost chamber, and the animal is able to propel itself by ejecting sea water through a tubular siphon.   Other cephalopods do not possess an outer shell but contain a small internal hard part which serves as a structural element in the animal.   All cephalopods possess tentacles around the mouth.

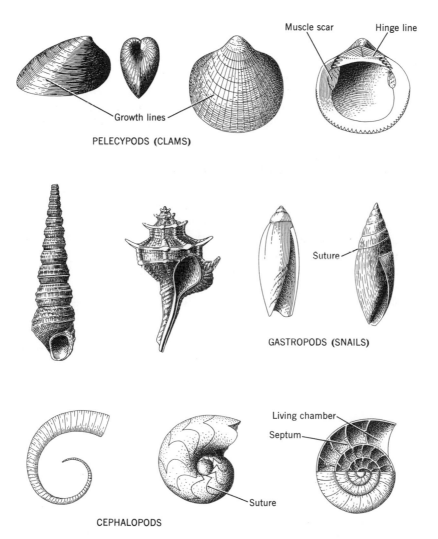

Figure 14-6.   Sketches of some fossil mollusks.   (After Karl A. von Zittel, 1899, *Textbook of Paleontology*, The Macmillan Co., New York.)

Ordovician mollusks include a large variety of snails, a few clams, and some remarkably large cephalopods, which were probably the largest animals of Ordovician time. Some small Ordovician cephalopods can be seen in (Fig. 14-2*B* and *G*).

THE SILURIAN PERIOD

The Taconic orogeny left the nothern part of the Appalachian geosyncline emergent long enough for the upended Cambrian and Ordovician rocks to be eroded and planed down. Eventually, however, the lands again were depressed and a new episode of encroachment by epicontinental seas began. The name Silurian, which is applied to this segment of geologic time, comes from a geographical district in the Welsh Borderland country. Fossil correlation between Great Britain and other parts of the world justifies the use of the term Silurian on other continents.

Besides the common sedimentary rocks such as sandstone, shale, and limestone, the Silurian seas contained deposits of chemically precipitated compounds among which were salt (sodium chloride),

gypsum (calcium sulfate), and anhydrite (calcium sulfate). Collectively these deposits are known as *evaporites* and they indicate environmental conditions that apparently were not widespread in earlier geologic periods.

Rocks of Silurian age are well exposed in the eastern United States, not only in the Appalachian Mountains but also in the Great Lakes region and southern Manitoba. One of the most famous exposures of Silurian rocks occurs in the gorge of the Niagara River in New York and Ontario. Niagara Falls owes its very existence to the hard layer of Silurian dolomite known as the Lockport dolomite (Fig. 14-7). This resistant formation can be traced from New York state, across southern Ontario, and into the Northern Peninsula of Michigan, from where it curves parallel to the west shore of Lake Michigan in Wisconsin. The edge of this nearly continuous layer is better known as the Niagaran escarpment.

The Cordilleran geosyncline received much less sediment during Silurian times than it did during the Cambrian or Ordovician periods, and was apparently dry during most of the early part of Silurian time.

The next younger sequence of rocks are

Figure 14-7. Diagrammatic cross section of Niagara Falls showing some of the stratigraphic units visible in the Niagara Gorge. (Based on the section described by F. B. Taylor in *Guidebook* 4, 16th International Geological Congress, 1933.)

Devonian in age and they are practically conformable with the Silurian strata. This means that no pronounced orogenic movements took place between Silurian and Devonian times, although in the Appalachian area field evidence shows that the Silurian beds were eroded before Devonian deposition began.

■ LIFE OF THE SILURIAN. Outstanding among the Silurian fossils are the *eurypterids,* scorpion-like creatures that inhabited the Silurian sea floor (Fig. 14-8*D*). Eurypterids are extinct today. As a matter of fact, they occupied only a very limited span of geologic time and did not even survive the Paleozoic era. These creatures belong to the advanced group of invertebrates known as the *arthropods,* and are akin to the trilobites. Although most of the Silurian eurypterids were only a few inches long, some attained a length of over 7 feet.

The Silurian seas also contained corals of great diversity including the colonial forms which grew in such profusion that they formed reefs similar to the great coral reefs fringing many islands of the South Pacific (Fig. 14-8*E*). Other invertebrates common to the Silurian were the brachiopods and crinoids; the crinoids were extremely prolific. Graptolites had already declined by Silurian time, but the trilobites were still common. Fossilized fish remains are present but rare in Silurian strata.

A noteworthy form of life new during the Silurian has been found in the scattered remains of very primitive land plants. Although the fossils are rare, they represent the first indication that plants existed on dry land. To what extent the Silurian landscape was covered with vegetation is not known, but probably no large trees or forests existed that early in geologic time. It is interesting to note, however, that terrestrial plants were established in a land environment long before animals invaded the continents.

THE DEVONIAN PERIOD

One of the best-known formations in all geologic literature is the Old Red Sandstone, a name immortalized through the writings of Hugh Miller who published his account of these strata over a hundred years ago. The "Old Red" is a very conspicuous sequence of layered rocks in Scotland and its general stratigraphic position in the geologic column of Great Britain was known before the details of the earlier Paleozoic periods were untangled.

Today it is well established that the Old Red Sandstone belongs to the Devonian system of the Paleozoic. It is in reality a terrestrial deposit that has a counterpart in thick beds of marine strata laid down at the same time elsewhere in the world.

In North America, the Devonian beds are exceptionally well developed in New York State where all the early studies on Devonian rocks of North America were made. The Appalachian geosyncline received sediments through almost all of Devonian time. The western geosyncline did not reach its maximum stage of submergence until after the period was nearly half over. By then the trough was filled with marine waters from the northern coast of Alaska to Southern California. At the same time the sea which flooded the Appalachian geosyncline spread westward to Michigan. Possibly the eastern and western seaways joined across the southern margin of the Canadian Shield, but this speculation needs verification.

Late in Devonian time, an uplift of the old Taconic Mountains rejuvenated the streams flowing westward into the northern part of the Appalachian geosyncline. These rivers deposited coarse clastics on a broad plain marginal to the Devonian sea and carried only the finer muds to the sea itself. The terrestrial beds produced during this last surge of Devonian

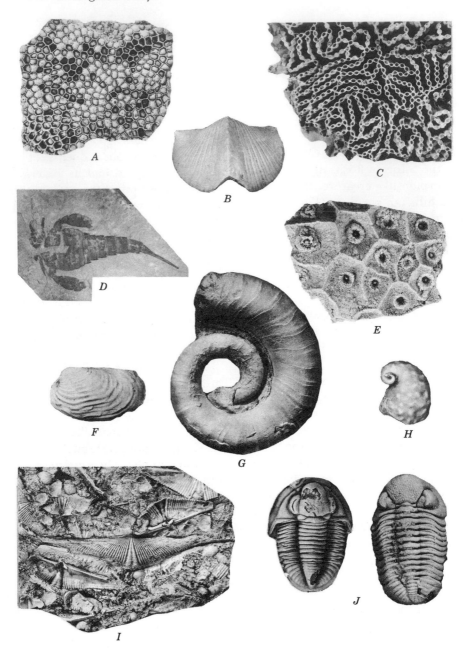

Figure 14-8.   Silurian and Devonian fossils.   About one-third natural size.   *A*. Silurian honeycomb coral (Michigan).   *B*. Devonian brachiopod.   *C*. Silurian chain coral (Michigan).   *D*. Silurian eurypterid (New York).   *E*. Silurian colonial coral (Michigan).   *F*. Devonian pelecypod (New York).   *G*. Devonian cephalopod.   *H*. Devonian gastropod (Ohio).   *I*. Devonian brachiopods (Michigan).   *J*. Devonian trilobites (New York).   (*A, B, C, E, F, G, H, I,* and *J* by George M. Ehlers and Erwin Stumm, University of Michigan Museum of Paleontology; *D* by Robert Sloan, University of Minnesota Paleontological Collection.)

history are known today as the *Catskill red beds*, and they bring to mind the similar events associated with the origin of the Old Red Sandstone in Great Britain. The Catskill red beds are conspicuously visible in Pennsylvania, especially where the highway engineers have excavated deep cuts for the Pennsylvania Turnpike.

Even before the Devonian seas received their last grain of sediment, the *Acadian* orogenic movements began. The New England area as well as eastern Canada was strongly affected by the Acadian orogeny near the end of the Devonian time. Devonian and pre-Devonian strata were strongly folded, metamorphosed, faulted, and intruded by magma during the Acadian surge of mountain building.

■ LIFE OF THE DEVONIAN. The Devonian period is commonly referred to as "the Age of Fishes." This designation is appropriate because, for the first time in

the history of the earth, a group of vertebrate animals occupied a prominent part of the organic world. To be sure, the invertebrates were also present because fossil crinoids, corals, and brachiopods are found in great numbers in Devonian rocks (Figs. 14-8 and 14-9). But the student's attention cannot help being focused on this new and quite diversified group of animals, the fishes.

Fishes are cold-blooded aquatic animals that breathe by means of gills. Many of the Devonian fishes were bizarre in comparison with modern types. Some possessed no moveable jaws but instead had a vacuum-cleaner type mouth which suggests that the animal lived near the bottom and gathered in his food by a sucking process. These same primitive vertebrates were flat horizontally rather than vertically, a fact that also points to a bottom-dwelling habitat.

Many of the Devonian jawless fishes

Figure 14-9. Restoration of a Devonian sea bottom showing various forms of invertebrate animals that inhabited the shallow water. (Diorama from University of Michigan Museum of Paleontology.)

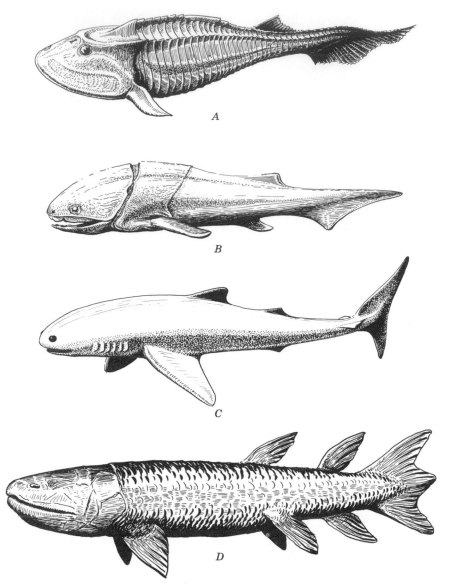

Figure 14-10. Devonian fishes. *A.* Ostracoderm. *B.* Placoderm. *C.* Shark. *D.* Crossopterygian. (After Edwin Colbert, 1955, *Evolution of the Vertebrates,* John Wiley and Sons, New York.)

had no scales. Their bodies were covered instead with bony plates. The entire early group of jawless and armoured fishes, known collectively as *ostracoderms* (Fig. 14-10*A*), was indeed diverse and varied. The *placoderms* (Fig. 14-10*B*) on the other hand, had primitive jaws with sharp bony plates that functioned as teeth. The placoderms flourished briefly,

and most of the Devonian forms did not survive that period, although some attained gigantic sizes.

Two other groups of fishes appeared on the Devonian scene, the *sharks* and *bony fishes*. The sharks of the Devonian had streamlined torpedo-shaped bodies and were sharklike in appearance (Fig. 14-10*C*). They had a skeleton of cartilaginous material, as they do now, and have always been confined to a salt water environment.

The bony fishes possessed heavy scales and a skeleton of true bony material. They had true teeth embedded in articulating jaws. The first fossil bony fishes were discovered in fresh water Devonian sediments, but marine forms are also known. One group of bony fishes, the *lungfishes,* was able to breathe air when the lakes or rivers in which they lived dried up during part of the year. This deduction is based on the similarities between the skeletons of the Devonian lungfish and the modern varieties of these strange creatures which today live in Africa, Australia, and South America. Although the ability to breathe air for extended periods suggests that the lungfish represents an intermediate evolutionary stage between fishes and terrestrial vertebrates, the paleontologists consider the living lungfishes and their Devonian relatives (Dipnoi) too highly specialized to be in the direct line of descent from fishes to land animals.

A related group of air-breathing fishes that is the most likely intermediary form between fishes and land-living vertebrates is the one known as *crossopterygians,* or lobe-finned fishes (Fig. 14-10D). The reasons for this statement lie in the many similarities between the crossopterygians and the earliest land dwellers. The Devonian specimens of this group have a skull that closely resembles the skull of early land vertebrates, and their teeth possess a structure similar in many details to those of their dry-land successors. But above all, the crossopterygians possessed paired lobate fins with a structure that is suggestive of the limbs of early amphibians, the next higher category of vertebrate animals.

Sometime during the Devonian period, the transition from water to land was accomplished, an evolutionary change that must be regarded as one of the greatest advances of the organic world. Paleontologists working in Greenland have turned up an undoubted skeleton of an amphibian from beds of Devonian age.

The statements made occasionally that this or that kind of animal appeared "suddenly" on one geologic period or another, leaves the unwary reader with the impression that these new forms literally sprang into existence overnight. What is really meant is that new fossil forms appear suddenly in the geologic record, and since it is a foregone conclusion that the geologic record is very fragmental, the sudden appearance of a new kind of fossil in some stratum does not necessarily mean that this marks the first occurrence of that particular creature in time. Its previous history might well be lost forever or it may yet be uncovered through new discoveries.

TERRESTRIAL PLANTS. As if the magnificent development of fishes during the Devonian was not sufficient to set this period off from all the rest, still another noteworthy fact is associated with it. Trees from the Old Red Sandstone and other Devonian strata represent the first large land plants. Possibly the Devonian landscape was "forested" although this is speculative. Certainly it is not beyond the realm of possibility that dense stands of primitive trees existed in localities favorable to their growth.

THE MISSISSIPPIAN PERIOD

One almost becomes bored at the repeated statement that the Paleozoic seas advanced and then retreated, only to readvance and withdraw again. Nevertheless this repetition of spreading and shrinking seas further emphasizes the fact that the earth is not a static body and that the features of the continents seen today are transient when viewed in the perspective of geologic time.

The Mississippian period was a time of widespread encroachment of marine waters on the continental blocks. In North America both the eastern and western geosynclines were submerged, and before the period drew to a close, the marine inundation had spread over much of the central and eastern states as well as into Alberta, British Columbia, and northern Alaska.

In the Rocky Mountain region, a vast sheet of limestone was deposited. Known as the *Madison limestone* in the northern Rockies, this widely occurring limestone formation indicates that a remarkable uniformity of environmental conditions must have prevailed during its accumulation.

The same statement holds true for the central interior of the United States where the Mississippian limestones are more than 2000 feet thick in places. Eastward, however, the limestones give way to sandstone because they were close to a source of clastic sediments from the newly formed Acadian Mountains marginal to the eastern shore of the Appalachian geosyncline. Some of the most prominent ridges of the Appalachian Mountains are the upturned edges of the Mississippian sandstone. Two of these, the *Pocono* and *Mauch Chunk* are especially prominent in Pennsylvania.

The Mississippian limestone of Kentucky and Missouri contains a remarkable network of underground caverns, and the Indiana limestones of Mississippian age have been quarried for many years and used as a building stone, especially where intricate carvings and scroll work are required. Other economic products associated with the Mississippian strata are discussed briefly at the end of this chapter.

■ LIFE OF THE MISSISSIPPIAN. The warm seas of the Mississippian time provided a home for a great variety of marine life of which the crinoids and blastoids (Fig. 14-11*E, F,* and *G*) were especially well represented. So prolific was the crinoid population that their fossil remains contributed materially to the bulk of some Mississippian limestones.

Another contributor to the making of Mississippian sedimentary rocks was the *bryozoa* or *moss animal* (Fig. 14-11*C* and *J*), minute colonial forms which first appeared in the Cambrian but never really amounted to much in the fossil record until mid-Paleozoic times. Because of their colonial habit, the fragmental remains of the bryozoans were incorporated in large accumulations of other debris on the shallow sea floor, a mass that was eventually consolidated into rock.

The simplest of all animals, the *protozoa,* were extremely abundant in the Mississippian seas. The subdivision of the protozoans known as *Foraminifera,* tiny one-celled animals with external shells called *tests,* were so prolific in Mississippian time that the accumulation of their remains on the sea floor became discrete masses of limestone. Although the "forams" date from the Cambrian, they did not become prominent rock formers until the Mississippian.

THE PENNSYLVANIAN PERIOD

Together, the Mississippian and Pennsylvanian periods comprise what is still known as the *Carboniferous* in Europe. In the United States, the Pennsylvanian period was characterized by the widespread development of swamps, an environment well suited for the growth of luxuriant vegetation. The remains of these great forests went into the making of the thick beds of coal found in central and eastern North America as well as in Europe and Russia. All the major coal fields of the world had their origin in the Pennsylvanian period.

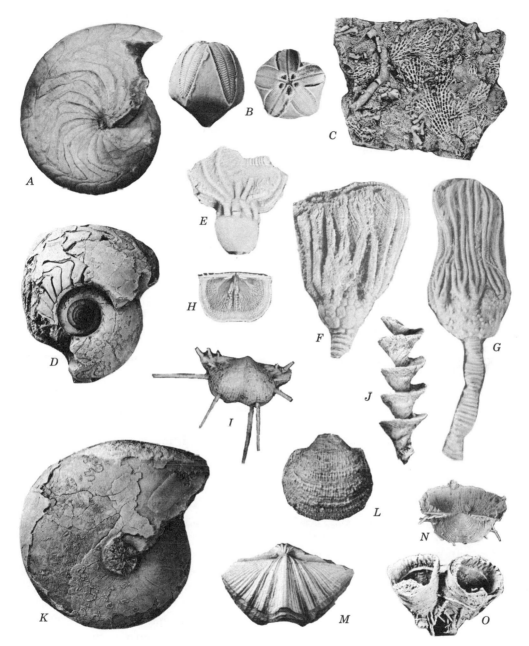

Figure 14-11. Mississippian, Pennsylvanian, and Permian fossils. (*A*) Mississippian cephalopod, × ¾. (*B*) Mississippian blastoid, × ¾ (Illinois). (*C*) Mississippian bryozoa, × ¾ (Kentucky). (*D*) Pennsylvanian ammonite, × ¾ (Texas). (*E, F,* and *G*) Mississippian crinoids, × ¾. (*H*) Pennsylvanian brachiopod (interior) × 1, (Texas). (*I*) Permian brachiopod, × ¾ (Texas). (*J*) Mississippian bryozoa, × ¾. (*K*) Permian ammonite, × ¾ (Texas). (*L*) Pennsylvanian brachiopod, × ¾ (Texas). (*M*) Pennsylvanian brachiopod, × ¾ (Illinois). (*N* and *O*) Permian brachiopods, × ¾ (Texas). (*A, C, G, I, J, L,* and *M,* from University of Michigan Museum of Paleontology. *B, D, E, F, K, N,* and *O,* courtesy of W. Charles Bell, University of Texas.)

In the south-central United States, however, marine sediments were accumulating in great thicknesses, especially in Arkansas, Oklahoma, and Texas. In Pennsylvanian time, uplift began in southern Oklahoma and the Texas Panhandle forming a southeasterly-trending range of mountains which extended into northern Arkansas. Uplift in this entire area was to occur intermittently through the rest of the Paleozoic, so the crustal unrest at this time was only a prelude to what was still to follow.

The succession of tectonic events that took place during the Pennsylvanian period in the south-central United States is exceedingly complex. The sediments alone attest to this fact since the many thousands of feet of detrital material that accumulated in Arkansas and Oklahoma required source areas of rapid and repeated uplift. Nor was the tectonic activity restricted to Arkansas, Oklahoma, and northern Texas, for a mountain range was developed in northern Colorado and southern Wyoming.

A southern landmass called Llanoria supplied the sediments for a depressed submerged area to the north in northern Texas, Oklahoma, and Arkansas. Sedimentary rocks of Pennsylvanian age in Texas alone have a total thickness of about 15,000 feet.

The swampy lands of central and eastern United States were alternately above and below sea level. Coal beds are interbedded with marine shales and brackish water limestones, a sequence of layers repeated so often in Pennsylvanian strata that some geologists believe in a rhythmic or cyclic oscillation of the sea to account for it. Whether or not this explanation is the correct one, the many limestone-shale-coal sequences seem to call for some sort of regulatory mechanism that enabled the same sequence of beds to be laid down time and time again.

■ LIFE OF THE PENNSYLVANIAN. The fossil remains of both vertebrate and invertebrate animals are found in Pennsylvanian rocks. The marine animals included members of many of the previously mentioned categories, especially brachiopods, mollusks, and a foraminiferan known as the *fusiline,* an elongated rice-shaped one-celled animal that existed in great profusion.

Land animals were also present. The amphibians increased in numbers and varieties, and the insects attained gigantic sizes. Cockroaches, spiders, scorpions, and the many-legged centipedes were common inhabitants of the low swamp lands bordering the Pennsylvanian seas. A winged insect resembling the modern "dragon fly" had a wing span of more than 2 feet. Small reptiles are known from the later part of this period, but fossils are extremely rare.

PLANTS. But not even the hundreds of species of insects nor the sprawling forms of amphibians can overshadow the ancient trees and ferns of the Pennsylvanian landscape. The Pennsylvanian period is appropriately known as the Coal Age, and the coal measures yield a fossil flora that is unlike anything before or after. The trees were primitive types, most of which have long been extinct, but a few of them are represented in the modern plant kingdom by small related forms.

The ferns were perhaps the most common inhabitants of the Pennsylvanian coal swamps, having reached their climax of speciation. In general appearance, the ferns of late Paleozoic time resemble the modern ferns that flourish in the shade of the present day forests. Both the primitive ferns (*Pteridophytes*) and the extinct "seed" ferns (*Pteridosperms*) are represented in fossil plants of Pennsylvanian age. The seed ferns reproduced by bearing seeds, an evolutionary advantage over Pteridophytes which reproduced by means of spores.

The modern horsetail or scouring rush is all that remains of a tribe of giant coal measure plants known as *Calamites.* Fossilized remains of these plants reveal that they consisted of a single jointed trunk with vertical ribs and no branches save a ring of short leaves at each joint (Fig. 14-12*B, D*).

The great "scale" trees of the Pennsylvanian swamps were probably the most unusual plants of that time. One group, the *Sigillaria*, was characterized by the hexagonal markings on the trunk (Fig.

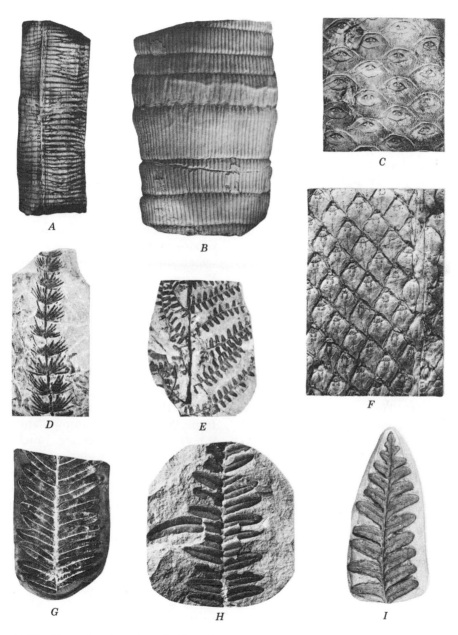

Figure 14-12.   Pennsylvanian plant fossils.   About one-third natural size.   *A. Cordaites* (Alabama). *B. Calamites.   C. Sigillaria* (Pennsylvania).   *D. Calamites* foliage (Ohio).   *E.* Fern (Oklahoma). *F. Lepidodendron* (Pennsylvania).   *G.* Seed fern (Illinois).   *H.* Seed fern (Michigan).   *I.* Seed fern (Kansas).   (Reproduced by permission of McGraw-Hill Book Co. from Chester A. Arnold, 1947, *An introduction to paleobotany,* New York.)

14-12*C*).   These represent cushions or
pads on the trunk from which the leaves
became detached as it increased in height.
In reality, then, the "scale" trees did not
possess scales at all, only scars of detached
leaves.

Another one of the scale trees was the
Lepidodendron (Fig. 14-12*F*).   Its leaf scars
were diamond shaped and arranged in
diagonal rows that spiraled around the
trunk.   *Lepidodendron* and *Sigillaria* attained heights of more than 100 feet, but
Sigillaria had no branches whereas *Lepidodendron* had a system of paired branches.

The only Pennsylvanian trees that resembled modern trees at all in general
form were the *Cordaites* (Fig. 14-12*A*).
The cordaites were the forerunners of
the modern conifers (cone-bearing trees).
They averaged 1 to 2 feet in diameter
and had a crown of branches with leaves
and seeds.   Cordaites were about 50 feet
high when mature.

There have been many attempts by
artists to recapture the arboreal scenes of
the Pennsylvanian forests through restorations based on fossil plant remains.
Unfortunately, however, because a plant
has no counterpart of the skeleton of an
animal, it does not lend itself to good
preservation.   Furthermore, land plants
are prone to dismemberment upon death,
a fact that accounts for the lack of complete plant fossils.   But in spite of the
rarity of complete specimens, the character of the coal measures forests has been
fairly well established by paleobotanists
using fragments of leaves, foliage, roots,
and other incomplete specimens.

THE PERMIAN PERIOD

The contrast between the Pennsylvanian period and Permian period in terms
of climate and physical conditions at the
earth's surface is very great.   The name
Permian comes from the province of

Perm in Russia, but rocks of Permian age
are now widely known in many parts of
the world.   In the United States, Permian strata are exceptionally well exposed in western Texas and New Mexico.
Other Permian beds can be found in
Kansas and other western states, but in
eastern North America, beds of Permian
age are rare because most of the sea had
withdrawn from the Appalachian geosyncline by the time the midpoint of the
period was reached.

Two events set the Permian off from the
other Paleozoic periods.   First, it is the
last of the recognized periods in the Paleozoic era.   This has some significance in
view of the fact that the Appalachian
geosyncline ceased to exist before the
Permian period ended.   In its place was
a lofty belt of folded mountains, the
product of the great Appalachian orogeny
which brought the curtain down on the
Paleozoic era.

The second event of marked importance was the pronounced change in climate.   The widespread warmth and hu-
midity which produced the lush foliage of
the coal measure swamps during the
previous geologic period gave way to
conditions of local aridity and glaciation
of the Permian.   Two lines of evidence
from Permian rocks throw light on the
question of paleoclimate (ancient climate).   One is the widespread occurrence
of evaporites, such as salt and gypsum,
which are usually interpreted as signs of
aridity.   Second is the undisputed existence of Permian tillites (lithified glacial
tills) in such widely scattered areas as
Brazil, South Africa, Madagascar, southern India, Australia, and Antarctica.
The age of these glacial deposits cannot
be fixed exactly, and many geologists refer
to their age as *Permo-Carboniferous,* a designation implying that no sharp boundary
existed between the two periods in places
where the tillites are found.

The name *Dwyka tillite* has been applied to the ancient lithified morainal deposits of South Africa where the Permian strata contain *striated* boulders, and the ancient crystalline rocks over which the ice moved still bear the striations and grooves left by the Permo-Carboniferous ice sheet. The Dwyka tillite is not restricted geographically, so it cannot be considered the deposit of a local valley glacier. As a matter of fact, the widespread occurrence of these late Paleozoic tillites in the southern hemisphere is one of the strongest arguments yet advanced in support of the idea of an ancient protocontinent of Gondwana. This continent was supposed to have existed all through the Paleozoic and Mesozoic eras, after which it separated into segments that drifted northward until the present distribution of continents was reached (Fig. 4-2). The supporters of continental drift argue that it is more plausible to regard the Dwyka and equivalent tillites as the product of a single ice cap centered in southern latitudes rather than as the result of several smaller ice sheets in each of the continents of Australia, Antarctica, Africa, South America, and Southern Asia (Fig. 14-13). The hypothesis is still

more compelling when it is pointed out that undisputed tillites occur in close proximity to the equator, a situation wholly incompatible with independent ice sheets in all of these areas. To be sure, valley glaciers today lie on flanks of mountains very near the equator, but the Permo-Carboniferous tillites are more widespread than could be explained by relatively narrow glaciers at high altitudes.

During the last stages of Permian time, sediments accumulated in the Guadalupe basin which encompassed what is now western Oklahoma, western Texas, and part of New Mexico. This basin, although connected to the open sea to the southeast, was apparently in a very arid region where evaporation was great enough to cause precipitation of the evaporites, salt and anhydride. Beneath the evaporites occur several thousand feet of shales and limestones, many of which are richly fossiliferous. Some of the best preserved Permian fossils come from the Glass Mountains of western Texas where Permian strata are exposed.

The Permian *Capitan* limestone of western Texas and southeastern New Mexico

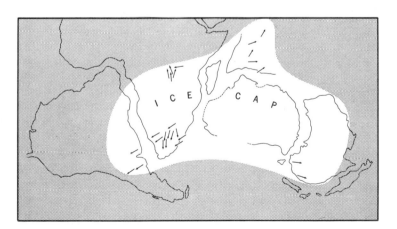

Figure 14-13. The hypothesis of continental drift has been invoked by some geologists to explain the occurrence of Permo-Carboniferous tillites in Africa, South America, Australia, and India. Arrows show the direction of ice movement inferred from striations. (After A. L. Du Toit, 1937, *Our wandering continents,* Edinburgh, Oliver and Boyd.)

is an ancient *reef,* several miles wide, hundreds of miles long, and thousands of feet thick. Modern reefs are accumulated masses of lime-secreting marine algae and corals which thrive in countless millions in warm shallow seas. Comparisons between the forms of modern reefs, such as the ones around Bikini Atoll and others in the Marshall Islands, and the Permian and other Paleozoic reef forms show, beyond a doubt, that they originated under similar ecological conditions.

■ APPALACHIAN OROGENY. The last marine sediments deposited in the Appalachian geosyncline were the thin shale beds of the *Dunkard* group of Ohio and West Virginia. Except for the few shales that bear fossil shark's teeth, the Dunkard deposits are mostly non-marine. They represent an accumulation of alluvium on a broad plain which was occasionally below sea level. Because the Dunkard beds are the youngest Paleozoic strata east of the Mississippi, and because they are folded along with the other Paleozoics, their age provides a maximum date for the Appalachian orogeny.

The Appalachian Mountain system is one of the best known in the world. It consists of a north-easterly trending belt of folded Paleozoic sediments flanked on the southeast by metamorphic rocks of the Piedmont and Blue Ridge and on the northeast by the gently warped layers of the Appalachian Plateau (Fig. 14-14). The structural features of the Appalachian Mountains range from simple folds to complex overthrusts and igneous intrusions.

The major forces responsible for the Appalachian folding were directed toward the northwest as indicated by the overturned folds and thrust faults of the southern Appalachians. In the New England states, the Appalachian orogeny was accompanied by intrusive activity which resulted in the emplacement of granite batholiths and other igneous rocks.

In a brief summary of the Appalachian orogeny, it is difficult to give a complete picture of this great event. Yet, even without the minute details, it is abundantly clear that the growth of the Appalachian Mountains marked a turning point in the geologic history of eastern North America. Whereas the western geosyncline was little affected by orogeny at the end of the Paleozoic, the depositional history of the great Appalachian geosyncline, in which the total thickness of sediments was nearly 10 miles, came to an end.

Some geologists speak of the Appalachian orogeny as a *revolution.* It was revolutionary in that a great change took place, but certainly we must not get the impression that this change was as abrupt as the term revolution implies. The Permian period lasted about 50 million years, and perhaps two-thirds of this time was consumed by the growth of the Appalachian Mountains.

■ LIFE OF THE PERMIAN. Turning now from the realm of physical geology to the organic world, the Permian fossil record provides us with abundant evidence of what the flora and fauna of that period were like.

The vertebrates were well established on the land and were represented by both the amphibians and reptiles. Amphibians are animals that are born into an aquatic world and do not invade the terrestrial environment until maturity is reached. The young bear little resemblance to the adults; for example, tadpoles are strictly aquatic in contrast to their frog parents, equally at home on land or in the water. Although the true amphibians date back to the Devonian, they were not abundant until the Pennsylvanian and Permian periods. The best known Permian form is *Eryops,* a sprawl-

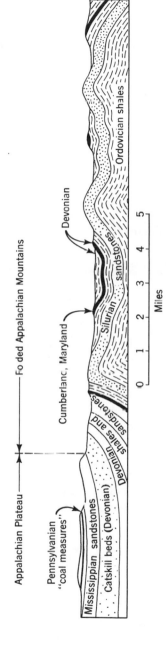

NORTHWEST

SOUTHEAST

Appalachian Plateau ↑ ├──────── Fo ded Appalachian Mountains ────────┤

Cumberland, Maryland

Pennsylvanian "coal measures"

Mississippian sandstones

Catskill beds (Devonian)

Devonian shales and sandstones

Devonian

Silurian sandstones

Ordovician shales

Miles
0 1 2 3 4 5

Figure 14-14. Geologic cross section in Maryland showing folded Paleozoic beds of the folded Appalachian Mountains. (After Charles Butts, Guidebook 3, 16th International Congress, 1933.)

Figure 14-15.   *Eryops,* a Permian amphibian.   (Restoration by Thomas Coates, after Edwin Colbert, 1955, *Evolution of the vertebrates,* John Wiley and Sons, New York.)

ing amphibian of modest size, perhaps not more than 6 or 8 feet in length (Fig. 14-15).

Reptiles also occupied an important niche in the Permian world. These animals are cold-blooded like the amphibians, but beyond that there is only a superficial resemblance. When hatched from their shells, young reptiles look like their adult parents and are able to begin life on land without the necessity of a transitional period in an aquatic habitat. Reptiles are known from the Pennsylvanian, but by Permian times they are fairly well represented by fossil remains.

One odd-looking Permian reptile, *Edaphosaurus* (Fig. 14-16), possessed a row of long spines down his back. To this day, paleontologists are uncertain as to the function of this anatomical structure. One idea is that the spines were connected by a web of skin which may have functioned as a temperature-regulating mechanism for the animal.

The Permian invertebrates provide us with the last glimpse of many marine creatures that became extinct by the end of the Paleozoic. The trilobites, horn corals, many of the crinoids, and all of the blastoids did not survive the Permian period. On the other hand, some of the brachiopods lost many of their older characteristic features, especially the pedicle. The Permian brachiopods possessed spiney appendages which served as a means of attachment, either to the sea bottom or to other brachiopods (Fig. 14-11 *I, N* and *O*). These distinct forms grew in such profusion in the Permian seas of western Texas that the rocks in which they occur as fossils consist almost wholly of brachiopod shells cemented together by limestone.

Cephalopods were well represented in the Permian seas by a group known as the *ammonites* (Fig. 14-11*K*). These coiled animals differ from snails in that the ammonite shell is separated into chambers and the fleshy part of the animal occupies the outer and largest chamber only. Early Paleozoic cephalopods, or *nautiloids,* had simple walls (septa) between chambers. The ammonite septa, on the other hand, were highly irregular in shape, and where the edges of the septa were attached to the shell wall, an irregular line or *suture* was formed. Permian ammonites with highly intricate sutures (Fig. 14-6) provide a means of correlating formations from widely separated areas.

PERMIAN PLANT LIFE. Many of the Pennsylvanian forms such as the scale trees and calamites persisted until early Permian time, but eventually these forms succumbed to the aridity and cold which prevailed over vast areas of the Permian world.

Probably the best-known and certainly one of the most controversial groups of plants associated with the geologic record is the *Glossopteris* flora. These plants were seed ferns with a very distinctive foliage, and their fossil remains are associated with the Permian beds of the Southern Hemisphere, notably South America, Australia, Antarctica, and Africa, as well as with India in the Northern Hemisphere. The Australian tillites of Permian age yield spores that are the same as those that occur elsewhere with Glossopteris flora living at the time of the Permian glaciation in the Southern Hemisphere. This fact is used as an argument in favor of the existence of the continent of Gondwana. How else, say the driftists, can the widely dispersed Glossopteris flora be explained than by a physical connection between the continents of the Southern Hemisphere? To this reasoning, their opponents argue that the widespread occurrence of the Glossopteris flora does indeed require a land connection, but such a connection need be only in the form of "land bridges," chains of islands that could provide a migratory path for both plants and animals. Protagonists on both sides of the controversy agree that physical connections of the continents is necessary to account for the widespread distribution of the Glossopteris flora, but basic disagreement on the kind of connection will provide fuel for arguments for years to come.

Many paleontologists argue against the hypothesis of continental drift on the basis that climatic analysis of fossil assemblages does not require any closer proximity of continents than exist today. Some fossil groups, they say, which according to the drift concept occurred in close proximity to each other, show marked differences that require isolation rather than an interchange of forms.

MINERAL RESOURCES IN PALEOZOIC ROCKS

Raw materials are the lifeblood of production in this highly industrialized age. Not only does the industrial world

Figure 14-16. The skeleton of *Edaphosaurus,* a finbacked Permian reptile from Texas. The function of the long spines is still a mystery. (University of Michigan, Museum of Paleontology.)

need mineral resources for fabrication into useful products, but it also needs tremendous quantities of fuel to supply power for machinery. Both fuels and raw materials are of geologic origin, and a large quantity of each comes from rocks of all geologic ages in the United States and Canada.

■ FUELS. A fuel is a combustible material that produces heat. Among the common fuels are wood, coal, gas, and oil. The last three are produced by geologic processes and warrant some discussion here, although full treatment cannot possibly be given in a text of an introductory nature.

COAL. Coal is a rock consisting of plant material that has been chemically and physically altered in varying degrees. The physical and chemical changes account for the different kinds or *ranks* of coal. Three major ranks are recognized; lignite (lowest), bituminous (intermediate), and anthracite (highest). Increase in rank reflects the natural processes whereby the carbon content of the coal is increased while the volatiles (chiefly hydrogen and oxygen) are expelled.

From a study of the fossil plants associated with coal beds, geologists have concluded that coal represents an aggregation of vast quantities of partially decayed plants that accumulated in the places where they grew. Many different environments suitable for such an accumulation of plant material are known, such as coastal swamps, inland lakes and swamps, high moors, and deltas, but it is generally agreed that the *major* coal fields all had their origin in coastal fresh water swamps. This conclusion is based on the fact that extensive coal beds are interbedded with marine strata, indicating an alternation of marine and fresh water conditions common to coastal areas.

The change from lignite to anthracite, is, in reality, a metamorphic process in which both physical and chemical changes occur. Generally speaking, the older the coal, geologically, the more likely it is to be of higher rank. Pressure on the coal beds, induced by folding, accentuates the metamorphic process and increases rank. Anthracite beds in eastern North America are all associated with strongly folded sediments of Pennsylvanian age, whereas the bituminous coals, also of Pennsylvanian age, occur in gently folded strata. Sedimentary strata containing coal beds are called "coal measures," and consist of alternating beds of sandstone, shale, and in some cases, limestone.

The Appalachian Coal Field in the eastern United States contains most of the coal produced in North America and includes the states of Pennsylvania, Ohio, West Virginia, and Virginia, as well as Kentucky, Tennessee, and Alabama (Fig. 14-17). Both anthracite and bituminous coals are mined in the Appalachian Field.

The Eastern Interior Field of the United States yields Pennsylvanian age coals that are mined by open pit methods in Illinois, Indiana, and Kentucky. Pennsylvanian coal was also mined in Michigan until 1952 when production ceased.

The coal reserves of the United States are sufficient to last for hundreds of years at the present rate of consumption, and although the use of fuel oil and natural gas have made great inroads on the coal industry, coal is still one of the greatest sources of energy in the industrial world.

OIL AND GAS. The origin and occurrence of oil and gas is discussed in Chapter sixteen. In the United States a great deal of crude oil is produced from Paleozoic rocks, but the bulk of the world's oil production comes from rocks of younger geologic age, especially the Tertiary.

■ SALT AND BRINE. For many years salt (sodium chloride) was almost as important to the welfare of mankind as drinking water, but in the twentieth century this domestic use has been greatly over-shadowed by the use of salt and associated minerals in the chemical industry.

Abundant salt occurs in sedimentary beds which range in age from the Silurian to Recent. Although the Permian was perhaps the period of greatest salt deposition, most of the production in the United States comes from the Silurian

deposits of Michigan, New York, and Ohio.

Silurian salt is mined by underground methods in the Detroit area (Fig. 14-18) or pumped to the surface from brine wells. Brine is regarded as fossil sea water. Besides sodium chloride, brine wells yield other salts of the halogen family such as bromine and iodine com-

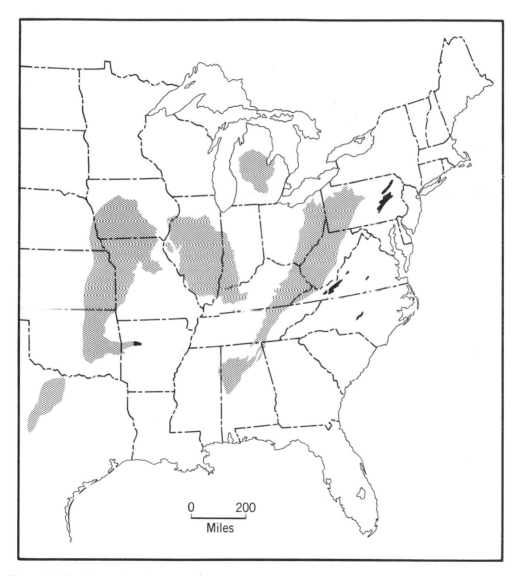

Figure 14-17. Pennsylvanian coal fields of the eastern United States. Bituminous coal is produced from the shaded areas, and the regions of anthracite coal are shown in black. (After the United States Geological Survey, 1942, *Coal fields of the United States,* Washington, D.C.)

Figure 14-18. A salt mine beneath the city of Detroit, Michigan. The salt occurs with beds of dolomite and anhydrite. These and other deposits like them are of Silurian age. (International Salt Company.)

pounds as well as magnesium and calcium chlorides. These are valuable raw materials in the manufacture of various chemicals used in industry, medicine, and agriculture. Most of the aspirin produced in the United States probably originated in a brine well penetrating a Paleozoic formation.

■ LIMESTONE AND DOLOMITE. The greatest use for these two sedimentary rocks is in the making of Portland Cement and as a flux in blast furnaces. Many limestones are used as building stones (dimension stones), especially if they are massive and uniform in composition. A good example of this type of deposit is the famous "Indiana Limestone" of Mississippian age extensively quarried near Bedford, Indiana (Fig. 14-19). This deposit is made up of tiny fragments of one-celled animals, cemented together to form an easily quarried rock. It is used for intricately carved stones around windows and doorways and as a structural stone in such famous edifices as the Washington Monument.

■ GYPSUM. This evaporite is quarried extensively from Paleozoic rocks of Silurian age in Michigan, New York, Ohio, and Indiana, as well as from younger beds in Texas. Its chief use is in the manufacture of plasters, plaster board, and quick-setting building cements for interior purposes.

■ MARBLE. The famous Vermont marble is an Ordovician limestone metamorphosed during the Taconic and Appalachian orogenies. Vermont and other marbles are used chiefly as interior decorative stones (Plate IV, N, and P).

■ IRON ORE. The major iron-producing rocks are Precambrian, but an important occurrence of Paleozoic sedimentary iron-bearing strata is the Clinton Iron Ore of Silurian age. The deposits occur as sedimentary beds containing 35–60 per cent iron and crop out in the eastern United States from New York to Alabama. At Birmingham, Alabama, a large steel industry has been developed around the Clinton ores, not only because of the ore itself, but also because of the availability of coal and limestone (also of Paleozoic age) from nearby localities. Both coal and limestone are needed in the process of steel making.

■ LEAD AND ZINC. The Tri-State District is comprised of parts of Missouri, Kansas, and Oklahoma and is one of the largest zinc districts of the world. Some lead is mined since it is commonly associated with zinc. Flat-lying cherty limestones of Mississippian age contain many solution cavities and other openings in which the lead-zinc ores accumulated.

Geologic opinion is divided as to the origin of these important strategic metals. Some hold to a cold-water origin whereby ground water dissolved the metals from older rocks and redeposited them at a later date. The balance of opinion, however, seems to favor an origin that involves the precipitation of the lead and zinc compounds from hot mineralized waters that originated from an igneous source at depth.

In either case, it is probably not entirely correct to say that the deposits are of Mississippian age because the Mississippian rocks act only as the host in which the ore was trapped. As a matter of fact, it is quite possible that the mineralization was accomplished long after the Mississippian beds were deposited, possibly during the Mesozoic Era.

SUMMARY

The Paleozoic Era began when the first fossiliferous strata of the Cambrian seas were deposited on top of the eroded Pre-

Figure 14-19.   Quarry in the Indiana Limestone of Mississippian age near Bloomington, Indiana. (Indiana Geological Survey.)

cambrian rocks. Throughout most of Paleozoic time two geosynclines were receiving sediments eroded from flanking land masses. The Appalachian geosyncline was supplied with sediment from Appalachia to the east and the Cordilleran or Rocky Mountain geosyncline received sediments from Cascadia to the west. The central part of the United States was a low-lying plain partially inundated by marine waters from time to time during the Paleozoic.

Paleozoic rocks range in composition from the normal marine clastics to limestones and evaporites. Continental sediments include conglomerates, floodplain deposits, and tillites. The latter suggest continental glaciation in the Southern Hemisphere during late Paleozoic time and give strong support to the theory of continental drift.

Orogenic movements are unequally dispersed during the Paleozoic in the United States. The Taconic orogeny followed the Ordovician, the Acadian followed the Devonian, and the great Appalachian revolution began in the later Paleozoic and culminated in the Permian. Igneous activity accompanied all of these orogenic episodes.

Early Paleozoic life was dominated by the invertebrates, especially trilobites, brachiopods, corals, graptolites, cephalopods, and eurypterids. Fishes appeared on the scene in the Ordovician but did not become prominent until the Devonian. Amphibians made the transition from sea to land during the Devonian and reptiles were well established by the end of the Paleozoic.

Economic products from Paleozoic rocks include the vast coal deposits of Pennsylvanian age; Silurian salt and iron ore; Mississippian lead and zinc; and petroleum, limestone, and dolomite formed in many of the Paleozoic periods.

REFERENCES

Butts, C. G. S. Stose, and A. I. Jona, 1933, *Southern Appalachian region,* International Geological Congress, Guidebook 3.

Carey, S. Waren, *et al.,* 1958, *Continental drift, a symposium,* Geology Department, University of Tasmania, Hobart.

Colbert, Edwin, 1955, *Evolution of the vertebrates,* John Wiley and Sons, New York.

Dunbar, Carl O., 1960, *Historical Geology,* 2nd ed., John Wiley and Sons, New York.

Durham, J. Wyatt, 1962, *The "drifting" continents,* Natural History, April 1962, p. 30–39.

DuToit, A. L., 1937, *Our wandering continents,* Oliver and Boyd Ltd., Edinburgh.

Eardley, A. J., 1962, *Structural geology of North America,* 2nd ed., Harper and Row, New York.

King, P. B., 1959, *The evolution of North America,* Princeton University Press, Princeton, N.J.

Ladd, Harry S., 1961, Reef building, *Science,* **134,** 703–715.

Ruedmann, R., and R. Balk, 1939, Geology of North America, *Geologie der Erde,* 1, Gebruder, Berlin.

Russell, R. J., 1955, *Guides to southeastern geology,* Geological Society of America, Guidebook for the 1955 Annual Meetings.

Shrock, R. R., and W. H. Twenhofel, 1955, *Principles of invertebrate paleontology,* McGraw-Hill Book Co., New York.

U.S. Geological Survey, 1932, *Geologic map of the United States,* Compiled by George W. Stose.

XV

The Mesozoic Era

. . . the organised Fossils
. . . may be understood by all,
even the most illiterate . . . .

William Smith

By the end of the paleozoic, animals were well established on dry land. The Mesozoic, which means "middle life," was a time during which the backboned animals became firmly entrenched in every conceivable environment. The Mesozoic era saw the rise and fall of one of the greatest animal dynasties of all time, the reptiles. Not only did these creatures become the dominant animal on dry land, but many returned to an aquatic habitat and still others conquered the skies.

In this chapter, the geologic history of the three Mesozoic periods, the Triassic, Jurassic, and Cretaceous, will be presented.

THE TRIASSIC PERIOD

The type locality of rocks of Triassic age is in Germany where three formations constitute the geologic record of this period. The Alps, too, contain exposures of Triassic rocks and in North America a well-documented record of Triassic time is revealed in sedimentary rocks of the same age.

■ EASTERN NORTH AMERICA. The Appalachian orogeny left the eastern half of the North American continent in an elevated position so that stream erosion was the dominant geologic process. Sediments were carried eastward beyond the present Atlantic coast where they presumably lie buried beneath younger strata. A deep boring at Cape Hatteras on the North Carolina coast penetrated sedimentary rocks of Triassic age, as is indicated by micro-fossils found in the samples.

The only record of Triassic sedimentation on the present continental area in the eastern United States dates from late Triassic time when a number of structural fault troughs came into existence. These areas were local in extent and apparently not interconnected (Fig. 15-1). Sediments that collected in the sinking troughs include conglomerates, sandstones, and shale, with interbedded lava

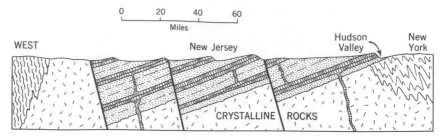

Figure 15-1.   Geologic cross section of the Newark beds of Triassic age. The clastic sediments are interbedded with and intruded by basaltic igneous rocks in the form of lava flows and sills. (After C. R. Longwell, 1933, *Guidebook* 1, 16th International Geological Congress.)

flows.   The imprints of dinosaur tracks and fossil land plants show conclusively that these Triassic beds were nonmarine. The remains of fresh-water fishes as well as the red color of some of the sediments point to a continental environment. Good exposures of red Triassic strata and associated lava beds near Newark, New Jersey, account for the name *Newark series* given to these strata (Fig. 15-2).

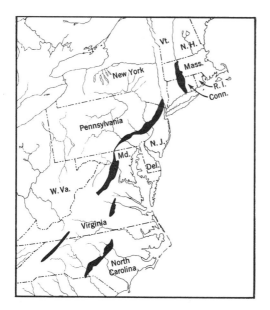

Figure 15-2.   Map showing the distribution of the Newark series of Triassic age in the eastern United States. (From the Geologic Map of the United States, 1932, United States Geological Survey, Washington, D.C.)

The Newark beds were tilted during the *Palisades disturbance,* which began with the faulting that formed the troughs in which the Triassic sediments accumulated.   The faulting continued while the Newark beds were being laid down and was accompanied by the intrusion of dikes and sills, and extrusion of lava. The Watchung "Mountains" in New Jersey are hogback ridges underlain by three lava flows of the Newark series, and the famous and picturesque Palisades of the Hudson River is an eroded edge of a thick sill near the base of the Newark series.

■ WESTERN UNITED STATES.   West of the Mississippi River the Triassic deposits range from a thick marine sequence in California, Idaho, and Wyoming, to the colorful continental beds in Arizona, Colorado, New Mexico, and Utah. These continental deposits are especially interesting because they yield an array of plant and animal fossils that tell of the organic world during the Triassic period.

THE JURASSIC PERIOD

The type locality of Jurassic rocks is in the Jura Mountains of Europe. Jurassic rocks crop out in the United States west of the Great Plains.   In the eastern United States Jurassic strata are encountered only at depth in oil wells of the

Gulf Coast region. The Appalachian Mountains and adjoining uplands to the west were being eroded at the time so that no sediments of Jurassic age crop out anywhere in eastern North America.

■ WESTERN UNITED STATES. California contained a sedimentary trough which more or less paralleled the long axis of the state. It received about 30,000 feet of sediments consisting of black shale and volcanics, the latter of which were derived from high volcanic peaks of an archipelago chain along the western flank of the trough.

From the Arctic the *Sundance Sea,* a narrow seaway, invaded the area now covered by Montana, Wyoming, the western Dakotas, and the Colarado Plateau (Fig. 15-3). The Sundance Sea was separated from the California trough by a land mass that prevented intermingling of the two arms of the sea, but it contributed sediments to both. The Cali-

fornia trough persisted throughout all of Jurassic time but the Sundance Sea did not reach its full extent until the latter part of the period.

Perhaps the two best-known formations of Jurassic age in the western interior are the Navajo sandstone and the Morrison formation. The Navajo sandstone is one of the oldest Jurassic formations and is a massive accumulation of dune sand, as is indicated by its typical eolian crossbedding. It is a prominent cliff-former in the Colorado Plateau region and is responsible for some of the most spectacular scenery in the southwestern part of the United States.

The Morrison formation is the youngest of the Jurassic strata in the western interior. It contains beds of conglomerate, sandstone, and shale, and has yielded a great variety of fossils, especially dinosaurs, for which it is particularly famous.

Marine strata of this period are

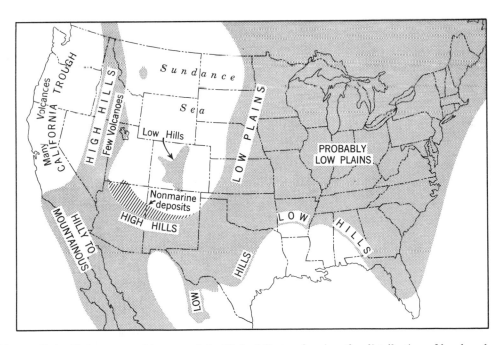

Figure 15-3. Paleogeographic map of the United States showing the distribution of land and sea during the late Jurassic period. (From Ralph Imlay, 1956, *Paleotectonic maps, Jurassic system, Misc. Geol. Investigations,* Map 1–175, United States Geological Survey.)

younger than the Navajo but older than the Morrison and are usually classified as Middle Jurassic in age. The Middle Jurassic sediments in eastern Utah, Wyoming, and western South Dakota are characterized by gypsiferous red beds. These indicate a shallow lagoon bordered by low land masses across which sluggish streams flowed. The gypsum suggests an arid climate for that region.

■ JURASSIC OROGENY AND IGNEOUS ACTIVITY. The Jurassic and Triassic strata of the California trough were subjected to severe compressional forces at the end of the Jurassic period. At the same time, great masses of granitic magma invaded the sediments in California and British Columbia. This great display of crustal deformation and igneous intrusion is known as the *Nevadian* orogeny.

In California Paleozoic rocks were thrust eastward over Jurassic strata and the great Sierra Nevada batholith, 16,000 square miles in surface area, was intruded. The largest of all igneous masses, the Coast Range batholith was intruded in western British Columbia during the Nevadian orogeny (Fig. 15-4). This granitic mass crops out over an area of 73,000 square miles.

THE CRETACEOUS PERIOD

The word Cretaceous means chalk, and was first applied to the rocks which form the well-known "White Cliffs of Dover." Rocks of Cretaceous age occur extensively on every continent. During late Cretaceous time deposits accumulated in an epeiric sea that probably was equalled only by the Ordovician marine invasions of the Paleozoic.

■ WESTERN UNITED STATES. In the western interior of the United States, Cretaceous sediments were laid down in the Cordilleran geosyncline that at times stretched from Mexico to the Arctic

Ocean. This geosyncline was not always occupied by marine waters during the Cretaceous period because the nature and distribution of the sediments and their organic content indicate a fluctuating sea. Early in the period the marine waters were more restricted in areal extent than later (compare Figs. 15-5 and 15-6) when the Cretaceous seas reached their greatest extent.

The sediments are generally coarser near the western margin of the trough, which suggests that the chief source of sediments in the Cordilleran geosyncline was from the west. On the other hand, the finer-grained shales and clays near the eastern margin of the geosyncline indicate that the borderland on that side was low-lying with sluggish streams carrying fine mud and silt.

■ EASTERN UNITED STATES. The Atlantic coastal plain and Gulf Coastal regions received sediments from the eastern United States land mass, which, by Cretaceous time, was pretty well worn down. Appalachia was no longer in existence and was not a source of sediment for Cretaceous seas. The Cretaceous beds overlap unconformably on the deformed late Paleozoic beds and dip gently seaward (Fig. 15-7). The Cretaceous shoreline of the eastern United States was undoubtedly farther inland than the landward edge of the present Cretaceous sediments. One interpretation suggests that most of the folded Appalachian belt was eroded to a peneplain by the end of Jurassic time, thereby permitting the transgressing Cretaceous seas to advance inland a considerable distance. Although it is plausible, this hypothesis lacks supporting field evidence because no Cretaceous deposits are found anywhere in the Appalachian Mountains.

■ LARAMIDE OROGENY AND THE END OF THE MESOZOIC. The sedimentary history of the Mesozoic Era in the western United States was brought to a close when the

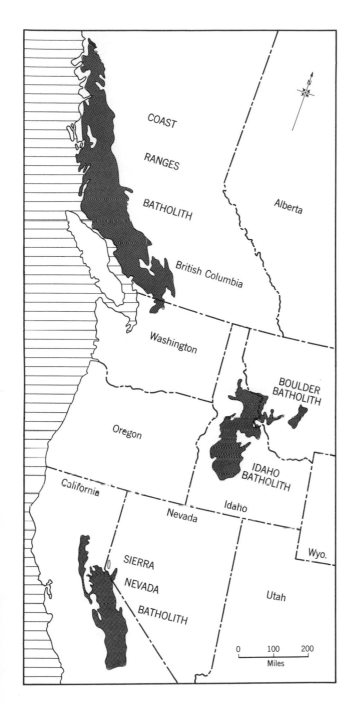

Figure 15-4. Map of the batholiths intruded during the Mesozoic Era. (Based on the Geologic Map of North America, published by the Geological Society of America, 1946.)

Cretaceous seas retreated in response to horizontal forces which uplifted and deformed the Cretaceous and older strata. This great orogeny has been named the *Laramide Revolution.* Once considered a single violent event, the Laramide orogeny is now known to have begun in late Cretaceous time and to have continued through the early part of the Tertiary period.

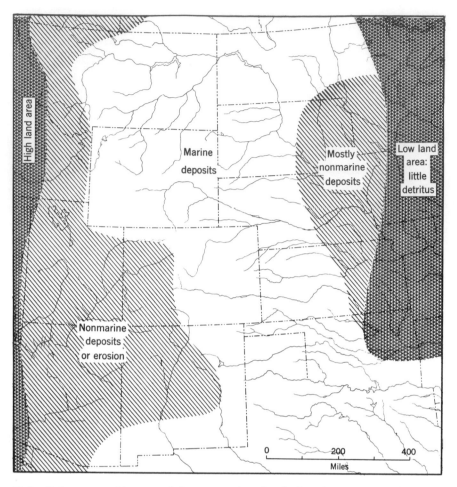

Figure 15-5. Paleogeographic map of the western interior during the early part of the Cretaceous period. (After Geological Society of America, 1957, Memoir 67, *Treatise on marine ecology and paleoecology,* vol. 2, *Paleoecology,* Chapter 18, Paleoecology of the Cretaceous seas of the western interior of the United States, by John Reeside.)

The Laramide orogenic movements were essentially compressional and resulted in the formation of folded mountains, extensive thrust faults, and igneous intrusions.

The Rocky Mountains of Wyoming and Colorado were strongly folded into broad anticlines in which the Precambrian cores were exposed by later erosion. The upturned edges of the late Paleozoic and Cretaceous sediments in Colorado attest to the magnitude of this folding (Fig. 15-8).

The great Laramide thrust faults of the Rocky Mountain region have attracted attention from structural geologists ever since they were first discovered in the last century. Although several dozen are known from this area, perhaps none has received so much attention as the Lewis overthrust in Alberta and Montana (Fig. 15-9). This fault has a northwest-southeast trend and is gently inclined toward the southwest. During the Laramide orogeny, compressional forces deformed the Proterozoic and Paleozoic sediments into broad folds, but eventually the folding gave way to faulting so that a large segment of the Precambrian rocks was shoved eastward over Cretaceous strata. Little Chief Mountain in Glacier National Park is an erosional remnant of the overthrust mass.

■ LARAMIDE IGNEOUS ACTIVITY. The largest igneous mass associated with the Laramide orogeny occurs in Idaho with an exposed area of 18,000 square miles. It is known as the *Idaho batholith* (Fig. 15-4). The *Boulder batholith* in western

Montana is of special interest because of its relationship to the great copper deposits of Butte, Montana.

LIFE OF THE MESOZOIC

The panorama of life during the Mesozoic era presents an interesting contrast, not only to the fauna and flora of the present day, but also to the life of the earlier Paleozoic. Both the plants and animals of the Mesozoic are found fos-

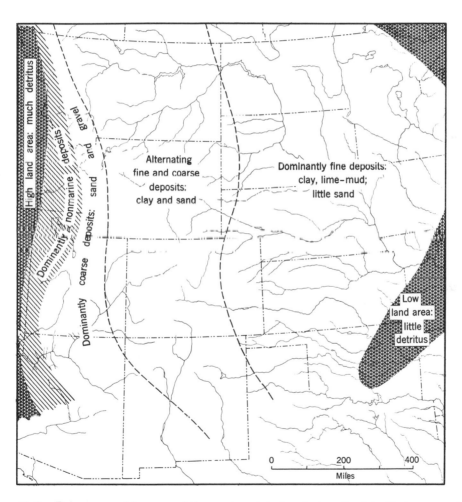

Figure 15-6. Paleogeographic map of the western interior during the late Cretaceous. (After Geological Society of America, 1957, Memoir 67, *Treatise on marine ecology and paleoecology,* vol. 2, *Paleoecology,* Chapter 18, Paleoecology of the Cretaceous seas of the western interior of the United States, by John Reeside.)

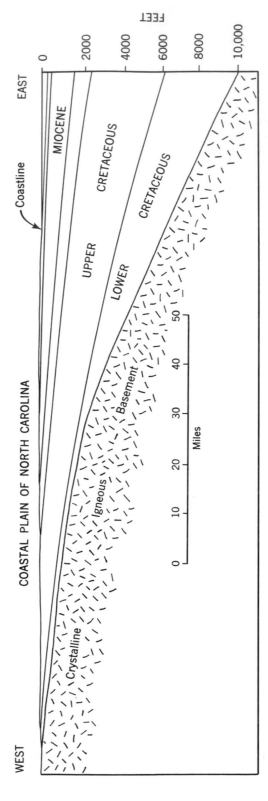

Figure 15-7. Geologic cross section of the Atlantic Coastal Plain through Cape Hatteras, North Carolina. (After W. B. Spangler, 1950, Subsurface geology of Atlantic coastal plain of North Carolina, *Bull. Amer. Assoc. Petroleum Geol.*, **34**, 100.)

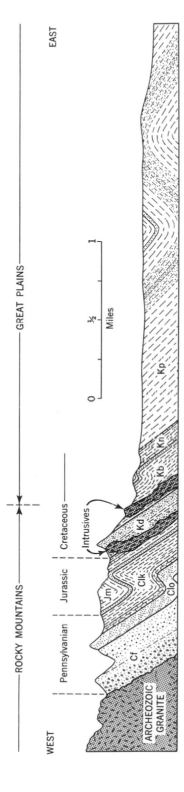

Figure 15-8. Geologic cross section of the Front Range of the Rocky Mountains about 30 miles north of Denver, Colorado. The folding of the Paleozoic and Mesozoic strata was accomplished by the Laramide orogeny. Symbols refer to formational names: Cf, Fountain formation; Clo, Lyons sandstone; Clk, Lykins formation; Jm, Morrison formation; Kd, Dakota formation; Kb, Benton shale; Kn, Niobrara formation; Kp, Pierre shale. (After R. D. Sample and J. W. Low, 1933, *Guidebook* 19, 16th International Geological Congress.)

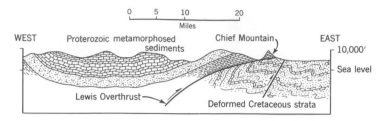

Figure 15-9. Geologic cross section showing the Lewis overthrust in northwestern Montana. Precambrian beds lie on Cretaceous strata. (After C. H. Clapp, 1932, *Geology of a portion of the Rocky Mountains of northwestern Montana,* Montana State Bureau of Mines and Geology, Memoir 4.)

silized in many different parts of the world, thus affording a means for the correlation of strata from widely separated localities.

■ INVERTEBRATES. The Mesozoic seas contained a variety of invertebrate creatures including mollusks, reef corals, crinoids, and others. But two members of the mollusk tribe stand out above all other inhabitants of the Mesozoic seas. These were the cephalopods known as the *belemnites* and the *ammonites* (Fig. 15-10).

The belemnites were squidlike cephalopods with an internal shell that gave rigidity to the elongate body. Like other cephalopods, the belemnites darted backward through the water, and like their relatives the squids, were capable of discharging a black inky fluid for protection. These unusual creatures make their first appearance in rocks of Triassic age, but by the Jurassic they reached their peak of development and abundance. The belemnites lived on into the Cretaceous period but declined severely in numbers until they finally became extinct at the end of the Mesozoic.

The ammonites are perhaps the most distinctive of all Mesozoic marine invertebrates. These coiled cephalopods were holdovers from the Permian, but the Mesozoic forms far surpassed their Permian ancestors in ornamentation and variation. The ammonite septa were beautifully intricate and amazingly complex, and it is this very feature which permits the paleontologists to classify this important group of animals. After a rise to a high degree of diversification in the Jurassic, the ammonites lost ground during the Cretaceous. Today there are no survivors of this ancient race of ornamental shell fish, because they died out *en masse* at the end of the Mesozoic.

Many other invertebrates lived in the Mesozoic seas but the listing of their names alone would fill a volume. One observation is significant, however, and that pertains to the Cretaceous mollusks. The snails and clams of that final Mesozoic period were remarkably modern in appearance, a fact that clearly demonstrates that many of the present-day creatures have a lineage reaching back nearly 100 million years.

■ REPTILES. It is no overstatement to say that the reptiles dominated the life scene during the Mesozoic era. Even though the Permian reptiles were already firmly established in the animal kingdom, their climax of development did not come until the Mesozoic.

Reptiles are cold-blooded, egg-laying vertebrates that include crocodiles, snakes, and lizards, as well as the extinct dinosaurs, marine reptiles, and flying reptiles. The word "dinosaur" is over a hundred years old and literally means "terrible lizard." Yet like so many other names in the scientific world, the term dinosaur is not entirely accurate, for many close relatives of these creatures were very small and could hardly be considered "terrible." Furthermore, the dinosaurs were so diversified in their habitats that they scarcely could be classified technically as lizards. Nevertheless, the term dinosaur is useful and is well entrenched in the language.

The first dinosaurs appeared in late Triassic time and were small compared to their successors in the Jurassic and Cretaceous periods. The first Triassic dinosaurs were about 8 feet long and moved about on their hind legs (i.e., they were *bipedal*). A long slender tail served as a counter balance, thereby permitting full use of the front limbs for grasping and tearing food. This anatomical pattern was repeated in many of the flesh eating (carnivorous) dinosaurs of the Jurassic and Cretaceous periods such as *Allosaurus* (Jurassic) and *Tyrannosaurus* (Cretaceous) (Fig. 15-11).

Anatomically, the dinosaurs can be grouped into two categories, the *saurischians* and *ornithischians*. The basic difference between the two kinds is in the structure of the pelvic bones, but other

Figure 15-10.   Restoration of a late Cretaceous sea bottom showing three kinds of cephalopods common during that time. The large ammonoid in the foreground has a diameter of 19 inches; the intricate sutures are not visible on its shell because they are covered by the outer layer of shell material. *Baculites* is straight except for a small coil at the very apex of the cone. *Belemnites* has no external shell but possess an internal hard part to give the body rigidity. (Diorama, University of Michigan Museum of Paleontology.)

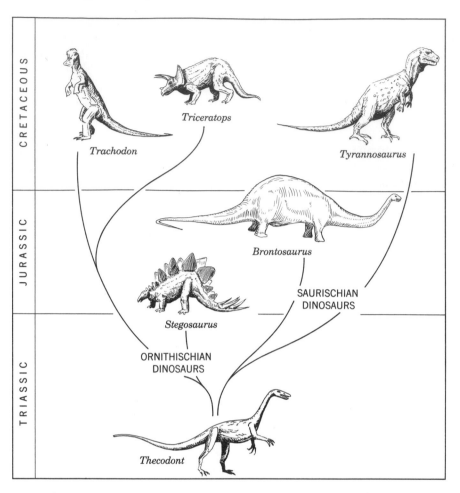

CRETACEOUS

Trachodon

Triceratops

Tyrannosaurus

JURASSIC

Brontosaurus

Stegosaurus

SAURISCHIAN
DINOSAURS

ORNITHISCHIAN
DINOSAURS

TRIASSIC

Thecodont

Figure 15-11.   Some Mesozoic dinosaurs, which are thought to have had a common ancestor.   Not to scale.   (After Edwin Colbert, 1955, *Evolution of the vertebrates,* John Wiley and Sons, New York.)

characteristic differences also exist.   For example, the ornithischians were all herbivorous, as is indicated by their teeth, which were highly adapted for cutting or chewing vegetation.   *Stegosaurus* (Jurassic) and *Triceratops, Iguanodon* (Fig. 15-12), and *Trachodon* (Cretaceous) are examples of the ornithischians.

The saurischians, such as *Coelophysis* (Triassic), *Allosaurus* (Jurassic), and *Tyrannosaurus* (Cretaceous) were generally carnivorous.   An exception is *Brontosaurus* (Jurassic and Cretaceous) who was not only herbivorous but had departed from the general anatomical pattern of other

saurischians to the extent that he was quadrupedal.

The dinosaurs reached gigantic sizes during the course of their evolutionary development.   The bones of their massive hulks have awed museum-goers the world over, and even the most objective vertebrate paleontologist experiences a thrill when he discovers the fossilized remains of these giants, some of which were 80 feet in length and weighed 50 tons or more.

■ MARINE REPTILES.   Although it may seem strange that land animals should return to a marine environment, the whole paleontologic record indicates that given time, and in the absence of competition, animals tend to occupy all available ecological niches. The marine reptiles of the Mesozoic evolved from a stock of land reptiles rather than from Paleozoic amphibians, and filled the niche available for highly active marine predators.

Two of the best-known Mesozoic marine reptiles are *Icthyosaurus* (Fig. 15-13*A*), a fishlike reptile which first appears in the Triassic, and *Plesiosaurus,* a long-necked reptile that vaguely resembled a turtle (Fig. 15-13*B*). *Icthyosaurus* was comparable to a modern porpoise in size and was like a big fish in its mode of life, but its skeleton is distinctly reptilian and not that of a fish. Both *Icthyosaurus* and *Plesiosaurus* were air-breathing carnivores, and it is quite probable that their chief source of food was fish.

■ FLYING REPTILES. The drama of Mesozoic life was full of new forms which appear in the fossil record quite suddenly. No less spectacular than the debut of the marine reptiles was the advent of flying reptiles or *pterosaurs* in the Jurassic. To envision the process by which the reptiles acquired their flying ability requires considerable intuitive thought. For one thing, the process of flying requires a high rate of metabolism because the body is in need of a constant source of energy during flight in order to overcome the force of gravity. By analogy with modern reptiles it is assumed that the Mesozoic reptiles did not have a high and constant metabolic rate and hence were not warm blooded. This has led to the argument that perhaps the flying reptiles were really not good fliers at all, but rather, were capable only of

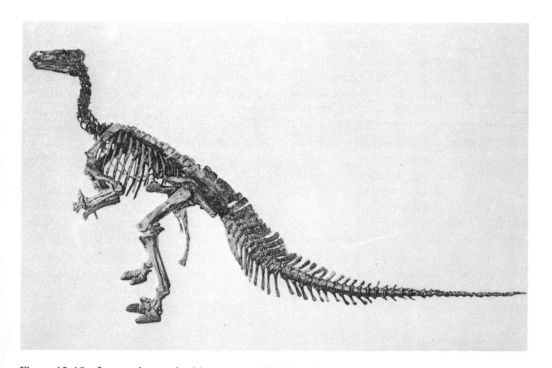

Figure 15-12. Iguanodon, an herbiverous ornithischian dinosaur from lower Cretaceous rocks near Mons, Belgium. They are also known from the lower Cretaceous beds of southern England. These animals may have been ancestral to the Trachodonts of the upper Cretaceous. (Courtesy of the Royal Museum of Natural History, Brussels, Belgium.)

Figure 15-13.   Icthyosaurs (*A*) and plesiosaurs (*B*) were marine reptiles that inhabited the Mesozoic seas.   (After Charles Knight, *Before the dawn of history*, 1935, McGraw-Hill Book Co., New York.)

gliding or swooping down from lofty cliffs near the sea.   It has also been argued that the flying reptiles may have achieved independently a high metabolic rate.

But whatever their abilities were as heavier-than-air flying animals, the reptiles such as *Rhamphorhynchus* (Jurassic) or *Pteranodon* (Cretaceous) were distinctly reptilian.   Their skulls were characteristically like those of other reptiles and their jaws had sharp rows of teeth indicative of a carnivorous diet.

The pterosaur wing consisted of a membrane stretched between an elongated fourth finger and the hind limbs, although the fossil remains are not adequate to establish the exact function of the back legs.   The elongated skull of *Rhamphorhynchus* plus the lack of a tail makes one wonder just how such an animal ever got aloft.   By comparison with modern birds, the flying reptiles must bear the same relationship to birds that the Wright brothers' first crude aircraft bears to the jet aircraft of the atomic age!

■ BIRDS.   As if the dinosaurs and flying reptiles did not present enough of a spectacle of variation in the Mesozoic world,

we have yet to consider the startling appearance of the Jurassic birds.   From an anatomical point of view, the bird skeleton is closely akin to the reptilian skeleton.   Paleontologists admit that, were it not for the imprints of feathers in the Solenhofen limestone of Germany from which two excellent skeletons were obtained, the fossils would have been classified with the reptiles.   But the presence of feathers, a singularly distinctive feature of all birds past and present, definitely proves that these Jurassic creatures were true birds (Fig. 15-14).

Archaeopteryx, the earliest known bird was about the size of a raven.   Unlike modern birds, *Archaeopteryx* had teeth and a long bony tail with feathers attached on either side.   The forelimbs or wings were unlike those of present-day birds in that the outer wing bones were separate instead of coalesced, and retained three of the fingers as clawlike appendages.

By cretaceous time, aquatic birds such as *Hesperornis* and *Ichthyornis* were present.   *Hesperornis* was a diving form whose adaptation to an aquatic life resulted in the loss of the ability to fly, as is indicated by dwarfed wings. *Ichthyornis* had powerful wings and possibly inhabited the coastal areas in search of food. The fossil record of birds is woefully inadequate, more so than any other large group of vertebrates. But our knowledge of avian ancestors and their evolutionary history indicates that they did not evolve from flying reptiles, although both birds and flying reptiles may have had a common ancestor.

■ MAMMALS   The appearance of birds and flying reptiles in the Jurassic period are important milestones in the evolutionary history of backboned animals. But still another "first" must be added to the Jurassic period, the mammals. Four different kinds of mammals are known from Jurassic sediments but only two of these groups survived into the Cretaceous.

The distinguishing characteristics of mammals are numerous. Some are anatomical and others are physiological. Among the former are the enlarged brain case as compared to reptiles, and the differentiation of the teeth. Physiologically, the mammals differ from reptiles in that they are warm blooded with a constant body temperature and give birth to their young alive. Young mammals are nourished by milk from the mother and receive parental care, a decided contrast to reptiles who lose interest in their offspring before they are hatched from the eggs.

Even though the Cretaceous was dominated by the dinosaurs, two categories of mammals, the *placentals* and *marsupials* made their first appearance during that period. Placentals are mammals that nourish the fetus within the body until it is fully developed, whereas the marsupials carry the prematurely born young in a pouch during a period of further growth and development. Most modern mammals are placentals whereas the marsupials, such as the kangaroos and opossums, are poorly represented except in the isolated areas of Australia, New Zealand, and South America.

■ MESOZOIC PLANT LIFE.   The flora of the Mesozoic until the middle of the Cretaceous period was predominantly composed of *cycadophytes* or *"cycads"* which look very much like the modern palms (Fig. 15-15). In spite of this superficial resemblance, however, the Triassic and Jurassic cycads bear no genetic relationship to the palm trees. Ferns were also fairly well abundant in the Triassic period, and the conifers of the first two Mesozoic periods were comparable in size

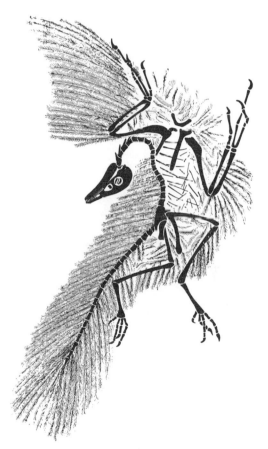

Figure 15-14. Drawing of the skeleton of the first bird, *Archaeopteryx*, as it was found in the Solenhofen limestone of Germany, Jurassic in age. (With permission of John Wiley and Sons, from *Evolution of the vertebrates*, by Edwin H. Colbert, 1955.)

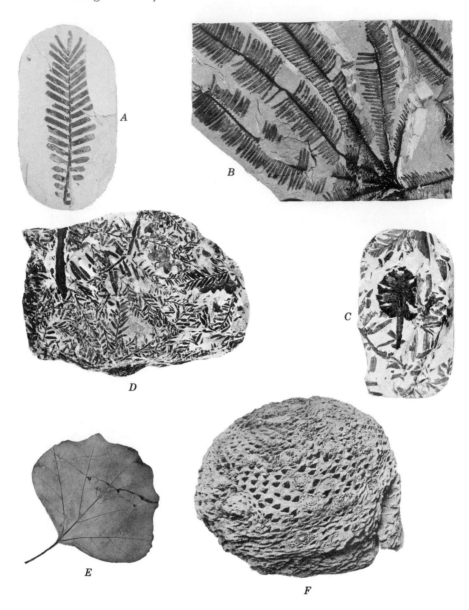

Figure 15-15. Some Mesozoic plant fossils. All are about one-fourth natural size except *C*, which is about one-half size. *A*. Jurassic cycad (Yorkshire). *B*. Triassic fern (Arizona). *C*. Cone of a Cretaceous conifer (Alaska). *D*. Foliage of Cretaceous conifers (Alaska). *E*. Leaf of a Cretaceous sycamore tree (Kansas). *F*. Trunk of a Cretaceous cycad-like tree (South Dakota). (*A*, *B*, and *F* reproduced by permission of McGraw-Hill Book Co. from Chester A. Arnold, 1947, *An introduction to paleobotany,* New York, *C*, *D*, and *E* by Arnold and Lowther, University of Michigan Museum of Paleontology.)

to the largest pine trees of today. A spectacular occurrence of fossil Triassic conifers can be seen in the Petrified Forest National Monument of Arizona where coniferous tree trunks up to 7 feet in diameter and 125 feet in length were buried in volcanic ash after they drifted into a shallow lake. Petrifaction of the logs resulted in the brilliant colors displayed in the exhumed giants of a Triassic forest.

The second half of the Cretaceous period is in marked contrast to the previous part of the Mesozoic in terms of the floral communities, because with the beginning of Upper Cretaceous, the plant world became distinctly modern in appearance. Not that the Upper Cretaceous forests weren't different from present-day wooded regions, because some of the older forms were still present, but the great increase in *angiosperms* or the "flowering plants" gave the Upper Cretaceous plant world a new appearance. Angiosperms bear seeds contained in a closed case and include such diverse forms as the flowers, grasses, legumes, and hardwood trees.

Among the Cretaceous angiosperms were such forms as willows, sassafras, oak, and poplars. Paleobotanists do not know exactly where or when the angiosperms originated because when they first appear in the geologic record they are completely developed. A few angiosperms are known from the Jurassic, but no plant fossil has ever been discovered that can be regarded as transitional between the angiosperms and earlier types.

ANIMAL EXTINCTION AT THE END OF THE MESOZOIC

One of the most frustrating problems of the paleontologist is the unsolved question of widespread extinction of animals in the geologic past. Why, after millions of years of successful life in various ecological niches did entire segments of the animal world vanish forever from the face of the earth? This has happened several times in the geologic past, but perhaps the most dramatic example was the disappearance of the dinosaurs at the end of Cretaceous time. On the one hand we

argue that the dinosaurs were able to adapt themselves to practically every conceivable environment such as swamps, the uplands, the sea, and the air, yet, on the other hand we must find some logical reason why they were unable to survive the environmental changes that came with the Laramide orogeny. Not only did the dinosaurs fail to survive the transition from the Mesozoic to the Cenozoic, but the marine reptiles and flying reptiles also vanished completely at that time. The lizards, snakes, turtles, and crocodiles were the only Mesozoic reptiles that survived into the Cenozoic, except for one unfamiliar reptile (*sphenodon*) living on only a few islands off the coast of New Zealand.

Perhaps the establishment of more varied temperatures and the stronger delineation of climatic zones due to the geographical changes which attened the Laramide orogeny had something to do with the mass extinction. But this suggested answer to an intriguing problem is very unsatisfactory, and it must be quite honestly admitted that the real answer lies beyond our grasp. A scholarly account of the problem of animal extinction during past geologic ages was written by Professor Newell of Columbia University. It is highly recommended (see reference list at the end of this chapter).

MINERAL RESOURCES ASSOCIATED WITH MESOZOIC ROCKS

Cretaceous coal from the western United States and petroleum from eastern Texas are among the chief mineral resources produced from Mesozoic rocks. Gold associated with Sierra Nevada batholith of Jurassic age, and other metalliferous deposits such as copper, zinc, and silver found in the Butte, Montana region are also important economic resources of Mesozoic age.

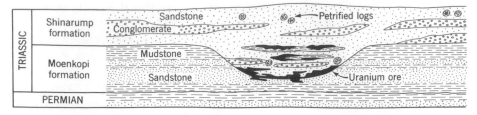

Figure 15-16.   Cross-sectional diagram of the uranium-bearing Shinarump conglomerate in the Colorado Plateau.   (After T. W. Mitchell and C. G. Evensen, 1955, Uranium ore guides, Monument Valley district, *Economic Geology,* **50,** 2, 172.)

But all these resources have been somewhat overshadowed by the post World War II discoveries of uranium minerals in sedimentary rocks of Mesozoic age in the southwestern United States and Rocky Mountain regions.   Fabulous wealth has come to some prospectors but thousands of others never made significant discoveries.

Important deposits have been discovered in the Colorado Plateau from formations ranging in age from Permian to Tertiary, but the principal sources have been sandstones or conglomerates from Triassic formations known as the Shinarump and Chinle, and the Morrison formation of Jurassic age.

Generally speaking, the uranium of the Colorado Plateau occurs as pitchblende or other dark uranium-bearing minerals associated with fossil organic material such as logs, bones, or plant debris which appears to have acted as a precipitating agent.   The ore bodies are most prevalent in sandstones of fluvial origin, especially those which are interbedded with mudstones or shale (Fig. 15-16).   The significance of the fluvial host rock is apparently its high permeability, which afforded the uranium-bearing solutions easy lateral passage along the strata.   Fluvial deposits are also more likely to contain lenses or "pockets" of organic material washed in during flood stages.

Probably the largest single deposit of uranium in the country was discovered in 1955 on the southern fringe of the Colorado Plateau in New Mexico.   There at Ambrosia Lake, a black asphaltic substance was encountered during the sinking of a drill hole in search for petroleum. The material was strongly radioactive and turned out to be high in uranium content. The Ambrosia Lake deposits of Morrison age contain a reserve of some 25 million tons of uranium ore.   This is more than 35 per cent of the total United States reserves, estimated by the Atomic Energy Commission at 71 million tons as of January 1, 1962 (see Table 15-*a*).

Age   determinations   (lead-uranium method) of the uranium from the Colo-

Table 15-*a*.   *Reserves of Uranium Ore in the United States**

STATE	MILLIONS OF TONS OF ORE
New Mexico	34.0
Wyoming	25.0
Colorado	4.0
Utah	3.7
Others (principally Arizona, Washington, South Dakota and Texas)	4.3
Total	71.0 million tons

* January 1, 1962.   Estimated by Atomic Energy Commission.

rado Plateau give an age of around 60 million years. This indicates that the uranium deposits are late Mesozoic to Tertiary in age; that is, they are related to the Laramide orogeny.

SUMMARY

The Mesozoic era is subdivided into the Triassic, Jurassic, and Cretaceous periods. The Triassic deposits of eastern North America consist of clastic sediments interbedded with lava flows which were tilted during the Palisades disturbance. Continental deposits of Triassic age occur in the southwestern United States whereas thick marine beds were laid down in California. No Jurassic sediments occur above sea level in the eastern United States, but beds of this age are encountered at depth in the Gulf Coastal region. In the west, the Sundance sea invaded the Rocky Mountain geosyncline which was separated from the California trough by a narrow land mass. The Navajo sandstone of eolian origin and the red beds containing gypsum are Jurassic deposits which indicate an arid climate in the western United States. The Nevadian orogeny severely deformed Jurassic and older strata in the west and was accompanied by the emplacement of the Sierra Nevada and Coast Ranges batholiths.

The greatest marine invasion of North America came in the Cretaceous period when much of the Gulf and Atlantic coastal plains were submerged, and the Cordilleran geosyncline was flooded from the Arctic Ocean to Mexico. The Laramide orogeny began in late Cretaceous time and culminated in folding and thrust faulting of Mesozoic and Paleozoic strata. The Idaho and Boulder batholiths are also related to the Laramide orogeny.

Mesozoic life was dominated by the dinosaurs which first appeared as small bipedal forms in the Triassic. Before they became extinct at the end of the Cretaceous, the dinosaurs reached gigantic sizes and became adapted to the land, sea, and air. Birds made their first appearance in the Jurassic as did the mammals. The ammonites and belemnites were distinctive cephalopods of the Mesozoic but other invertebrates were also present. The plants of the Mesozoic consisted mostly of cyads, ferns, and conifers until the mid-Cretaceous when the angiosperms became dominant.

Coal, petroleum, gold, and other metalliferous deposits are produced from Mesozoic rocks. Since World War II, however, uranium deposits from the Triassic and Jurassic beds have received more attention from geologists than any other mineral deposits.

REFERENCES

Arkell, W. J., 1956, *Jurassic geology of the world,* Oliver and Boyd Ltd., Edinburgh.
Arnold, Chester A., 1956, Paleobotany, *The Encyclopedia Americana,* 21, 141–157.
Colbert, Edwin, 1955, *Evolution of the vertebrates,* John Wiley and Sons, New York.
Colbert, Edwin, 1961, *Dinosaurs,* E. P. Dutton, New York.
Eardley, Armand J., 1962, *Structural geology of North America,* 2nd ed., Harper and Row, New York.
Economic Geology, 1955, *Special Uranium Number,* Vol. 50, The Economic Geology Publishing Co., Lancaster, Pennsylvania.
Geological Society of America, 1957, Memoir 67, *Treatise on marine ecology and paleoecology,* Vol. 2, Paleoecology, Chapter 17, Paleoecology of Jurassic seas in the western interior of the United States, by Ralph Imlay, and Chapter 18, Paleoecology of the Cretaceous seas of the western interior of the United States, by John Reeside.
Ginoux, Maurice, 1950, *Stratigraphic geology,* W. H. Freeman and Co., San Francisco.
Knopf, Adolf, 1955, Bathyliths in time, *The crust of the earth,* Geological Society of America, Special Paper 62.

McKelvey, Vincent, 1955, *Search for uranium in the United States,* U.S. Geological Survey, Bulletin 1030-A.

Nairn, A. E. M. (ed.), 1961, *Descriptive palaeoclimatology,* Interscience Publishers, New York.

Newell, N. D., 1963, Crises in the history of life, *Scientific American,* February issue, 77–92.

Shrock, R. R., and W. H. Twenhofel, 1953, *Principles of invertebrate paleontology,* McGraw-Hill Book Co., New York.

XVI

The Cenozoic Era

Said the little Eohippus,
"I am going to be a horse!"

Charlotte Gilman

The winding trail through the geologic past leads ultimately to the present. The last 60 million years of earth history represents the final scenes on the stage of life and the last events in the drama of physical changes which our planet, Earth, has undergone during its long and dynamic development. If we were to base the coverage of geologic history on the length of each era, the Cenozoic would receive only a few pages in this book, because it covers only 1 or 2 per cent of all geologic time. On the other hand, the Cenozoic ranks among the most intriguing episodes of earth history because of the clarity of the record preserved in the sediments, some of which are hardly consolidated. Furthermore, because of its geologic recency the Cenozoic era provides us with the transitional link between the past and the present.

Most of the present-day landscape had its beginning during the Cenozoic, and many of the modern plants and animals ascended from closely related forms of early Cenozoic vintage. The principle of uniformitarianism is more easily invoked in the interpretation of Cenozoic geologic history than in any previous era. It is, perhaps, this reason alone that has compelled so many geologists to expend their energies toward the study of Cenozoic events.

Like the other geologic eras, the Cenozoic has subdivisions, each of which bears an identifying name. The two major time units of the Cenozoic era are known as the *Tertiary* and *Quaternary* periods. The Tertiary, which lasted about 63 million years, comprises the bulk of Cenozoic time, and the Quaternary consists of the Pleistocene, or Great Ice Age as it is sometimes known, and the Recent, the shortest of all geologic time subdivisions.

Actually, both of the terms Tertiary and Quaternary are holdovers from a very early attempt to subdivide geologic time. They were supposed to represent the last two units of a fourfold time scale in which the Primary was equivalent to the Paleozoic and Precambrian, and the Secondary included the Mesozoic. But strangely enough the terms, Tertiary and Quarternary, did not suffer the fate of "Primary" and "Secondary," and so we find the former firmly entrenched in the geologic vocabularies of all countries. Even though every geologist agrees that the original meaning of the terms has been discarded for more than a century, there is little likelihood of their being displaced by more meaningful terms.

The Tertiary period consists of five smaller subdivisions or epochs of unequal length which, from oldest to youngest are known as the Paleocene, Eocene, Olgiocene, Miocene, and Pliocene (Fig. 12-6).

Some of these names date back to the time of Lyell, who proposed a classification of the Tertiary formations of the Paris Basin in France on the basis of their percentage content of modern molluskan shells. Although this basis for classification is not as practical in the United States as in Europe, it represents the first attempt to subdivide a part of geologic time on a more or less quantitative basis.

PHYSICAL HISTORY OF THE CENOZOIC

Perhaps the most striking difference between the Tertiary landscape of North America and previous ones was the absence of any extensive inland seas. To be sure, the Atlantic, Pacific, and Gulf Coastal regions were partially submerged and a very restricted seaway penetrated into the region of the Dakotas from the Gulf of Mexico during Paleocene time. But this was short lived because all of the later Tertiary sediments of the interior western United States were deposited in a continental environment.

Because the Tertiary landscape so closely resembled that of today, some comments on the various natural physiographic areas of the United States and their Tertiary history is the most logical

manner in which to approach this last episode of geologic history.

■ ATLANTIC AND GULF COASTAL PLAIN. This broad belt of land separates the highlands of the eastern United States from the present Atlantic Ocean. In the early part of the Cenozoic it was submerged beneath shallow marine waters just as the modern continental shelf is now submerged. The Eocene and Miocene strata are mainly marine and contain many fossil mollusk shells and shark's teeth which can be found wherever the present attack of the waves has eroded the exposed beds along the Atlantic shore. The coast of Maryland, especially, has yielded many Miocene fossils that so closely resemble their modern descendants living in the present near-shore environment that only an expert can tell them apart.

Farther south in Florida the early Cenozoic beds consist chiefly of marine limestones indicating that the Florida peninsula did not exist then but was, instead, a broad submarine bank covered by a warm shallow sea. Florida did not become emergent until the Miocene and is, in a geologic sense, the youngest state in the Union!

Along the Gulf Coast from Alabama to Mexico a belted outcrop pattern of Cenozoic strata testifies to a northward penetration of the Gulf of Mexico waters which, in the Paleocene, reached southern Illinois and the northern boundary of eastern Texas (Fig. 16-1). Oil wells drilled into the Gulf Coastal plain have penetrated over 20,000 feet of Tertiary sediments and recent studies in the Gulf of Mexico itself have revealed a total thickness of Cenozoic sediments of more than 40,000 feet. A modern geosyncline lies beneath the northern part of the Gulf of Mexico and adjoining coastal plain. It has been slowly subsiding since the Appalachian orogeny.

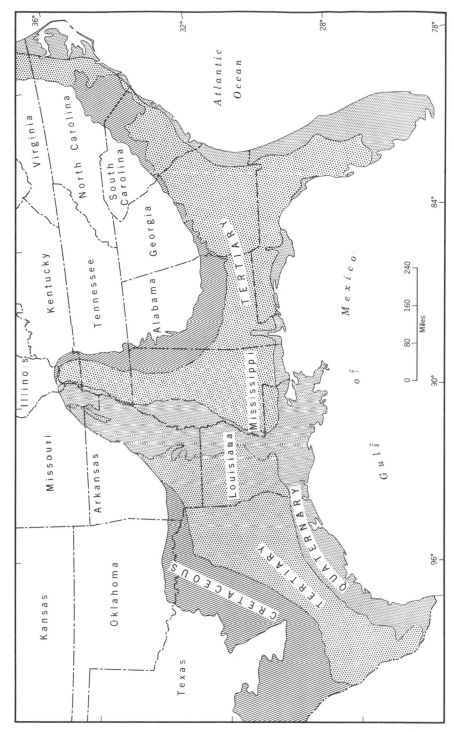

Figure 16-1. Geologic map of a part of the Coastal Plain of the southeastern United States. (From the Geologic Map of North America, published by the Geological Society of America, 1946.)

285

Figure 16-2.   Physiographic map of the western United States.   (Base map by Erwin Raisz. Physiographic boundaries after Fenneman.)

■ PACIFIC COAST. The states of Washington, Oregon, and California have had a complex Tertiary history. Basically, it involved the uplifting of two parallel mountain belts and the subsidence of an intervening trough which was invaded from time to time by Tertiary seas. The California trough lies between the massive Sierra Nevada on the east and the Coast Ranges on the west (Fig. 16-2), and contains about 50,000 feet of Tertiary marine and nonmarine sediments.

The Coast Ranges experienced resurgent uplift all through the Cenozoic, but the greatest vertical movement came in the mid-Pleistocene, and the many earthquakes of the California-Nevada area support the conclusion that this period of mountain building is not over yet.

The rugged Sierra Nevada is a gigantic fault block that was tilted westward along a 430-mile fault along its eastern flank. The uplift amounts to some 13,000 feet. Most of this was accomplished in mid-Pleistocene during what has been called the *Cascadian revolution*, which involved not only the Cascade Mountains of Washington and Oregon, the Pacific Coast Ranges, and the Sierra Nevada, but other parts of the world as well.

The Cascade Range is studded with a galaxy of magnificent volcanic peaks along its entire length from Washington to northern California. Many of them are snow-covered and some of them contain systems of radial glaciers flowing down their flanks. These volcanoes came into being during the Pliocene, but some show evidence of eruptive activity during the Pleistocene. Mt. Shasta, whose snow-clad peak rises 14,161 feet above the sea, contains a hot spring near its summit which indicates that hot lava may still exist below. Eruptions of Lassen Peak in northern California during the 1914–17 period spread hot volcanic ash down the slopes, thereby melting huge quantities of snow which caused extensive mud flows at lower elevations.

Crater Lake, Oregon, lies in the center of what was once a towering volcanic peak, Mount Mazama (Fig. 16-3). The top of this Tertiary volcano collapsed or foundered in Late Pleistocene times, but the presence of glacial deposits on its lower flanks indicates that Mount Mazama contained an array of valley glaciers before the final collapse took place. The depression itself is a *caldera* which is at least 2000 feet deep and 5 miles wide. Wizard Island is a small volcanic cone that represents the final stage of volcanic

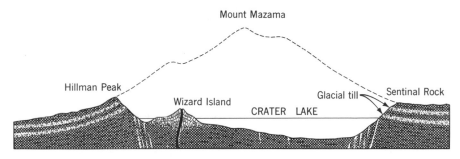

Figure 16-3. Geologic cross section of Crater Lake, Oregon. The water of the lake lies in a caldera, the huge depression left after the bulk of Mt. Mazama collapsed. Glacial deposits interbedded with volcanics on the lower flanks of Mazama attest to a former extensive system of valley glaciers flowing radially down its flanks. Wizard Island is a small volcanic cone formed during a final surge of eruptive activity. (After Wallace W. Atwood, 1940, *The physiographic provinces of North America,* Ginn and Co., Boston.)

Figure 16-4.   Wizard Island in Crater Lake, Oregon, is a small volcanic cone formed during the last stages of volcanic activity.   See Fig. 16-3.   (Photograph by United States Air Force.)

activity after the main collapse took place (Fig. 16-4).

■ COLUMBIA PLATEAU. An enormous volume of basaltic lava was extruded over the northwestern United States between the Cascade Mountains and the Rocky Mountains (Fig. 16-5). Interbedded with some of the flows are lacustrine beds containing Miocene plants, but in Idaho at the Craters of the Moon, eruptions continued almost until the present.

■ BASIN AND RANGE PROVINCE. The name "Basin and Range" refers to the region south of the Columbia Plateau between the Sierra Nevada and the Colorado Plateau (Fig. 16-2). It is characterized by north-south trending mountain blocks (ranges), and intervening valleys (basins) filled or partially filled with sediments derived from the surrounding mountains during Tertiary time. The ranges are uplifted blocks of deformed pre-Cenozoic rocks that were elevated along fault planes during the Miocene. Movement along these faults has been recurrent since then, and they are still active today

as evidenced by the numerous Nevada earthquakes.

■ COLORADO PLATEAU. This physiographic province is something of a geologic oddity. On all sides of it the earth's crust has crumpled under intense lateral stresses so that the rock strata are strongly folded and deformed. But for some reason the sedimentary rocks of the Colorado Plateau are still in a nearly horizontal position although they have been dislocated in some places along huge normal faults.

The Tertiary depositional history of the Plateau is represented by sedimentary beds of Paleocene age and the Eocene Wasatch formation, picturesquely displayed in Bryce Canyon National Park, Utah (Fig. 16-6). Since the end of the Eocene the Colorado Plateau has been recurrently uplifted so that the nearly horizontal rock layers have been partially stripped off by weathering, mass wasting, and stream erosion. This is exactly what is happening to the Wasatch beds in Bryce Canyon, and other strata exposed as buttes, mesas, and erosional remnants of the Plateau.

Igneous rocks of Miocene-Pliocene age occur as stocks, laccoliths, and basaltic lava flows scattered over the Plateau. The Henry Mountains of Utah are classic examples of laccolithic mountains.

The Colorado Plateau contains such an abundance of spectacular and colorful erosional scenery and provides so many outstanding examples of geologic principles that any person who is even slightly aware of his natural surroundings cannot help but learn simple lessons of geology from them. Everyone from the amateur "rock hound" to the professional geologist can find something of interest in this wonderful outdoor laboratory.

Geologists are not prone to the use of superlatives, but undoubtedly all would agree that the Grand Canyon is one of the most magnificent geologic spectacles, not only of the Colorado Plateau, but of the entire world (Fig. 16-7). An individual is dwarfed in space and time as he stands at the rim of this gash in the earth's crust and gazes into the awesome chasm carved by the Colorado River. It must be seen to be appreciated, for even the most eloquent words become

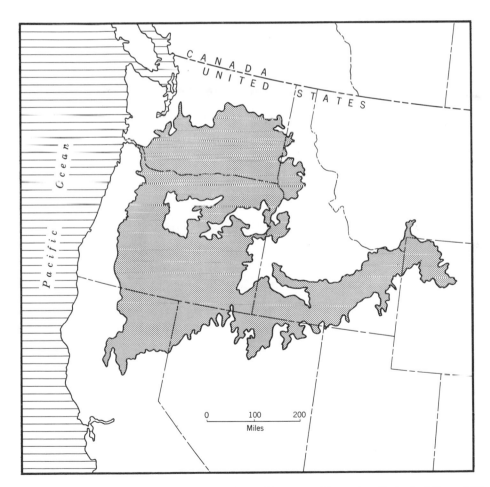

Figure 16-5. Map showing the Columbia Lava Plateau. (From the Geologic Map of North America, published by the Geological Society of North America, 1946.)

Figure 16-6.   Bryce Canyon National Park, Utah.   These erosional features are developed in the Wasatch formation of Eocene age.   The Colorado Plateau contains many formations that are slowly being stripped away by erosion, just as the Wasatch beds are being removed.   (Photograph by R. G. Luedke, United States Geological Survey.)

mere platitudes when used to describe its majestic grandeur and wondrous beauty. The Colorado River probably began its incision of the Colorado Plateau in late Pliocene time, although geologic opinion is divided on this matter.

■ ROCKY MOUNTAINS.   The Cenozoic history of the Rocky Mountains presents a marked contrast to the Mesozoic history of the same region, because the Laramide orogeny signaled the end of a marine environment which had dominated the geologic processes until that time.   With the withdrawal of the Cretaceous seas and the destruction of the Cordilleran geosyncline, the region now occupied by the Rocky Mountains en-

tered upon a new phase of landscape evolution.

The high mountains formed by the Laramide orogeny were vigorously eroded by streams cascading down their flanks. Some of these rushing torrents may have begun their downward course from the snouts of Alpine glaciers during the Eocene, because a scattering of Eocene conglomerates discovered in Colorado is interpreted by some geologists as till deposited by mountain glaciers at that time.   However, an equally valid argument is that the so-called Eocene tillites are, in reality, mudflows associated with volcanoes.

Ever since the Eocene, the Rocky

Mountains have been in the center of conflicting forces of uplift from within and the erosional forces from without. At times the erosional processes won out, because evidence of widespread planation exists in the form of beveled rock surfaces. But the fact that these peneplained surfaces are now high above sea level is an indication that the victory of downwearing of the land was nullified by renewed uplift. At least once during the Tertiary, the Rocky Mountains were worn down to a surface of gentle relief occupied by scattered monadnocks. This Rocky Mountain Peneplain, as it is known among geologists, is strikingly visible from many vantage points in many parts of the present ranges.

The final surge of uplift came in the Miocene, continued into the Pliocene, and is still going on today. This last pulsation of uplift caused the superposi-tion of many rivers across geologic struc-tures such as the Black Canyon of the Gunnison River and the Royal Gorge of the Arkansas River in Colorado. These rivers, like many others flowing in the Rocky Mountains, maintained pre-existing courses by incising mountain ranges that rose across them. There seems to be no other explanation for the more than two dozen river gorges that slash across resistant geologic structures when they could have selected easier and less tortuous routes only a few miles on either side.

But the Tertiary history of the Rocky Mountains is not all erosive because inter-spersed between the various mountain ranges are structural basins which filled with sediments derived from the sur-rounding mountains. Some of these basin sediments are fluviatile and others are clearly lacustrine, for example, the

Figure 16-7. The Grand Canyon of the Colorado River is a mile-deep gash in the Colorado Plateau. The initial cutting of this magnificent canyon probably began in late Pliocene time. (Photograph by N. W. Carkhuff, United States Geological Survey.)

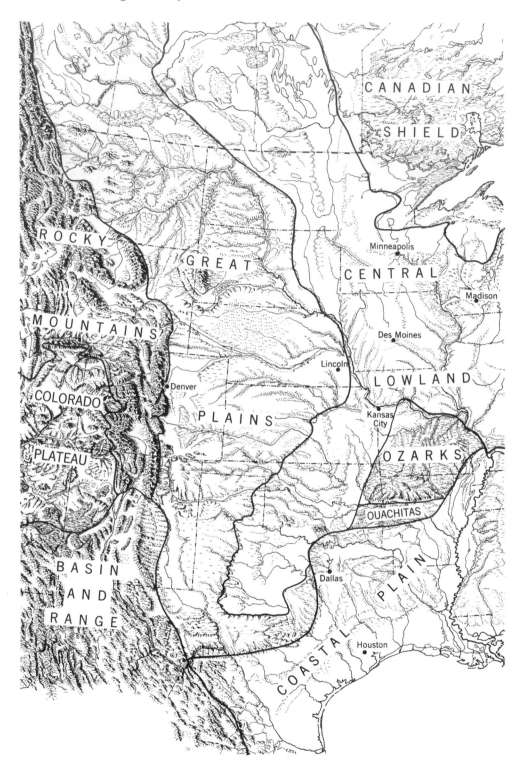

Figure 16-8.   Physiographic map of the Great Plains and adjoining areas.   (Base map by Erwin Raisz.   Physiographic boundaries after Fenneman.)

2000 feet of laminated shales of the Green River formation (Eocene) which contain fossil fresh-water fish remains. The Tertiary basin deposits are local in extent and do not extend beyond the confines of the individual basins in which they accumulated.

■ THE GREAT PLAINS. Lying between the Rocky Mountains and the lowlands of the Mississippi Valley and extending from the Arctic Ocean to the Rio Grande is the vastness of the Great Plains (Fig 16-8). Never the scene of orogeny since before the Cambrain, the Great Plains possess a rather simple geologic structure of flat or almost flat-lying sediments ranging in age from Paleozoic to Pleistocene. The present surface of the Great Plains slopes eastward away from the Rocky Mountains, a fact that accounts for the genetic kinship of the two areas.

During the Tertiary period, streams originating in the Rocky Mountains debauched eastward carrying sediments worn from the craggy new mountains. During the Eocene, some of these sediments were trapped in the structural basins within the Rocky Mountains, but by Oligocene time a blanket of terrestrial sands, silts, and clays was laid down over much of the Great Plains. These beds constitute what is known as the *White River series* and are famous for their content of terrestrial mammal fossils. In the Big Badlands of South Dakota almost anyone can find a fossil bone or tooth within a few hundred feet of the main highway passing through this national monument (Fig. 16-9).

In the Pliocene, a network of east-flowing streams originating in the Rocky Mountains spread their gravelly deposits over most of the Great Plains forming the *Ogallala formation*. Much of the present Great Plains surface is mantled with the Ogallala gravels.

In western South Dakota the Black Hills rise abruptly from the surrounding plains owing to a dome structure which developed during the Laramide orogeny. The outcrop pattern of sedimentary rocks of Paleozoic and Mesozoic age is concentric around a Precambrian core which has been exposed by erosion during the Cenozoic. Actually, the Black Hills structure is an outlying part of the Rocky

Figure 16-9.   Geology students hunting fossils in the Badlands National Monument of South Dakota.   The strata are known as the White River series and are Oligocene in age.

Mountains, hence both have similar Cenozoic histories.

■ TERTIARY HISTORY OF THE APPALACHIAN MOUNTAINS. By the beginning of the Cenozoic era the folded pre-Tertiary strata of the Appalachians were eroded to a surface called the Schooley peneplain. The rivers flowed eastward to the Atlantic Ocean across the regional trend of the upturned rock strata deformed during the Appalachian orogeny at the close of the Paleozoic. Sometime during the Tertiary, an epeirogenic (not orogenic) movement uplifted the Schooley peneplain and caused rejuvenation of the streams which began their process of erosion once again. The uplift was not rapid enough to cause deflection of the streams, thereby permitting them to maintain their pre-existing courses across the regional structural elements. The present Appalachian Mountains are therefore the result of broad uplift accompanied by differential stream erosion on folded strata (Fig. 16-10).

Evidence for the Schooley peneplain exists in the form of *accordant* summits of the long ridges which characterize the topography of the Appalachians. *Water gaps* are notches cut in these ridges by streams that maintained their courses in spite of the uplift of the Schooley surface. The Susquehanna River flows through such a water gap at Harrisburg, Pennsylvania.

LIFE OF THE TERTIARY

The mammals unquestionably dominated the Tertiary animal kingdom as is shown by the great variety of their remains excavated from the continental deposits of Tertiary age. Many of the early Tertiary forms became extinct by the end of the Eocene, and it was not until the Oligocene and Miocene that the more modern forms made their appearance. By the Pliocene the mammals were distinctly modern in form, although many species living then did not survive to the present. A detailed account of the mammalian Tertiary fauna would take us far beyond the purpose of this book, but one example of the changes undergone by one stock of animals will serve as an illustration of Tertiary evolution.

■ THE EVOLUTION OF THE HORSE. One of the best documented accounts of evolutionary change in a single group of animals is the development of the horse in North America. The accompanying chart (Fig. 16-11) summarizes the evolutionary history of the horse during the Cenozoic. Changes in size of the animal are very striking for the early *Eohippus* (Eocene) was about the size of a small fox terrier. But more meaningful in terms of evolutionary change is the evidence of modification of the skull, teeth, limbs, and feet.

Specifically, the muzzle increased in length so that the eye sockets came to occupy a position back of the molar teeth. The teeth of *Eohippus* were stubby (low-crowned) and suited for browsing whereas the dentitions of *Pliohippus* (Pliocene) and *Equus* (Pleistocene) were high-crowned and well adapted for grazing. To accommodate the increasing height of the teeth, the jaws deepened vertically.

The increase in length of the limbs from *Eohippus* to *Equus* was accompanied by a change in the feet. The front feet of *Eohippus* had four functional toes, and the back feet had three. In *Mesohippus* (Oligocene) the rear feet had only three functional toes, and although *Merychippus* (Miocene) also had three toes on the front and back feet, only the middle was functional. In other words, *Merychippus* walked and ran on his middle toe. This trend of reduction and final loss of the lateral toes and increase in the size of the middle toe culminated in the hoofs of *Equus*. The feet of *Eohippus* and *Meso-*

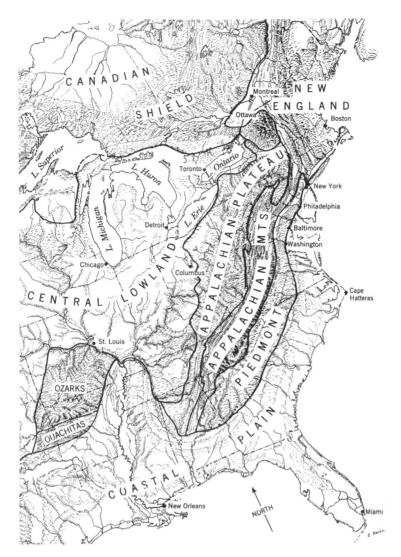

Figure 16-10. Physiographic map of the eastern United States. (Base map by Erwin Raisz. Physiographic boundaries after Fenneman.)

hippus were padded, but this feature, like the lateral toes, was lost during the course of evolutionary change.

No more positive example of organic evolution could be cited than that of the horse, although in the sequence just described, some intermediate forms of the main line of evolution as well as forms which branched off in the Miocene are not mentioned. *Equus* became extinct in North America before the end of the Pleistocene, but managed to immigrate to the old world via Asia where it survived to the present.

■ OTHER CENOZOIC ANIMALS. The rhinoceroses, camels, and elephants have evolutionary histories revealed by their fossil remains in North America. The early Cenozoic ancestors of the rhinos and camels were much smaller than their living relatives, but they increased in stature and were modified in other respects

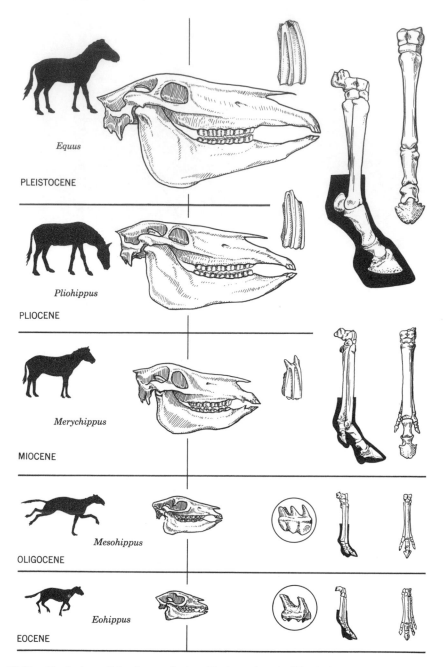

Figure 16-11. Evolution of the horse during Tertiary time in North America. Drawings in each vertical column are to scale except the teeth of *Mesohippus* and *Eohippus* (circled) which are enlarged. (Bodies and limbs after Simpson, G. Gaylord, 1953, *Life of the past,* Yale University Press, New Haven; teeth after Stirton, R. A., 1940, Phylogeny of North American Equidae, *Bull. Dept. Geol. Univ. Calif.,* **25,** 165–198; skulls after Romer, Alfred S., 1945, *Vertebrate paleontology,* 2nd ed., University of Chicago Press, Chicago; Colbert, Edwin H., 1955, *Evolution of the vertebrates,* John Wiley and Sons, New York; and specimens in the University of Michigan Museum of Paleontology furnished by Claude W. Hibbard.)

as Cenozoic time progressed. Although the camels and rhinos both originated from North American stock, the elephants began their evolutionary development in Africa but migrated to North America during the Miocene.

One extinct animal tribe prominent during the Cenozoic is known as the *titanotheres,* which in appearance resembled the rhinoceroses to which they were remotely related. These brutes were bulky and their skulls were adorned with bony appendages that protruded from the region of the nose (Fig. 16-12).

In the sea, Eocene whales represent the first adaptation of mammals to a marine environment. In the air, birds must have flourished in great abundance but their fossil remains are extremely rare. Lakes and streams contained many fishes which closely resemble modern forms and are among the best preserved fossils of the Tertiary; those of the Eocene Green River formation of Wyoming (Fig. 16-13) are examples.

Rodents, snakes, turtles, dogs, cats, deer, pigs, and many other animals began their evolutionary development during the Tertiary, but only passing reference to them is possible here.

■ TERTIARY PLANTS. The ancestors of modern land plants were already established by the end of the Cretaceous, and their Tertiary history is merely a continuation of the evolutionary trend that began in the late Mesozoic (Fig. 16-14). The angiosperms (flowering plants) increased in kinds and numbers and are found fossilized wherever fine-grained sediments accumulated, such as in the Florissant lake beds of Miocene age in Colorado. Fossil plants provide the best evidence for climatic conditions of the past, and the distribution of Tertiary plants strongly suggests a general cooling from the Eocene to the Pleistocene. Along with this came a condition of progressively less rainfall over much of continental North America, which may have aided to some degree in plant differentiation.

MINERAL DEPOSITS OF CENOZOIC AGE

■ PETROLEUM. Since the first oil well was finished by Colonel Drake at a depth of 69 feet in Paleozoic strata on August 27, 1859 near Titusville, Pennsylvania, the petroleum industry has become a gigantic business, not only in the United States, but over the entire face of the earth. About half of all professional geologists

Figure 16-12. *Brontotherium,* a titanothere from the Tertiary of western North America. (Restoration by Thomas Coates, after Charles Knight.)

Figure 16-13.   An Eocene fish skeleton from Two Creeks, Wyoming.   (University of Minnesota Museum of Paleontology.)

are actively engaged in the exploration or production of petroleum products.

The industry has come a long way since 1859 when Colonel Drake's discovery unleashed a new rush for riches and unfolded new horizons for the good of all mankind.   Not the least of the reasons for the skyrocketing advances in the discovery of new oil fields has been the use of the internal combustion engine in the automobile, airplane, and other mechanized means of transportation. The oil from early wells went mostly for the manufacture of kerosene for lamps, but today petroleum products are put to hundreds of different uses, the most important of which are fuels and lubricants.

Oil, as it comes out of the ground, is called crude oil, and consists of a mixture of hydrocarbon compounds.   Most geologists concur that oil originated as an accumulation of organic matter on the sea bottom, although it must be admitted that hydrocarbons can be produced in the laboratory by the combination of certain inorganic substances.   But not one of the

chemicals used in these laboratory experiments is known to exist in nature, so it is logical to rule out the inorganic theory of origin on this basis alone.   On the other hand, new observations on certain organic deposits in *fresh-water* lakes definitely show that oil-producing hydrocarbons can and do exist in fresh-water sediments.

One point of fundamental importance in the science of oil finding is the fact that oil does not remain in the sedimentary rocks in which it originates.   Instead it migrates until it becomes entrapped in a geologic structure called an *oil trap* (Fig. 16-15).   Oil migrates through rock pores because it occurs with water.   The oil, being of a lower specific gravity than water, and for all practical purposes insoluble in water, will tend to separate itself from the associated water by moving in the direction of least resistance, usually upward.   If no impermeable barrier such as shale stops the oil migration, the oil eventually reaches the surface and forms an *oil seep,* but if geologic conditions are favorable, the oil accumulates in a sub-surface oil trap, forming an *oil pool*.

The term oil pool is really a misnomer because oil does not occur in underground "pools" in the strict sense of the word. Instead, the oil occupies the voids between mineral grains or other existing openings.

The search for oil is in reality the search for oil traps. Some traps are barren but others contain more oil than originally anticipated. There is no known way whereby the actual presence of oil beneath a particular place on the earth's surface can be detected by surface methods alone. Geologists and geophysicists determine the structural features by geologic methods but only the drilling of a

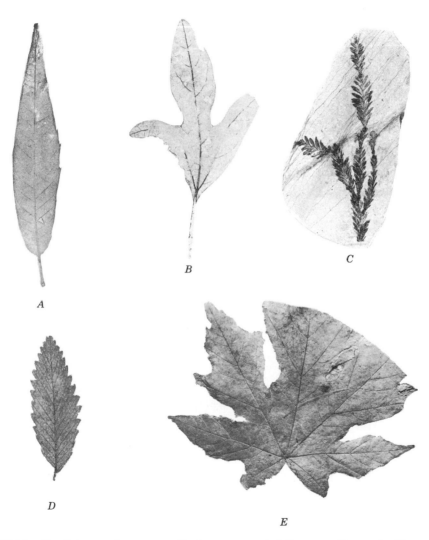

Figure 16-14. Fossil leaves from some Tertiary trees. *A*. Miocene willow oak (Oregon). *B*. Miocene sassafrass (Oregon.) *C*. Oligocene sequoia (British Columbia). *D*. Oligocene birch (Colorado). *E*. Miocene maple (Oregon). (*A*, *C*, *D*, and *E* by Chester A. Arnold, University of Michigan Museum of Paleontology; *B* reproduced by permission of McGraw-Hill Book Co., from Chester A. Arnold, 1947, *An introduction to paleobotany,* New York.)

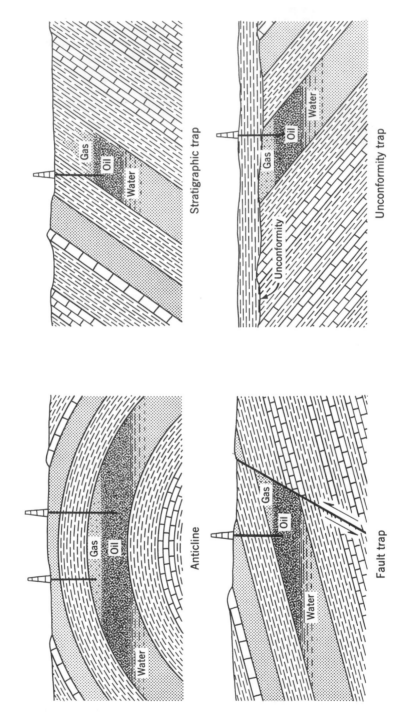

Figure 16-15. Geologic cross sections showing some common types of oil and gas traps.

hole in the ground gives the final answer. On the average, about ten dry holes are drilled for every producing one in the United States. Annual world production of crude oil in 1961 amounted to about 8 billion barrels, of which the United States produced about 32 per cent (See Table 16-*a*). The deepest producing oil well in 1956 was drilled to a depth of 21,465 feet in Coastal Louisiana and produced 206 barrels of oil per day.

Oil is found in sedimentary rocks of all ages from Cambrian to Pliocene, but the occurrence of oil in a bed of one age or the other has no particular significance in view of the fact that the oil may have accumulated during an earlier geologic period and migrated into a trap existing in strata of entirely different age. Hence we can only conclude from the ubiquitous geologic occurrence of oil that conditions for its formation must have existed ever since the Cambrian. Indeed, crude oil probably is being formed at this very moment somewhere in basins of deposition where organic matter is accumulating under favorable circumstances.

About half the total world production of crude oil comes from sediments of Tertiary age, and in the United States

large quantities of Tertiary oil are produced from California and from the Gulf Coastal plain. The offshore drilling in the Gulf of Mexico near the delta of the Mississippi River has already resulted in production from Tertiary sediments.

An almost unlimited amount of liquid hydrocarbons is available from the "oil shales" of Colorado and Wyoming. A process has been perfected whereby oil can be generated from these highly organic shales by distillation. This source is largely untapped but stands as an immense reserve available when the more conventional oil deposits diminish appreciably. Crude oil production figures for the United States are shown in Table 16-*b*.

■ SALT. Along the Gulf Coast in Louisiana and Texas, salt occurs in the form of vertical pipelike masses that were forced upward from great depth through the Tertiary strata. The salt was undoubtedly intruded while in a plastic state but the cause of the intrusion or the exact mechanism by which it took place is not known. The rocks through which the salt plugs were injected were arched upward or bent into dome-shaped structures which provide excellent oil traps.

Table 16-*a*. *World Crude Oil Production and Reserves for 1961**

COUNTRY	AVERAGE DAILY PRODUCTION (BARRELS)	ESTIMATED RESERVE (BILLIONS OF BARRELS)
USA	7,188,000	35.50
Europe	314,000	1.73
Africa	475,300	9.71
Middle East	5,629,100	188.20
Western Hemisphere, exclusive of USA	4,516,600	29.71
Asia-Pacific	557,800	10.87
Total free world	18,680,800	275.72
USSR and Communist Bloc Areas	3,650,000	34.25
Total World	22,330,800	309.97

* Source of Data: *The Oil and Gas Journal*, January 29, 1962.

*Table 16-b. Annual Crude Oil Production and Proved Reserves in the United States**

STATE	PRODUCTION 1961 (BARRELS)	RESERVES AS OF JANUARY 1, 1962 (BARRELS)	(PER CENT OF U.S.)
Texas	894,486,000	15,061,000,000	42.5
Louisiana	366,586,000	6,039,000,000	17.1
California	298,709,000	3,956,284,000	11.2
Oklahoma	190,997,000	2,275,000,000	6.4
Wyoming	143,619,000	1,420,500,000	4.0
New Mexico	110,402,000	1,072,000,000	3.0
Kansas	112,412,000	953,000,000	2.7
Utah	33,136,000	647,000,000	1.8
Illinois	79,477,000	596,000,000	1.7
Mississippi	53,100,000	589,500,000	1.7
North Dakota	22,873,000	414,000,000	1.2
Montana	31,040,000	394,000,000	1.1
All others†	178,932,000	1,970,600,000	5.6
Total U.S.	2,515,769,000	35,387,884,000	100.00

* Source of Data: *The Oil and Gas Journal,* January 29, 1962.
† Includes Alabama, Alaska, Arizona, Arkansas, Colorado, Florida, Indiana, Kentucky, Maryland, Michigan, Missouri, Nebraska, Nevada, New York, Ohio, Pennsylvania, South Dakota, Tennessee, Virginia, Washington, and West Virginia.

The salt itself is mined from deep shafts.

■ METALS. Many metallic ores in the Rocky Mountain states are mined from rocks older than Tertiary, but evidence points to a Tertiary age for the ore-bearing solutions themselves. Of special interest are *placer* gold deposits of California which are accumulations of stream gravels derived from gold-bearing rocks in the Sierra Nevada during the Tertiary. The California gold rush of 1848 involved the *panning* of stream gravels for their content of gold particles.

SUMMARY

The Cenozoic era lasted about 63 million years. Marine sediments were restricted to the Atlantic and Gulf coastal areas during most of the Tertiary except for a narrow marine arm that penetrated north to Montana and Wyoming during the Paleocene.

Continental deposits of fluvial and lacustrine origin as well as vast amounts of lava and other volcanics characterize the Tertiary deposits of western United States. The Cascadian period of mountain building uplifted the Rocky Mountains after a period of long erosion in the early Tertiary, and similar forces of epeirogenic uplift gave rise to the Sierra Nevadas, Cascade Mountains, and Coastal Ranges. Normal faulting in the Basin and Range province produced a series of north-south trending mountain ranges with intervening basins in which terrestrial sediments accumulated. Structural basins in the Rockies also acted as sedimentary traps.

Erosion predominated during late Cenozoic time on the Colorado Plateau where flat-lying Mesozoic formations were gradually stripped back during the

Tertiary, but on the Great Plains east-flowing streams laid down sands and gravels derived from the Rocky Mountains.

Mammals flourished in great numbers and diversity of kinds all during the Tertiary, but some of them, such as the titanotheres, failed to survive into modern times. Excellent examples of evolutionary development can be seen in the fossil remains of camels, horses, rhinoceroses, and elephants. Modern types of plants were already established at the beginning of the Tertiary but some new species evolved in response to progressively cooler and drier climate.

Tertiary mineral deposits include nearly three-fourths of the world's petroleum production, large amounts of salt from Gulf Coast salt domes, and many different kinds of metals from the western United States.

REFERENCES

Atwood, Wallace W., 1940, *The physiographic provinces of North America,* Ginn and Co., Boston.

Briggs, Lyman, J., 1962, When Mt. Mazama lost its top, *National Geographic Magazine,* Vol. 122, No. 1, p. 128–148.

Colbert, Edwin H., 1955, *Evolution of the vertebrates,* John Wiley and Sons, New York.

Fenneman, Nevin M., 1931, *Physiography of western United States,* McGraw-Hill Book Co., New York.

Hinds, Norman E. A., 1952, *Evolution of the California landscape,* San Francisco, California Division of Mines, Bulletin 158.

Hunt, Charles B., 1956, *Cenozoic geology of the Colorado plateau,* U.S. Geological Survey, Professional Paper 279.

Maxson, John H., 1961, *Geologic map of the Bright Angel quadrangle, Grand Canyon National Park, Arizona,* Grand Canyon Natural History Association, Box 219, Grand Canyon, Arizona.

Raymond, Percy E., 1939, *Prehistoric life,* Harvard University Press, Cambridge.

Romer, Alfred S., 1945, *Vertebrate paleontology,* 2nd ed., University of Chicago Press, Chicago.

Scott, William B., 1937, *A history of land mammals in the western hemisphere,* The Macmillan Co., New York.

Simpson, George Gaylord, 1953, *Life of the past,* Yale University Press, New Haven.

Stirton, R. A., 1940, Phylogeny of North American Equidae, *Bull. Dept. Geol. Univ. Calif.,* **25,** 165–198.

Van Houten, F. B., 1957, Appraisal of Ridgeway and Gunnison "tillites," southwestern Colorado, *Bull. Geol. Soc. Amer.,* **66,** 383–388.

Van Houten, F. B., 1961, Maps of Cenozoic depositional provinces, western United States, *Am. Jour. Sci.,* **259,** 612–621.

XVII

The Pleistocene Epoch

The Earth is a vast cemetary . . .
The rocks are tombstones on which the buried
dead have written their own epitaphs.

Louis Agassiz

The pleistocene deposits as a group are so variable in origin that it is impossible to base the definition of the Pleistocene on any one particular kind of deposit as is sometimes done with older strata. Instead, a more inclusive basis for differentiating the Pleistocene epoch from older periods is employed—this basis is climate.

The chief distinction of Pleistocene time is that it embraced a number of marked climatic fluctuations during the last million years, fluctuations that are still in progress today. These variations in climate have ranged from cool and moist to warm and dry. The expansion of continental glaciers until nearly a third of the earth's land surface was covered by glacier ice was unquestionably the most spectacular effect of the climatic changes. But indirect effects of this glaciation were widespread, and because it appears that the climatic fluctuations were worldwide, climate seems to be the only logical peg on which to hang the discussion of the Pleistocene.

GLACIATED REGIONS OF THE WORLD

Ice sheets or continental glaciers, such as those which exist today on Greenland and Antarctica, covered areas on the earth which are among the most heavily populated today. Besides the North American ice sheet, which will be discussed in the next section of this chapter, other parts of the northern hemisphere experienced similar glacial conditions.

The Scandinavian ice sheet covered all of Norway, Sweden, and Denmark, and expanded eastward across the Baltic to north-central Siberia in the USSR, southward into Germany and Poland, and westward across the North Sea to the British Isles. A separate ice cap developed independently in the Alps although several peaks were left unglaciated and protruded above the general level of the ice cap as nunataks. Eastern Siberia was at least partially glaciated, and Greenland was ice covered as now but the average ice thickness was greater and the total area covered, larger.

In the Southern Hemisphere, Antarctica was undoubtedly glaciated, and the Highlands of southern South America (Patagonia) were dominated by large valley glaciers. In fact, mountain ranges the world over carried valley glaciers of greater extent than those which persist in the same areas today.

THE GLACIATED REGION OF NORTH AMERICA

The great North American ice sheet reached a maximum southern limit roughly equivalent to the Missouri and Ohio Rivers. One main center of original snow accumulation was in the highland regions of Labrador and eastern Quebec. Other local centers may have developed later on, due to shifting of storm tracks and other meteorological factors. A second major center of glaciation persisted in the Canadian Rockies.

The ice advanced in lobate fashion, each lobe being guided by major topographic lowland areas, especially large river valleys. Eventually, however, the entire land area north of the Ohio and Missouri Rivers was engulfed in glacier ice, except for a tract in southwestern Wisconsin known as the "Driftless Area," which may have escaped glaciation altogether.

The classic area of Pleistocene glacial deposits is the Upper Mississippi Valley. This area has received the attention of glacial geologists for over 75 years, and is the type area for most of the Pleistocene drift sheets.

A major stride toward better understanding of the Pleistocene was the discovery of multiple glaciation. Until the late nineteenth century, geologists assumed that one major advance of the ice was followed by one major retreat. But recognition of two drift sheets separated by *interglacial deposits* led to the concept that more than one advance of the ice

had taken place, and that each major advance or *glacial age* was separated in time by an *interglacial age*. In fact, fossils from one of the interglacial deposits near Toronto indicate that a climate *warmer than today's* existed before the last major advance of the ice in that region.

Studies since this important concept was recognized have revealed that the Pleistocene consisted of four major glacial and three interglacial ages. Each of these has been named, and the fourth or youngest of the glacial ages has been further subdivided into subages. Table 17-*a* gives the commonly accepted subdivision of the Pleistocene of North America, and Fig. 17-1 shows the distribution of the most recent or Wisconsin drift sheet in the Great Lakes region.

RADIOCARBON DATING

A recent development in the field of radioactive materials has led to a process that permits the assigning of an age in actual years to certain of the drift sheets. This process is known as the *radiocarbon* method. It is based on the fact that atmospheric nitrogen changes to carbon 14 (C_{14}), a radioactive isotope of carbon. Plants incorporate C_{14} along with regular carbon (C_{12}) into their systems as carbon dioxide (CO_2). Because animals feed on plants, they too have some C_{12} and C_{14} in their systems. In the live tis-

Table 17-a. A Classification of the Pleistocene

GLACIAL AGES	INTERGLACIAL AGES
Wisconsin	
	Sangamon
Illinoian	
	Yarmouth
Kansan	
	Aftonian
Nebraskan	

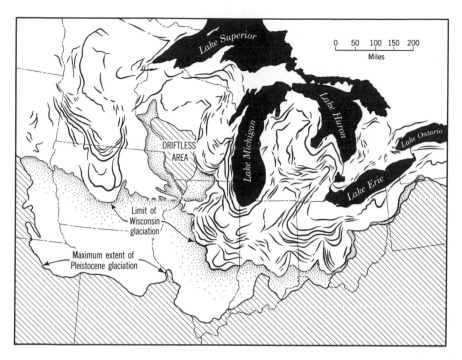

Figure 17-1. Map of the Great Lakes region showing the general distribution of the end moraines formed during the Wisconsin stage of the Pleistocene. The moraines are shown in heavy black lines. The shaded area was never covered by the Pleistocene ice sheet. The area between the Wisconsin drift boundary and the maximum extent of glaciation is covered with pre-Wisconsin Pleistocene deposits. (After the Glacier Map of North America, published by the Geological Society of America, 1945.)

sue of a plant or animal the ratio of C_{12} to C_{14} remains constant, but upon death of the organism, the amount of C_{14} slowly dwindles because it changes by radioactive decay back to nitrogen. The amount of C_{14} contained in organic matter buried in glacial or interglacial deposits is thus an index of the length of time the organism has been dead, and hence "dates" the deposit in which it is contained. Extension of this absolute chronology back to the very early Pleistocene is not possible because of the extremely weak radioactivity of C_{14} in deposits older than 50,000 years. For the period between the present and 50,000 years ago, the radiocarbon method provides the basis for the construction of an absolute chronology and opens the way for the correlation of deposits of diverse origin on an inter-continental basis.

PRE-WISCONSIN GLACIATION

The best-known phase of the Pleistocene is the Wisconsin or fourth glacial, yet a much greater time span was involved in the glacial and interglacial ages prior to the advance of the Wisconsin ice sheet.

The older glacial deposits, especially the Nebraskan and Kansan drifts, have been deeply weathered and eroded. They no longer possess the youthful topographic appearance of the later Wisconsin drifts. Drainage patterns are well established on them, no end moraines can be recognized, and the upper parts have been transformed by weathering into *gumbotils,* a compact, clayey material in which the clay minerals predominate. Gumbotils in excess of 10 feet indicate that long periods of interglacial time were

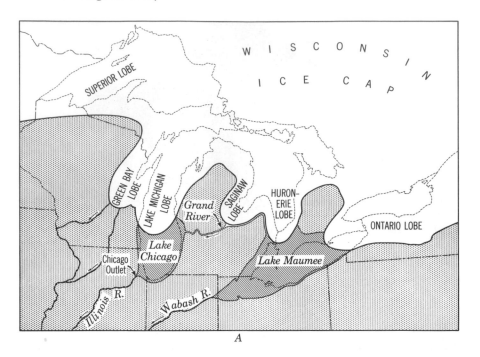

A

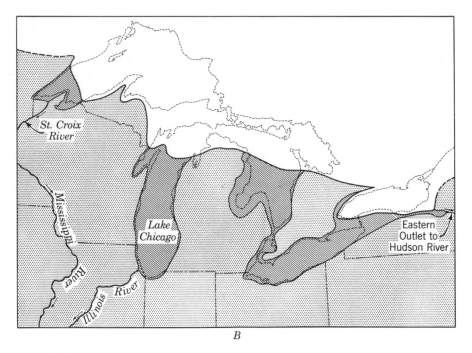

B

required to produce these residual clays. The Yarmouth interglacial, for instance, is estimated to have spanned over 100,000 years, although this figure is hardly more than an educated guess.

THE ORIGIN AND HISTORY OF THE GREAT LAKES

There are probably few episodes of late Pleistocene history that are more

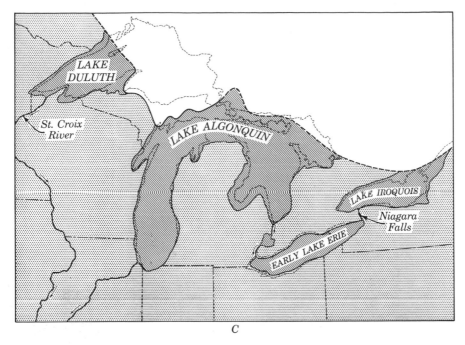

C

Figure 17-2. *A*. The ancestral Great Lakes came into existence when the lobate ice margin began its final retreat in late Wisconsin time. Lake Chicago and Lake Maumee were the first of the proglacial lakes to form. They drained to the Gulf of Mexico via outlets shown (about 14,000 years ago). *B*. Further retreat of the ice front opened an eastern outlet to the Atlantic Ocean via the Hudson River. Lake Chicago and the newly formed Lake Duluth still drained to the Gulf of Mexico (about 10,500 years ago). *C*. Niagara Falls came into existence when the Ontario basin became ice free about 8000 years ago. At the same time, Lake Algonquin existed in the Huron-Michigan basins and for a time had two functional outlets. One was the Chicago outlet and the other was the St. Claire-Detroit River channel near Detroit. (After Jack L. Hough, 1963, *The prehistoric Great Lakes of North America*, American Scientist, **51**, 84–109.)

intriguing or more compelling than the development of the Great Lakes. When we consider further that Lakes Superior, Michigan, Huron, Erie, and Ontario possess nearly 11,000 miles of shoreline, have a total area of almost 95,000 square miles, and constitute the greatest inland waterway system in the world, the impetus for a thorough understanding of their origin and history is greatly increased.

■ ANCESTRAL GREAT LAKES. The presence of vast areas of old lake bottoms and ancient shorelines in the vicinity of the present Great Lakes is the chief evidence for the former existence of larger and deeper water bodies in those regions. The evolution of these former water

bodies into the modern Great Lakes is a complex and remarkable sequence of events involving about 13,000 years of late glacial happenings, but only a brief outline of this detailed history can be given here.

The Great Lakes are youthful geologic features and did not exist in pre-Pleistocene time. The ancestral Great Lakes had their inception during the retreat of the lobate front of the Wisconsin ice sheet (Fig. 17-2*A*). Ice lobes protruding from the main glacier mass filled the lowlands now occupied by the Great Lakes. These lowlands, except possibly for the Superior lowland, were large river valleys formed by a pre-Pleistocene drainage system, although no firm agreement exists as to the direction of flow of these preglacial rivers. They were large enough, however, to have an influence on the general pattern of advance and retreat of the Wisconsin ice.

Until the beginning of the final retreat the meltwater issuing from the ice front flowed away from the glacier margin, but as the lobes shrank still more, lower land was uncovered and the meltwaters became impounded between the ice front and higher land. These water bodies were small at first but grew in extent as the various lobes diminished in size. Former shoreline features such as beaches, bars, and associated sand dunes permit the delineation of these early *proglacial lakes*. To differentiate them from the modern water bodies, names have been assigned to them. Lake Chicago and Lake Maumee were associated with the early retreat of the ice (Fig. 17-2*A*).

Each possessed an outlet or overflow channel, just as many modern lakes do, but different outlets were used at different times, because as deglaciation progressed, new and lower outlets became ice free. Lower outlets caused a drop in lake level, which in some extreme cases amounted to several hundred feet, but were usually less than 25 feet. If the new outlet persisted long enough, it would be represented by well-defined shoreline features, many of which are clearly visible today around the Great Lakes.

Early in the deglacial history the outlets of the proglacial lakes converged toward the Mississippi River which carried torrents of glacial meltwater to the Gulf of Mexico. As deglaciation continued, the drainage shifted to an eastern course (Fig. 17-2*B*), first through the Mohawk-Hudson valleys and later through the St. Lawrence lowland.

■ LOW-WATER STAGES. Until the early 1950's, glacial geologists pictured the sequence of events in the Great Lakes region as a succession of steplike lowerings

of water levels in the various lake basins, but recent evidence indicates that at least two major episodes of extreme low-water stages existed in the Michigan and Huron basins. Shallow-water sands containing shallow-water snail shells were discovered in deep water of Lake Michigan where silts and clays are now accumulating. This is interpreted as proof of a water level at least 350 feet lower than the present level of Lake Michigan, to which the name Lake Chippewa has been given (Fig. 17-3). Uplift of the land in the

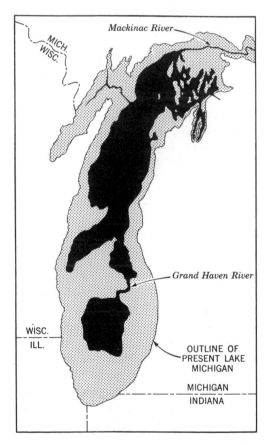

Figure 17-3. Map showing the extent of Lake Chippewa (in black) during a low-water stage in the Lake Michigan basin about 9500 years ago. Lake Chippewa was 350 feet below the level of modern Lake Michigan. (After Jack L. Hough, 1955, Lake Chippewa, a low stage of Lake Michigan indicated by bottom sediments, *Bull. Geol. Soc. of Amer.* **66,** 957–968.)

Figure 17-4. Niagara Falls, American side. Note the large blocks of limestone lying at the base of the escarpment in the upper right. The falls retreat as the underlying soft shale is eroded, leaving the Lockport dolomite unsupported. For details of the bedrock stratigraphy at Niagara Falls, see Fig. 14-7.

region of North Bay, Ontario near the outlet of Lake Chippewa, caused the water levels in the Michigan and Huron basins to return to their former elevation. The modern Great Lakes reached their present development shortly after this, roughly about 2500 years ago. Since that time their outlets have remained constant and their water levels have fluctuated only slightly compared to the great changes in levels that occurred during their early periods of development.

■ NIAGARA FALLS. The Niagara River flows from Lake Erie into Lake Ontario over the edge of a resistant dolomite layer, the Niagaran escarpment (Fig. 17-4). This drainage came into existence when the shrinking Wisconsin ice uncovered the escarpment and the Ontario basin less than 10,000 years ago. The waterfall thus created has since migrated upstream creating a gorge of scenic beauty. If the average rate of retreat (about 4 feet per year) is continued, Niagara Falls will reach Lake Erie in 25,000 or 30,000 years!

Geologists once thought that they could calculate "postglacial" time simply by dividing the total gorge length by the retreatal rate. Evidence brought to light later, however, indicated that not only was the gorge history more complex than formerly realized, but also the discharge of the Niagara River had varied greatly since its inception. In view of these complicating factors, all attempts to use the retreat of Niagara Falls as a geologic clock are doomed to failure. Geologists now rely on the radiocarbon method for establishing late Pleistocene chronology.

■ OTHER LATE PLEISTOCENE LAKES. A flat plain of thousands of square miles occupies most of southern Manitoba, a large part of southwestern Ontario, and great tracts of land in northwestern Minnesota and eastern North Dakota. This flat land marks the former extent of an immense fresh-water body, called Lake Agassiz (Fig. 17-5) which came into being during the final retreat of the Wisconsin ice sheet. Its early outlet was south through the valley presently occupied by the Minnesota River, now a tributary to the Mississippi, but then a river of immense proportions. In a later stage of Lake Agassiz's history, the ice retreat finally uncovered a lower outlet to Hudson Bay. Today only remnants of this once vast fresh-water lake remain, such as Lake Winnipeg in Manitoba and the Red Lakes of Minnesota.

PLEISTOCENE HISTORY OF NORTH AMERICA OUTSIDE THE GLACIAL BOUNDARY

■ ROCKY MOUNTAIN GLACIATION. During the advance and retreat of the continental ice sheet, valley glaciers also expanded and contracted in the Rocky Mountains of the United States. The existing glaciers and glacierettes now present in Colorado, Wyoming, and Montana are only remnants of former, much expanded valley glaciers.

Correlation of Pleistocene glaciation between the mountainous regions and the Upper Mississippi Valley has not been accomplished. Whereas the evidence for four major glacial stages separated by three interglacials is quite positive in the Upper Mississippi Valley, no such clear-cut arrangement of glacials and interglacials has been deduced for the Rocky Mountain Pleistocene.

■ PLEISTOCENE OF THE GREAT PLAINS. While the Pleistocene ice caps were waxing and waning, climatic changes were felt beyond the limits of the continental glaciers. On the uplands near the major rivers such as the Platte and Missouri, thick deposits of loess accumulated in Kansas and Nebraska during glacial advances. During interglacial times the loess deposits were stabilized by vegetation and soils were developed. Renewal of glaciation farther north brought the interglacial climates to an end, and the interglacial soils were covered with fresh loess. The soils thus became "fossilized" or buried soils. One of the best examples of a soil formed during interglacial times is the Loveland soil of Sangamon inter-glacial age. This soil has been recognized buried beneath younger Wisconsin deposits from Kansas and Nebraska to Illinois and Iowa. It is one of the best stratigraphic markers in the glaciated and nonglaciated regions and has been developed on a variety of parent materials including Illinoian till, loess, and Cretaceous shale. Its consistent red color suggests a warm, humid—perhaps subtropical—climate for the central United States during the Sangamon interglacial. No widespread agreement exists on this interpretation of climate, however.

Sand and gravel deposits of Pleistocene age in the high plains area, especially Kansas, Nebraska, and Oklahoma, are attributed to eastward-flowing streams originating in the Rocky Mountains. Many of these terrestrial stream deposits now lie several tens of feet above the modern river valleys, and are thus exposed in cross section where modern streams have cut through them. Correlation of the nonglacial deposits of the High Plains with the standard glacial sequence of the Upper Mississippi Valley is based on fossil evidence and the tracing of buried soil horizons between the two regions.

■ BASIN AND RANGE PROVINCE. Today in the arid western United States there are several lake basins, some like Great Salt Lake, partially filled with concentrated saline waters, others completely dry. Old shore lines above these modern basins are well preserved and testify to a once wetter climate when the basins contained more water (Fig. 17-6).

The two largest Pleistocene lakes, Bonneville and Lahonton, are represented by shrunken remnants. Great Salt Lake, Lake Provo, and Lake Sevier occupy part of the Bonneville basin and Lakes Pyramid, Wennemucca, and Carson are the main descendents of Lake Lahonton.

Investigations of the deposits in these basins reveal a sequence of alternating

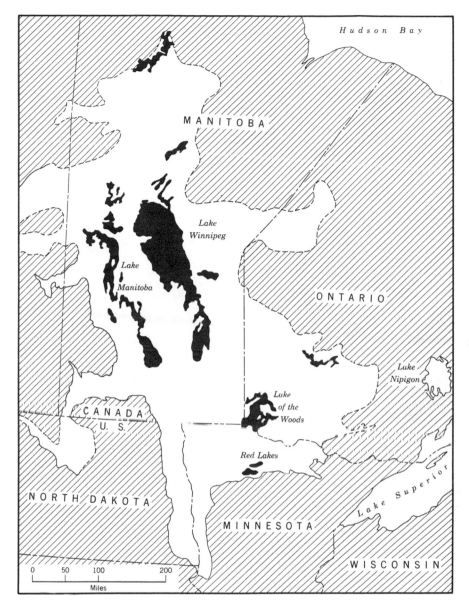

Figure 17-5. The large modern lakes shown in black are remnants of the largest single body of fresh water ever to cover the North American continent, Lake Agassiz. This body of water formed as the retreating Wisconsin ice sheet released large quantities of meltwater. Lake Agassiz discharged first down the Minnesota River which joins the Mississippi at Minneapolis and St. Paul. Later, however, the ice retreated farther north and uncovered a lower outlet to Hudson Bay. (From the Glacial Map of North America, published by the Geological Society of America, 1945.)

periods of high water and low water, which must be related to changes in precipitation during the Pleistocene. Most Pleistocene geologists now consider the wet periods or *pluvial periods* to be coincident with the glacial maxima, and the periods of desiccation to be correlatives of the interglacials.

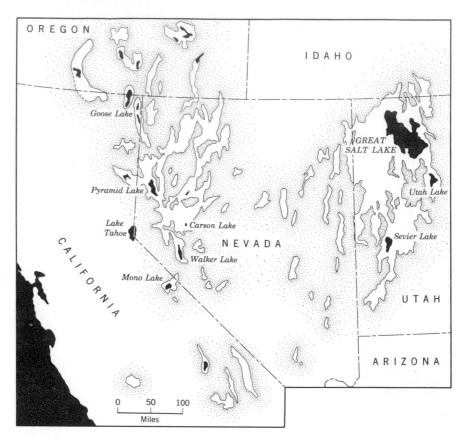

Figure 17-6. The white areas enclosed by the stippled pattern are basins occupied by lakes during the Pleistocene. The existence of these former lakes is evidence of a period of higher rainfall in what is now a semiarid land. The periods of higher rainfall are known as Pluvial periods, and they presumably are correlative with the times of glacial advance in the Great Lakes region. (From the Glacial Map of North America, published by the Geological Society of America, 1945.)

THE LOWER MISSISSIPPI VALLEY

Much of the meltwater from shrinking Pleistocene glaciers was returned to the ocean via the Mississippi River and its major northern tributaries, the Illinois, Ohio, and Missouri Rivers. North of Cairo, Illinois, Pleistocene geologists regard the variation in discharge of the Pleistocene Mississippi as the chief cause of changes in the Upper Valley. Terraces especially have been attributed to alternate periods of cutting and filling due to large variations in discharge and load. As a matter of fact, the valley train

deposits of the Pleistocene Mississippi are regarded as the source area for the loess cover that mantles much of the ground in the Mississippi Valley states (Fig. 7-10). In other words, we might say that geologists in the Upper Mississippi interpret Pleistocene history in the light of *upstream changes* of the glacial Mississippi River.

In contrast to this approach, workers in the Lower Valley (below Cairo, Illinois) have viewed Pleistocene history from the point of view that upstream changes in load and discharge have been minor in comparison to the *downstream* changes, especially the sea level fluctuations that accompanied the waxing and waning of the ice sheets. Lower sea levels during the glacial maxima caused valley cutting, and higher sea levels during interglacial times caused alluviation, according to this interpretation. The origin of certain terraces within the Mississippi Valley are thus in dispute because of the conflicting views held by Upper and Lower Valley geologists.

SEA LEVEL FLUCTUATIONS

The accumulation of snow and ice on the continents during the glacial advances caused a lowering of sea level, whereas the widespread melting of ice and snow during the interglacial periods caused the sea level to rise.

Ancient beaches and wave-cut features exist in many of the coastal regions of the world. These strand-lines are not easily correlated, however, either with each other or with the standard Pleistocene chronology, mainly because they have been uplifted or tilted since their origin. Evidence of lower sea level exists in the form of submerged shorelines such as extend along the continental shelf of the Atlantic Coast of North America.

The lowering of sea level during the Pleistocene can be estimated by computing the total volume of glacier ice on land during the various phases of Pleistocene glaciation. The area covered by Pleistocene glaciers is fairly well known because of the drift sheets associated with them, but the average ice thickness during the various glacial maxima can only be estimated. Using two different figures of the mean thickness of the Antarctic ice sheet as a guide, the following calculated values for the Pleistocene lowering of sea level can be given. The maximum sea level lowering, which occurred during the Illinoian glacial age, ranged between 450 and 520 feet. These values agree with the worldwide occurrence of submarine terraces at a depth range of 465 to 505 feet. They are also in accord with a prominent erosional terrace and shallow water deposits which occur at a depth range 475 to 520 feet along the continental shelf of eastern North and South America.

Melting of the Illinoian ice caused sea level to return to its normal interglacial level, but readvance of the ice during the last or Wisconsin glacial age again reduced the level of the oceans. Computed values for sea level lowering during the Wisconsin age are 345 to about 400 feet. These values are less than those for the Illinoian because the Wisconsin glaciation was less extensive than the Illinoian.

LIFE OF THE PLEISTOCENE

The plant and animal life of Pleistocene time were represented by two categories, those forms that are living today and those that became extinct in the Pleistocene. The major difference in the Pleistocene flora and fauna compared with the plants and animals of today lies in their distribution. That is to say, the present distribution of plants and animals is regulated by ecologic factors among which climate is of great importance. So long as the ecologic factors remain constant for a given area, the plant and animal population should remain more or less stable over a period of years. During the Pleistocene, however, we know that climatic changes were the rule, and as a consequence, the attending environmental changes forced widespread shift in range of plants and animals. Organisms that are now restricted to an arctic climate were forced southward into the more temperate regions as the continental ice sheets expanded. On the other hand, during the interglacial warming of the

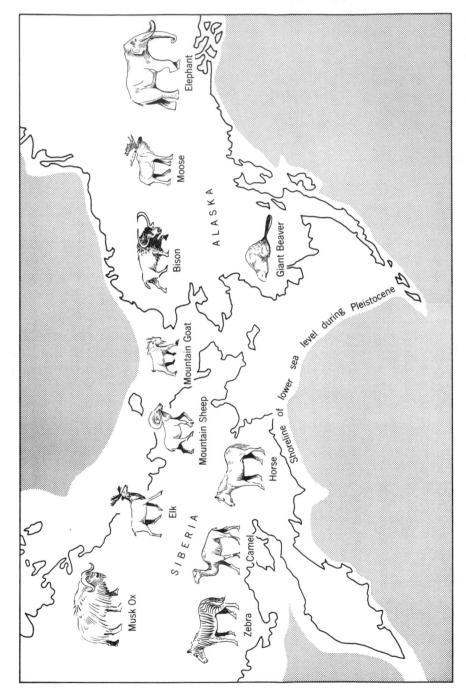

Figure 17-7. The Alaskan-Siberian land bridge which functioned as a migration route along which an interchange of animals took place between Asia and North America during the Pleistocene. (After Claude W. Hibbard, University of Michigan, Museum of Paleontology.)

climate, a northward spread of more southerly forms resulted.

The Pleistocene paleontologist, therefore, looks to the present distribution of plants and animals as an index of their climatic tolerance, so that when he finds fossils of these same or closely related organisms in Pleistocene deposits, he can read into their presence some interpretation of the climate prevailing at the site of their burial at the time of their death. Thus, a real understanding of the distribution of modern plants and animals as well as a thorough comprehension of their ecology is vital in the interpretation of the Pleistocene fossil record.

The fossil record of Pleistocene animals is far from complete, but we do have a rough idea of their general distribution. During the Pleistocene an interchange of animals occurred between North America and Asia by the way of the Alaskan-Siberian land bridge (Fig. 17-7), a stretch of dry land that persisted during the periods of lower Pleistocene sea levels.

■ EXTINCT PLEISTOCENE ANIMALS OF NORTH AMERICA. The horses and zebras originated in North America during the Tertiary and they roamed the western grass lands in large herds until they became extinct in late Pleistocene time. The so-called wild horses of the western plains were not native to North America but were progeny of horses introduced into Mexico during the invasion by the Spanish conquistadors in the sixteenth century.

An animal usually associated with Asia is the camel, but the camel also originated in North America. Pleistocene camels were numerous and varied, and ranged from Florida to Alaska. Of the many species of the Pleistocene camels the best known were the Camelops (one-humped Dromedary) and South American llama-like camels. The llamas of South America as well as the true Asiatic camels are descendents of the Pleistocene

forms, which are now extinct in North America.

Two of the largest creatures to roam the North American continent during the Pleistocene were the mastodon and mammoth (Fig. 17-8). Although both appeared to be elephant-like in appearance, only the mammoth was a true elephant, represented today by those in India and Africa.

In North America there were four species of the mammoth group, the Woolly Mammoth, Jefferson Mammoth, the Columbian Mammoth, and the Imperial Mammoth. The Woolly Mammoth is probably the most famous of all fossil mammals in view of the discovery of nearly complete carcasses in the permanently frozen tundra of Siberia and Alaska. Because some people have insisted that the frozen woolly mammoth carcasses require a catastrophic death, a further discussion of these creatures is given later in this chapter.

The Jefferson Mammoth inhabited the meadowed areas of the eastern woodlands as well as the stream valleys of Kansas and Nebraska. The Columbian mammoth had a more southerly range than his contemporary of the Arctic. His tusks were more recurved and he very likely lacked the shaggy coat of hair. The Columbian Mammoth was a prominent inhabitant of southern North America, ranging from Georgia and Florida to Arizona and Mexico during glacial times, and as far north as Nebraska in interglacial times.

Largest of all Pleistocene mammoths was the great Imperial Mammoth which stood over 13 feet, shoulder height. These giants roamed the Great Plains as far south as Texas and Mexico and extended from the Pacific Coast to the Gulf Coast area.

The American Mastodon, in contrast to the Pleistocene mammoths, was an in-

Figure 17-8. Restoration of a Pleistocene mastodon (above) and a Pleistocene Wooly Mammoth (below). A tooth of each is shown with a hand for scale. The crowned tooth of the mastodon was suitable for a diet of twigs, branches, and cones, whereas the infolded structure of the mammoth tooth was more adapted to a grass diet. (Restorations by Thomas Coates after Charles Knight, 1935, *Before the dawn of history,* McGraw-Hill Book Co., New York.)

habitant chiefly of eastern forests but also roamed along the timbered streams of the west and subsisted on a diet of twigs of coniferous trees. This eating habit classifies the mastodon as a browser rather than a grazer, and accounts for the difference in tooth structure.

Other animals that became extinct in late Pleistocene time include the large bison, ground sloths, giant beavers, sabretooth tigers, large jaguars, large wolves, woodland musk-oxen, and giant moose. The skeletons of many of these animals have been recovered from the famous Rancho La Brea tar pits in Los Angeles. The "pits" contain a natural asphaltic material in which thousands of animals became entrapped, either in attempting to cross it or in preying on other animals already caught in the death trap (Fig. 17-9).

■ THE FROZEN MAMMOTHS OF SIBERIA. The tundra of arctic Siberia has yielded some of the most spectacular fossils of the world in the form of frozen woolly mammoths which inhabited these treeless regions during the late phases of the Wisconsin age of the Plcistoccnc. At least thirty-nine discoveries have been made of frozen mammoth remains, some with soft parts preserved, but only four of these were nearly complete.

One of these, the so-called Berezovka mammoth (Fig. 17-10) is mounted and on display in the Zoological Museum of Leningrad. This hairy beast was discovered near the Arctic Circle in eastern Siberia as it was thawing out of the permafrost in which it had been entombed since the late Pleistocene. Save

Figure 17-9. Animals from the Rancho La Brea tar pits, Los Angeles County, Califonia. The photo inset shows a modern squirrel trapped in the present asphaltic material, just as the larger animals like the bison and elephants were caught in the death trap during the Pleistocene. (Photograph, Los Angeles County Museum. Animal silhouettes from Chester Stock, 1953, *Rancho La Brea*, Los Angeles County Museum.)

Figure 17-10. The Berezovka mammoth, displayed in the Zoological Museum of Leningrad in the position in which it was discovered, is a nearly complete cadaver. Only the front of the face and part of the trunk was missing. Broken bones in the animal's legs testify to an accidental fall; undigested food in the mouth and stomach almost demand sudden death, but not by freezing. (Courtesy of the Zoological Museum, Leningrad.)

for some skin on the face and part of the trunk, the animal was intact, and undigested food was found in the mouth and stomach.

Some popular writers have promoted the idea that the Berezovka and other woolly mammoths were victims of a climatic catastrophe which caused them to become frozen in a matter of a few hours' time. Unfortunately, these accounts are quasi-scientific at best, and are based on speculation which is hardly warranted by the facts. There is no direct evidence that any mammoth froze to death, either rapidly or slowly. A more likely explanation for their demise is that they perished suddenly by asphyxiation due to drowning in a lake or from being buried alive in a mudflow or river bank slide.

One of these heavy-footed mammals can be pictured browsing along the edge of a river bank in the late summer or early fall. Summer melting of the exposed permafrost weakened the bank to the point that it was unable to support the cumbersome beast who was feeding too close to the edge. As the cumbersome creature plunged to the bottom he was injured and helpless to free himself from further bank cave-ins which eventually buried him alive. The broken bones of the Berezovka mammoth give credence to such an explanation. The reader interested in further documentation of the conditions surrounding the death and preservation of the woolly mammoths would do well to study a summary account of this problem written by Farrand (see reference list at the end of this chapter).

■ LIVING FORMS. The distribution of some modern animals is a great contrast to their range during the Pleistocene. For example, the musk ox, a shaggy beast that still inhabits remote arctic areas northwest of Hudson Bay and in Greenland near the Arctic Circle, used to live as far south as Kansas and Oklahoma. Clearly, the growth of the North American ice sheet forced these animals southward. Other creatures that still inhabit arctic regions today were subject to the same force which pushed them southward into the now temperate regions of the United States. Among these are the woodland and barren ground caribou, the arctic wolf, and arctic hare.

The northward migration of southern forms during interglacial periods can also be deduced from fossil discoveries. Deposits containing such "warm faunas" are thus classified as interglacial in age. A striking example of this is the fossil occurrence in Kansas of a land turtle (gopher turtle) now restricted to Florida. Certainly the climate of the Kansas plains must have been much more humid than now to provide a hospitable environment for this subtropical reptile.

■ CAUSE OF PLEISTOCENE EXTINCTION. Extinction of a race or species of animals always poses a difficult question for the ecologist. We are still unable to account for the loss of the gigantic animals of the Pleistocene, even though many of them lived through at least one glacial and one interglacial age. Some paleontologists consider the chief cause of extinction to be competition from new forms better suited for survival in a changing environment. Others consider an increase of predators a real factor in extinction. Man himself contributed in a large measure to the extinction of the herds of wild bison that once roamed the western plains by the tens of thousands. Still another idea to account for extinction suggests that such animals as the Woolly Mammoth became so firmly chained to arctic conditions that they were finally unable to survive the warmer climate since the last glacial maximum. One other factor in extinction may have been the rapidity with which the glacier ice disintergrated at the close of the last glaciation. Picture the plight of the large mastodons as they attempted to follow the rapidly withdrawing ice margin in the vicinity of the Great Lakes Region, only

to find their northward route blocked by the ancestral Great Lakes. Such a natural barricade could result only in death for the stranded beasts.

■ PLANT LIFE DURING THE PLEISTOCENE. All statements made concerning the change in animal distribution as a result of the waxing and waning glaciers are equally apropos for plants. Northern plants had a more southerly range during the glacial advances and the warmth-loving vegetation extended northward during the interglacials. An example of plant succession induced by changing climate is vividly demonstrated in pollen records of the Great Lakes region. Pollen grains are extremely resistant to natural forces of decay and remain intact when buried in lake or bog sediments. When strata containing these microscopic plant fossils are studied, the relative percentage of tree pollen can be determined for any single layer in the strata. Theoretically, the pollen content of any one stratum should reflect the forest composition in the immediate vicinity of the settling basin. Care has to be exercised in the interpretation, however, because some pollen grains are transported hundreds of miles by wind, and other pollen grains are present in quantities that far exceed the percentage of trees producing the pollen. Overrepresentation and long-distance transport are thus two factors that complicate the interpretation of the pollen profile.

Notwithstanding these difficulties, however, the overwhelming evidence of gradual change in forest composition during the final retreat of the Wisconsin ice is well established for central and eastern North America and Europe. Near South Haven, Michigan (Fig. 17-11) a pollen profile collected in conjunction with radiocarbon samples revealed a 13,000-year record of forest changes from an early assemblage of spruce and fir species

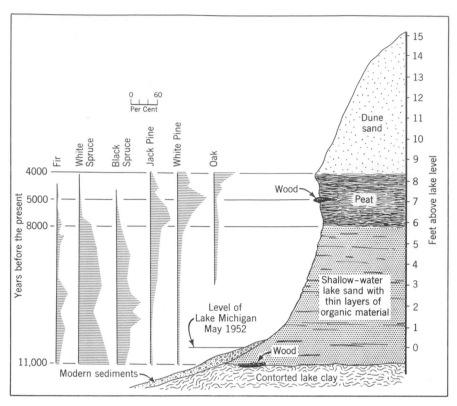

Figure 17-11.   Diagram of geologic section of South Haven, Michigan showing the change in percentage of tree pollen recovered from the various layers.   The peat bed has been correlated with the Chippewa low-water stage in the Lake Michigan basin (page 310).   Other pollen profiles from nearby indicate that the oak peak was reached about 3500 years ago, and since then oak has decreased and white pine has increased.   This has been interpreted as a revertence to a colder climate during the last 3500 years.   (Based on Zumberge and Potzger, 1956.   Late Pleistocene chronology of the Lake Michigan basin correlated with pollen profiles.   *Bull. Geologic Soc. America.* **67,** 271–288.)

when the ice first withdrew from southern Michigan, to the oak-pine forest of today. Other pollen studies in the same area indicate that the climatic trend of the last few thousand years (approximately) is one of cooling, evidenced by the return of a larger percentage of pine near the tops of some pollen profiles.   The South Haven profile is *truncated*.   That is, pollen deposition ceased when dune sand was blown over the peat layer 4000 years ago.   It may seem paradoxical that the pollen record indicates a cooling climate, whereas the present worldwide retreat of valley glaciers is a strong indication that

the climate is becoming warmer.   Possibly the pollen evidence represents a long-term trend of cooling whereas the widespread glacial retreat of the last few hundred years is a short-term trend of warming.

CAUSES OF CLIMATIC FLUCTUATIONS

Scientists have long sought the answer to the question, "What was the cause of the Ice Age?"   Their attempts to answer satisfactorily this intriguing query are so far unsuccessful.   Many hypotheses have been proposed and some have been discarded in the light of new knowledge.

In proposing an explanation for a natural phenomenon, one should first know precisely what is to be explained. We are now fairly well agreed that the Pleistocene involved worldwide climatic fluctuations, which when coupled with increased precipitation, were sufficient to cause the growth of continental glaciers four times during the last million years. Interglacial periods separated the glacial advances and during at least one interglacial the climate of North America was considerably warmer than it is today.

It is somewhat ironic that although the Pleistocene is probably the most complete of the geologic periods in terms of the record of *what* happened, geologists are still hard pressed to state with certainty the cause of the worldwide climatic changes during that time.

Meteorologists and their modern progeny, the climatologists, have delved into this perplexing problem. Many of them believe that some cause outside of the earth is basically involved. The most plausible extraterrestrial cause is the variation in amount of heat given off by the sun, or more precisely, the variation in the *solar constant*. But until we are able to know how a change in the amount of heat reaching the earth from the sun would affect the general circulation of air masses, any new hypothesis that attempts to explain climatic change on a worldwide basis must be purely speculative. Add to this the uncertainty of earthly factors such as topography, ocean currents, and the distribution of land and sea, and the problem appears to be anything but simple.

One of the most recent hypotheses set forth to explain the climatic fluctuations of the Pleistocene invokes the terrestrial rather than the extraterrestrial causes. The originators of the idea, Ewing and Donn of Columbia University, postulate

that the earth's poles gradually shifted from the open Pacific Ocean to the Arctic Ocean, according to the concept of polar wandering set forth in Chapter four of this book. The Arctic Ocean is isolated from the Pacific Ocean except for the narrow Bering Strait between Alaska and Siberia, and from the north Atlantic except for the stretch of water between Scandinavia and Greenland which contains a relatively shallow submarine ridge.

The Ewing-Donn hypothesis postulates an unfrozen Arctic Ocean kept ice-free because of the interchange of the relatively warm waters of the Atlantic with the Arctic Ocean. The ice-free Arctic Sea served as a source of moisture for winds that passed over its surface onto surrounding Arctic lands. Precipitation in the form of snow gradually accumulated and formed into ice sheets. The growth of these ice sheets caused a reduction of sea level until the circulation between the open Atlantic and the Arctic Ocean was markedly reduced because of the restriction on circulation imposed by the Greenland-Scandinavian submarine ridge. This situation resulted in a thermally isolated Arctic Ocean which then became covered with sea ice, thereby reducing the evaporation potential of the atmosphere and cut off the supply of snow for nourishment of the surrounding land glaciers. The glaciers, thus "starved," became reduced in size because of excessive melting over nourishment, and subsequently returned water to the ocean basins. The resultant rise in sea level re-established the circulation between the Arctic basin and the north Atlantic and caused the melting of the sea ice cover so that the Arctic Ocean again became a source of moisture for the nourishment of surrounding land glaciers. The cycle thus started anew.

Although quite intriguing and rather ingenious, the Ewing-Donn hypothesis suffers from one important defect. If true, the hypothesis would require the peripheral lands of the Arctic Ocean to contain evidence of heavy glaciation, but neither northern Alaska nor eastern Siberia bear any evidence of strong Pleistocene glaciation, presumably because of the lack of sufficient precipitation.

The Ewing-Donn hypothesis should not be discarded on this basis alone, however, because some other explanation may be forthcoming to account for the discrepancy between the apparent facts and the requirements of the hypothesis. Further testing of it by meteorologists, climatologists, and oceanographers seems worthwhile.

SUMMARY

The Pleistocene Epoch lasted about one million years during which time four major glaciations occurred. The final glacial age, the Wisconsin, lasted only 70,000 years according to evidence provided by radiocarbon dating. The Wisconsin glacial deposits are extremely youthful in appearance when contrasted with the drifts of Illinoian, Kansan, and Nebraskan ages.

The final retreat of the lobate glacier margin was accompanied by the development of proglacial lakes, which, after several changes in level due to the opening of new outlets and uplift of the land, evolved into the modern Great Lakes. The early proglacial lakes as well as their contemporary, Lake Agassiz, drained southward to the Gulf of Mexico; Lake Agassiz later drained to Hudson Bay, and the Great Lakes now drain to the Atlantic Ocean via the St. Lawrence. Niagara Falls has been in existence less than 10,000 years and has been retreating at an average annual rate of four feet.

Outside the borders of the continental glacier, now marked by the Ohio and Missouri Rivers, other events took place during the Pleistocene. Valley glaciers waxed and waned in the Rocky Mountains, and rivers originating on the east flank of the Rockies flowed across the High Plains, depositing sand and gravel. Loess accumulated on the uplands during the cold periods and was weathered during the warm interglacials. The pluvial lakes of Utah and Nevada greatly expanded during the glacial periods and shrank or became dry during the interglacials. Sea level became lower during the glacial maxima and higher during interglacial times.

Plants and animals shifted north and south with glacial retreats and advances. The solution to the Pleistocene distribution of plants and animals lies in a better understanding of the ecology of modern plant and animal populations. Many animals now native to Asia actually originated in North America, for example, the zebras, camels, and elephants. The cause of widespread extinction of many species that had already lived through most of the Pleistocene is not known.

The cause of worldwide climatic fluctuations which characterized Pleistocene time are unknown. Variations in the solar constant as well as the presence of mountainous areas in the temperate regions where ice sheets could get started seem to be logical factors in one explanation of the cause of the "Ice Age."

The Ewing-Donn hypothesis is attractive because it seems logical and plausible. Yet, unless some other reason can be found for the lack of Pleistocene glaciation in all of the peripheral arctic lands, a consequence demanded by the hypothesis, the hypothesis will not gain many adherents.

REFERENCES

American Geographical Society, 1953, *Glacier variations and climatic fluctuations.*
Charlesworth, J. K., 1957, *The Quaternary Era,* vol. 1 and 2, Arnold Press.

Donn, W. L., W. R. Farrand, and M. Ewing, 1962, Pleistocene ice volumes and sea level lowering, *Jour., Geology,* **70,** pp. 206–214.

Ewing, Maurice, and Donn, W. L., 1961, Pleistocene climatic changes, *Geology of the Arctic,* Vol. II, pp. 931–941, University of Toronto Press.

Farrand, William R., 1961, Frozen mammoths and modern geology, *Science,* **133,** 729–735.

Flint, R. F., 1957, *Glacial and Pleistocene geology,* John Wiley and Sons, New York.

Haag, William G., 1962, The Bearing Strait land bridge, *Scientific American,* January.

Hibbard, C. W., 1951, Animal life in Michigan during the Ice Age. *Michigan Alumnus Quaterly Review,* **57,** 200–208.

Hough, Jack L., 1958, *Geology of the Great Lakes,* University of Illinois Press, Urbana.

Scott, W. B., 1937, *A history of land mammals of the western hemisphere,* The Macmillan Co., New York.

Appendix A

Table A-1. Explanation of Plate I. Common minerals

A. Graphite: (locality unknown).
B. Diamond: South Africa.
C. Native Copper: *leaf copper*, Houghton, Michigan.
D. Quartz: *rock crystal*, Arkansas.
E. Quartz: *milky quartz*, (locality unknown).
F. Quartz: *greasy quartz*, (locality unknown).
G. Quartz: *smoky quartz*, (locality unknown).
H. Quartz: *rose quartz*, near Custer, South Dakota.
I. Limonite: *yellow ochre*, Mishawaka, Wisconsin.
J. Galena: crystals, (locality unknown).
K. Gypsum: *selenite*, (locality unknown).
L. Calcite: crystals, (locality unknown).
M. Calcite: double refracting cleavage fragment.
N. Flourite: crystals, England.
O. Muscovite: with quartz, Paris, Maine.
P. Biotite: (locality unknown).
Q. Feldspar: *Microcline*, Pikes Peak, Colorado.
R. Feldspar: *Plagioclase*, (locality unknown).

Table A-2. Explanation of Plate II. Igneous Rocks

A. Granite: *biotite granite*, Platte Canyon, Colorado.
B. Granite: *hornblende-biotite granite*, Cotopaxi, Colorado.
C. Granite: *biotite granite*, Mt. Airy, North Carolina.
D. Granite: *biotite granite*, Cockspit Point, Washington.
E. Diorite: *quartz diorite*, Mt. Stuart Quadrangle, Washington
F. Gabbro: Ashland, Wisconsin.
G. Peridotite: *dunite*, Jackson County, North Carolina.
H. Felsite: *rhyolite*, Big Butte-Snake River Desert, Idaho.
I. Felsite: *rhyolite*, Castle Rock, Colorado.
J. Andesite: *augite andesite*, Pauline Lake, Oregon.
K. Basalt: Wachung Mountains, New Jersey.
L. Felsite Porphyry: *hornblende-mica andesite*, Hoosac Mountain, Nevada.
M. Felsite Porphyry: *dacite porphyry*, Clear Creek, California.
N. Andesite Porphyry: *dolerite porphyry*, Cape Ann, Massachusetts.
O. Basalt Porphyry: *basalt dike*, Jakuben, Bohemia.
P. Pumice: Millard County, Utah.
Q. Obsidian: "glass rock," Yellowstone National Park, Wyoming.
R. Scoria: Mauna Loa, Hawaii.

Table A-3. Explanation of Plate III. Sedimentary Rocks

A. Sandstone: *banded sandstone,* Hot Springs, South Dakota.
B. Sandstone: *gray sandstone* (Berea grit), Berea, Ohio.
C. Fossiliferous Sandstone: *Marshall sandstone* (Mississippian), Jackson, Michigan.
D. Arkose: Rock Creek formation (Pennsylvanian), McCoy, Colorado.
E. Conglomerate: *quartz pebble conglomerate,* Titusville, Pennsylvania.
F. Breccia: Montpelier, Idaho.
G. Shale: shaley limestone from *Madison formation* (Mississippian), Cream Puff Mountain, Wyoming.
H. Fossiliferous Limestone: *Richmond formation* (Ordovician) with *Dalmonella meeki,* Oxford, Ohio.
I. Chert: *novaculite,* Hot Springs, Arkansas.
J. Chert: weathered black chert nodule, Baltic Coast, Denmark.
K. Rock Gypsum: East Tawas, Michigan.
L. Rock Gypsum: Grand Rapids, Michigan.
M. Diatomaceous Earth: Santa Barbara County, California.
N. Chalk: (locality unknown).
O. Rock Salt: drill core from *Salina formation* (Silurian), Detroit, Michigan.
P. Coquina: St. Augustine, Florida.
Q. Peat: northern Minnesota.
R. Anthracite: Pennsylvania.

Table A-4. Explanation of Plate IV. Metamorphic Rocks

A. Gneiss: *banded gneiss,* (locality unknown).
B. Gneiss: *granite gneiss,* boulder from glacial drift near Ann Arbor, Michigan.
C. Gneiss: *biotite gneiss,* Uxbridge, Massachusetts.
D. Quartzite: *jasper quartzite conglomerate,* north of Bruce Mines, Ontario.
E. Schist: *hematite schist,* Marquette Iron Range, Michigan.
F. Schist: *biotite schist,* Copper Queen Mine, Park, Co., Colorado.
G. Schist: *garnet-mica schist,* Southbury, Connecticut.
H. Schist: *garnet-mica schist,* Ötztal, Austria.
I. Schist: *garnet-mica schist,* Zäptan, Mahren.
J. Slate: Albermarle County, Virginia.
K. Slate: *red roofing slate,* Granville, Ohio.
L. Slate: *gray roofing slate,* Bangor, Pennsylvania.
M. Marble: *gray Derbyshire encrinal marble* (polished), Derbyshire, England.
N. Marble: *Westland Cippolino marble* (polished), West Rutland, Vermont.
O. Marble: *mottled onyx marble* (polished), Pelican Point, Utah.
P. Marble: *Lyonaise marble* (polished), Swanton, Vermont.
Q. Marble: *dark red Ashburton marble* (polished), Devonshire, England.
R. Marble: *red mottled Ogwell marble* (polished), Devonshire, England.

Index